third symposium on
the structure of low-medium mass nuclei

1.	J. P. Davidson	17.	J. A. Becker	X.	007
2.	G. Pipka	18.	P. Pronko	33.	I. Taylor
3.	P. M. Endt	19.	P. Goldhammer	34.	G. I. Harris
4.	A. E. Litherland	20.	J. G. Borse	35.	J. Risser
5.	D. S. Koltun	21.	S. Varma	36.	J. R. MacDonald
6.	E. C. Halbert	22.	F. E. Dunnam	37.	R. Davis
7.	J. P. Elliott	23.	R. G. Arns	38.	G. M. Griffiths
8.	J. W. Olness	24.	M. L. Roush	39.	R. C. Bearse
9.	A. Arima	25.	H. J. Hennecke	40.	J. Walinga
10.	M. Baranger	26.	W. R. Phillips	41.	J. C. Legg
11.	L. W. Seagondollar	27.	R. T. Carpenter	42.	R. W. West
12.	D. Kurath	28.	R. W. Krone	43.	P. Cockburn
13.	E. W. Titterton	29.	R. S. Cox	44.	N. Freed
14.	M. deLlano	30.	D. R. Tilley	45.	D. A. Gedcke
15.	R. Y. Cusson	31.	K. H. Purser	46.	H. Willmes
16.	S. A. Williams	32.	F. W. Prosser, Jr.	47.	R. Nordhagen

third symposium on
the structure of low-medium mass nuclei

Edited by

J. P. Davidson

Sponsored by:

The Nuclear Structure Laboratory

The University of Kansas

The Aerospace Research Laboratories

Wright-Patterson Air Force Base

University Press of Kansas
Lawrence and London

EDITOR'S PREFACE

This volume of the proceedings includes all of the invitational papers, formal comments and discussion following these which were presented in this third Symposium held at the University of Kansas on April 18 - 20, 1968. Professor Ralph W. Krone, Director of the Nuclear Structure Laboratory was a co-organizer of the Symposium. The invitational papers are denoted by the Roman numeral of the session and a capital letter while the formal comments are denoted by the session numeral and a lower case letter. The discussion was tape recorded and immediately transcribed. All of these transcriptions, except for session V, were examined and corrected by those commenting; therefore, the discussion has the flavor of spontaneous as well as considered comments. Editorial insertions, where deemed necessary or useful, are enclosed in square brackets.

Formal publication of these proceedings was decided on because the large numer of requests for proceedings of the previous symposia led us to believe that their appearance in the published literature would facilitate work in the field of low-energy structure of low and medium mass nuclei. The overriding principle, as before, has been the rapid publication of all of the written material and pertinent comments. Most of the manuscripts and drawings appear as provided by the participants; only a few had to be redone due mainly to the lack of an international typewriter font convention. Another lack of international convention, equally as serious, is apparent in the papers. This is, where the A numeral is to be placed in relation to the chemical symbol. These proceedings contain representative offerings by leftists and rightests (and even both in the same person). To have obtained complete uniformity would have required retyping and redrawing of a majority of the papers. I have taken the centerist position and eschewed uniformity.

The one innovation in this Symposium was the industrial session (Session V). All of the groups making electrostatic or electrostatic-type accelerators were invited to present papers on the current state of the art. We were highly gratified that the two major producers of such accelerators did accept our invitation. Their session was last so that the theorists could attend to more theoretical matters, including the enjoyment of Northeastern Kansas.

The papers and discussions were taped by W. A. Dobra and ably transcribed by Mrs. Carol Smith. I wish to thank Mrs. Bev North for many, many hours of tedious typing and retyping, without which the speedy appearance of these proceedings would not have been possible. I also want to thank the graduate students of the Nuclear Structure Laboratory for the many hours of help they freely gave. I wish to acknowledge the continuing efforts of Dr. Gale I. Harris and the other members of the Nuclear Structure Group of the Aerospace Research Laboratories which have made these symposia possible. And finally, I want to express my appreciation to the staff of the University Press of Kansas and especially to William E. Kukuk of the University of Kansas Printing Service for all of the technical advice they have given for these many months.

Lawrence, Kansas   J. P. Davidson
August, 1968

CONTENTS

Session V, Chairman: D. A. Gedcke

I.A. STUDIES IN THE 2s-1d SHELL
USING TRITON INDUCED REACTIONS[+]

J. A. Becker
Lockheed Missiles and Space Company
Palo Alto, California

I. INTRODUCTION

The 3MV electrostatic generator has been accelerating a triton beam at Lockheed since 1965, and triton induced reactions are proving quite useful for the study of nuclei in the s-d shell.[1] Some of the nuclei studied during this time are conveniently formed only via t,p and t, reactions, and relatively little is known about them beyond the mass of the residual nucleus and location of energy levels;[2,3] while for other nuclei, these reactions (because of their high Q value) have provided a simple means of access to energy regions heretofore limited to study employing higher energy accelerators or capture γ-ray reactions.

Tritons also have sufficient nuclear penetrabilities (for s wave particles and Z - 10, the penetrability of a 3-MeV triton is $\sim$ 50 times that of a 3-MeV He^3 ion) to be useful for 3 MV accelerators and s-d shell nuclei. Q values are also generally high for the (t,p), (t,α), (t,n) and (t,d) reactions, and a typical triton bombardment leads to a wealth of reaction products and activities, especially when the common contaminants C^{12} and O^{16} are included in the target material. For this reason, coincidence work is almost always the rule in γ-ray spectroscopy. Much of the work at Lockheed has consisted of γ-ray angular distribution measurements following t,$\alpha\gamma$ or t,pγ reactions. The particle γ-ray coincidence technique of Litherland and Ferguson[4] has been extensively employed to gain information on the γ-decay and character of levels in the residual nucleus, as well as multipole mixing ratios. This work is reviewed below.

Section II contains a brief discussion of the experimental arrangement, while Section III contains a discussion of the experimental results for the nuclei studied by this method. The discussion emphasizes points mentioned above, as well as interesting features of the resulting decay schemes. Section IV briefly describes some of the other

[+]Supported in part by the Lockheed Independent Research Fund and in part by the Office of Naval Research

work at Lockheed employing the triton beam.   Throughout,
only representative references are noted.

II. EXPERIMENT

In the Method II geometry of Litherland and Ferguson,
γ-ray angular distributions are measured in coincidence
with a reaction particle detected either at 0° or 180° to
the incident beam axis.   Thus, γ-radiation is detected from
decaying states in the residual nucleus aligned with (in
general) unequal populations in magnetic substates; and the
highest allowed magnetic quantum number m is equal to the
sum of the spins of the incoming and outgoing light particles and target nucleus.   For example, γ-ray angular distributions following the t,α reaction on an even-even
target nucleus are readily interpreted, as only magnetic
substates with m = ± 1/2 are involved.   Similarly for the
t,p reaction on an even-even target nucleus, m is restricted
to 0, ± 1.

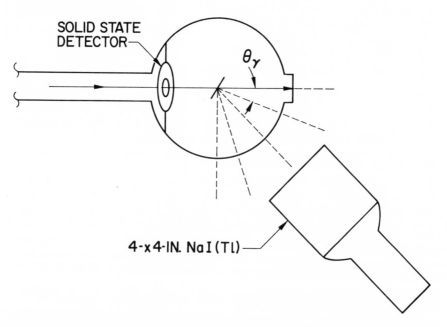

Fig. 1.   Schematic of the Method II Geometry.

Figure 1 illustrates the experimental arrangement used
to exploit the Method II geometry.   The target is mounted
coaxially in a 6" diameter cylindrical chamber.   After
acceleration and momentum analysis a well collimated beam
($\sim$ 1 × 1 mm) is allowed to strike the target.   The outgoing

light reaction particle is detected near 180° with respect
to the incident beam direction in an annular counter while
the γ-ray angular distribution is determined by measuring
the yield of coincident γ-rays at several angles to the
beam axis. Typically, the solid state counter has an active
area of 150 mm^2, with reaction particles detected between
166° and 176°. NaI(Tl) scintillators, 4" diameter × 4"
long and located 3.75" from the reaction site, are used for
γ-ray detection. Typical bombarding energies are near 2.7
MeV. Beam currents employed are on the order of 20 na, and
a typical distribution point requires ∿ 12 hours running
time. Data are collected with a good real: random ratio,
usually > 10:1 for a strong full energy absorption peak.

Thin targets are used, and the good resolution of the
solid state detector is relied upon to separate the
particles populating individual levels in the residual
nucleus into groups. Thus with coincidence techniques and
2 parameter pulse-height analysis, γ-rays associated with
individual levels may be studied. The data acquisition
system employed has dual 4096 channel ADC's interfaced with
a general purpose computer. Ample dispersion is thus available for both charged particle and γ-ray pulse-height
analysis. A magnetic tape is employed for record storage
so relatively unlimited memory is available.

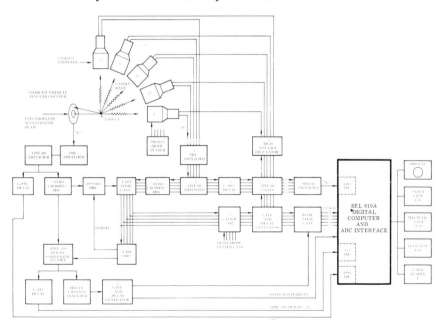

Fig. 2.   Block diagram of the proposed experimental
arrangement.

Significant experimental improvements and somewhat improved data collection time could be obtained if more than 1 NaI(Tl) detector were used. The flexibility of the computer has been utilized in a new system designed to record both real + random and random p-γ coincident pulse-height distributions between one charged particle detector and any one of 6 γ-ray detectors. The proposed system is illustrated in Figure 2. A somewhat limited version of this has recently been put into operation.

III. RESULTS

Nuclei studied with this technique are listed in Table I. Sample illustrations from the work are presented as each of the nuclei are discussed in turn.

TABLE I. Nuclei Under Investigation
Employing the Method II Geometry

Residual Nucleus	Reaction	Q (MeV)
O^{18}	$F^{19}(t,\alpha)$	11.82
O^{20}	$O^{18}(t,p)$	3.08
Ne^{24}	$Ne^{22}(t,p)$	5.59
Mg^{28}	$Mg^{26}(t,p)$	6.46
Na^{23}	$Mg^{24}(t,\alpha)$	8.12
Na^{25}	$Na^{23}(t,p)$; $Mg^{26}(t,\alpha)$	7.49; 5.66
Al^{29}	$Al^{27}(t,p)$; $Si^{30}(t,\alpha)$	8.68; 6.22

O^{18} and Na^{23}

The study of O^{18} employing the $F^{19}(t,\alpha)O^{18}$ reaction illustrates many points mentioned above. Figure 3 illustrates the charged particle spectrum coincident with γ-rays of energy > 600 keV. One can see that levels in O^{18} up to an excitation energy of 8-MeV are populated in this reaction, and those which do not decay by α particle emission are readily studied using α-γ coincidence techniques. By contrast, much of the previous work (apart from direct reaction studies) relied on the $C^{14}(\alpha,\gamma)O^{18}$ reaction[5,6] and

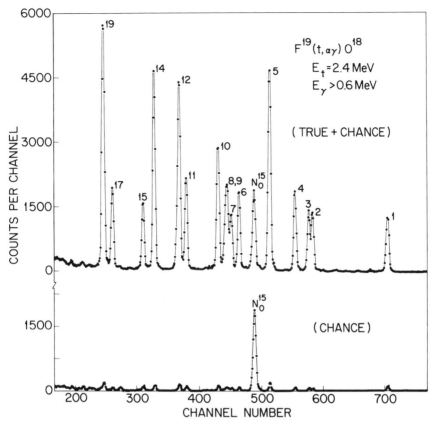

Fig. 3. Pulse-height distribution of α-particles coincident with γ-rays with energy > 600 keV following the F^{19} $(t,\alpha)O^{18}$ reaction. Levels are identified in Fig. 4.

the $O^{18}(p,p)O^{18}$ reaction[7]. While much information is usually obtained from the α,γ work only selective levels above the α particle binding energy are populated in the α,γ reaction and then one at a time. The $O^{18}(p,p)$ work studied levels only up to 5.52-MeV and employed a tandem Van de Graaff accelerator.

The entire α,γ coincidence matrix was measured for all these states (Fig. 3) simultaneously (for each θγ) employing dual 4096 channel ADC's and the computer based data acquisition system; the coincident events are written out on magnetic tape using the full 4096 × 4096 matrix and can be recalled for analysis using any desired dispersion. A wealth of data was obtained, and data reduction is still in progress. Figure 4 shows a partial level scheme for O^{18}.

Level assignments and γ–decay branching modes are not taken
from the literature and this work. One might note that
mostly the negative parity states do not decay to the ground
state, but prefer the 1.98–MeV level. The assignment[8]
$J^{\pi} = 0^{-}(1^{+})$ to the 6.86–MeV level is based on the isotropic
angular distributions for all the γ–ray decays originating
with this level, the fact that it does not α–decay, and its
γ–decay mode. Figure 5 illustrates the angular distribution
of the 1.98–MeV γ–ray following the decay of the 1.98–MeV

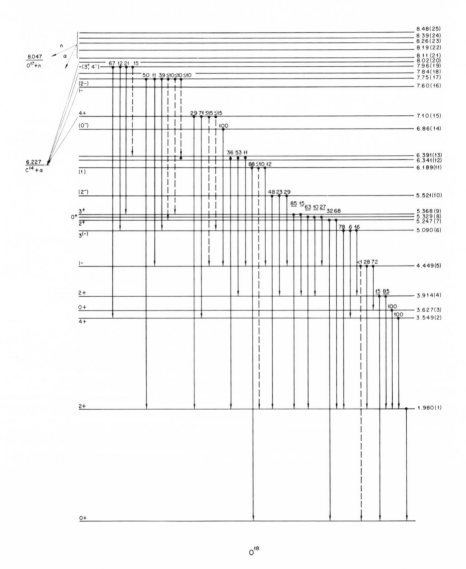

Fig. 4. Partial level scheme for O^{18}.

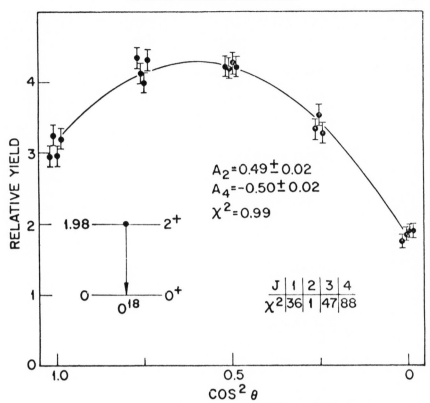

Fig. 5. Angular distribution of the O^{18} 1.98-MeV γ-ray following the $F^{19}(t,\alpha)O^{18*}$ (1.98) reaction.

level. Analysis of the data indicates the 1.98-MeV level has J = 2 and is populated mostly in the m = 0 substate. Note that the agreement among the 19 data points included in this distribution is quite good. Each data point has a 3% error, and χ^2 = 1.0 for the Legendre polynomial fit to this distribution. This agreement results from the normalization of the yields to the (simultaneously measured) isotropic yield of γ-rays from the 6.86-MeV level. Figure 6 illustrates the angular distribution of the 6.19 → 0 γ-ray following the population of the 6.19-MeV level. Analysis of these data indicate J = 1 for this level.

Na^{23} is another case where the triton beam is being used to extend the available information to higher regions of excitation energy. Figure 7 illustrates a partial level scheme for Na^{23}. Previous γ-ray angular distribution data was restricted to levels in Na^{23} below 3 MeV[9]. Using the

J. A. Becker

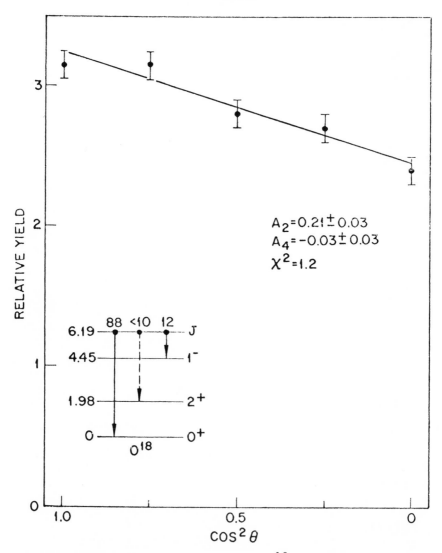

Fig. 6. Angular distribution of the O^{18} 6.19-MeV level fol-
         lowing the $F^{19}(t,\alpha)O^{18*}$ (6.19) reaction.

$Mg^{24}(t,\alpha)Na^{23}$ reaction, angular distribution data have been
collected for levels up to an excitation energy of 5.74-MeV.
These data are presently being analyzed. The 3.68-MeV level
is somewhat unusual, in view of its γ-ray decay modes.
Based on the angular distribution of the 3.68 → 2.64 transition, one can arrive at a spin assignment for this level.
The 2.64 and 3.68-MeV levels have $J^\pi = (1/2, 3/2)^-$ since

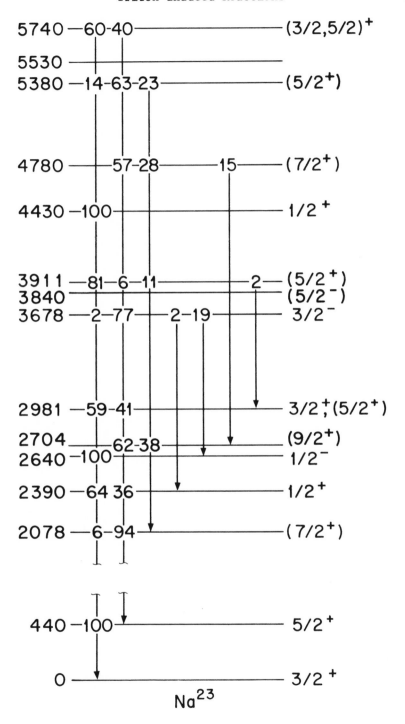

Fig. 7. Partial level scheme for Na²³.

J. A. Becker

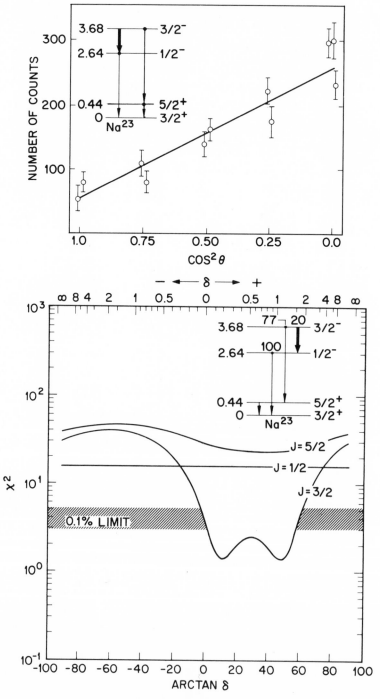

Fig. 8. Angular distribution and χ^2 fit to the Na^{23} 3.68
2.64-MeV transition.

they are both populated in an $\ell = 1$ transition via the
$Ne^{22}(He^3,d)$ reaction. Preliminary doppler shift experiments
indicate that the lifetime of the 2.64-MeV level, t_m,
$\leq 2 \times 10^{-13}$ sec ($\Gamma > 3.3 \times 10^{-3}$ eV). A 3/2 assignment to
the 2.64-MeV level together with the measured mixing of the
2.64 → 0 transition $\delta = -(0.26 \pm 0.05)$ requires $\Gamma(M2) >$
1.4×10^{-4} eV. The Weisskopf estimate, $\Gamma_w(M2)$, $= 1.56 \times 10^{-5}$
so a transition strength $|M|^2 > 9$ is required. As there is
no known M2 transition in the s-d shell with $|M|^2 > 1$, the
3/2 assignment for the 2.64-MeV level may be safely rejected,
resulting in a $J^\pi = 1/2^-$ assignment for the level. Fitting[10] the angular distribution (Figure 8) of the 3.68 →
2.64-MeV transition (19%), then, with $J = 1/2$ for the
2.64-MeV level requires $J = 3/2$ for the 3.68-MeV level,
with mixing ratio $0.07 < \delta(E2/M1) < 1.50$, while the angular
distribution of the 3.68 → 0.44 transition (77%) requires
$\delta(M2/E1) = (0.078 \pm 0.094)$.

$$Na^{25}, Al^{29}, Mg^{28}, O^{20}, Ne^{24}$$

Na^{25}

Measurement of the γ-ray angular distributions in Na^{25}
was made employing the $Mg^{26}(t,\alpha)Na^{25}$ reaction to populate'
the levels. Figure 9 illustrates a partial level scheme
for Na^{25}. The ground state has $J^\pi = 5/2^+$, while based on
lifetime measurements the 90-keV level has $J = 3/2$ or $5/2$.
Only a rough idea of the γ-ray branching was obtained from
the angular distribution work, because the resolution of
the NaI(Tl) detector is not adequate to separate the relative amounts of ground vs first excited state transitions.
(A study of the γ-transitions was undertaken employing a
Ge(Li) detector is described in Section IV.) The angular distribution of the 1.07 → 0.09 cascade γ-ray is isotropic,
consistent with the $J = 1/2^+$ assignment to the 1.07-MeV
level required by the angular distribution of He^3 particles
from the $Mg^{26}(d,He^3)$ reaction. The angular distribution of
the 2.20 → 1.07 cascade γ-ray requires $J = 3/2$ for the
2.20-MeV level if the 1.07-MeV level has $J = 1/2$, with
$\delta = -0.03 \leq 0.09 \leq 0.21$ or $1.07 \leq 1.43 \leq 1.88$. The 2.91-
MeV level has $J = 3/2$ or $5/2$ if the 90-keV level has spin
3/2. The comparison of Na^{25} with O^{19} is very interesting

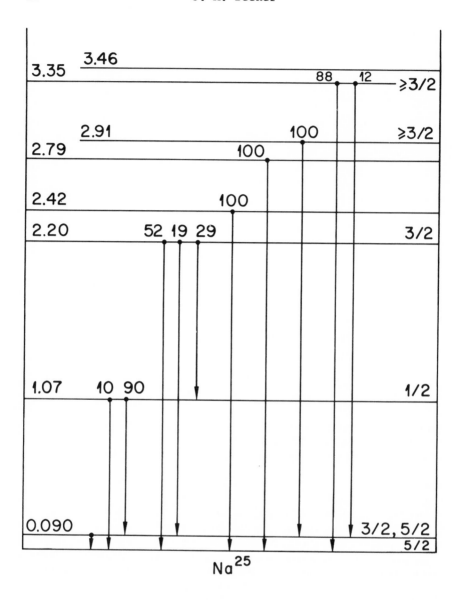

Fig. 9. Partial level scheme for Na^{25}.

(see Figure 10). Both are T = 3/2 nuclei, and one expects
the first few states to be shell model states characterized
by the $d_{5/2}^3$ configuration. This does seem to be the case.

Spacing of the energy levels is quite similar, and the
second excited states both have similar decay modes. Calculations[11] suggest that the J = 3/2 2.20-MeV level is a
good candidate for the $d_{5/2}^2(2)s_{1/2}$ level. It would be

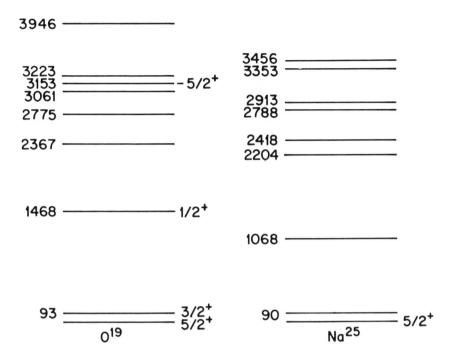

Fig. 10.   Comparison of the energy levels in O^{19} and Na^{25}.

especially interesting if the 2.42-MeV level has J = 9/2
as the excitation energy of the J = 9/2 level arising from
the $d_{5/2}^3$ configuration is predicted to be around 2.6-MeV.

Mg^{28}

This T = 2 nucleus was populated using the $Mg^{26}(t,p)Mg^{28}$
reaction. While magnetic substates with m = 0, ± 1 may be
populated here, interpretation of the distribution was
relatively straight forward as γ-ray angular distributions
were in general quite marked, and also because δ ≡ 0 for a
ground state γ-ray transition. Data have been reduced for
levels up to and including 4.87-MeV excitation energy
(Figure 11).   In all cases the spin assignments are in
agreement with those of Hinds and Middleton[12]. Figure 12
illustrates the angular distributions obtained for the 3.08-
and 1.47-MeV γ-rays following the decay of the 4.55-MeV
level, the second 2^+ state. Fitting these data requires
δ = 0 for the 3.08-MeV γ-ray. A similar fit to the 3.40-MeV
γ-ray following the decay of the 4.87-MeV level results in
δ = 0.36 ± 0.10 for the 3.40-MeV γ-ray.

J. A. Becker

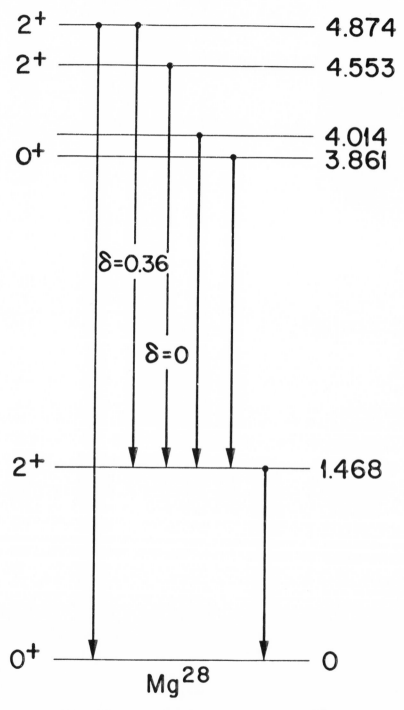

Fig. 11. Partial level scheme of Mg^{28}.

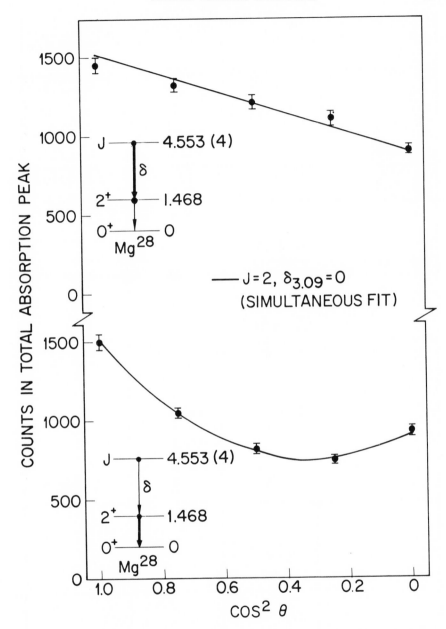

Fig. 12. Angular distributions of the Mg^{28} 4.55-MeV level.

Ne^{24}

Another T = 2 nucleus, Ne^{24} has been studied via the $Ne^{22}(t,p)Ne^{24}$ reaction. γ-ray angular distributions and

J. A. Becker

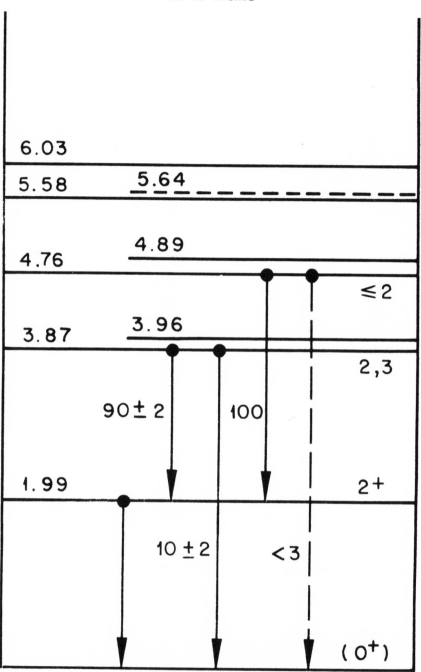

Ne^{24}

Fig. 13. Partial level scheme for Ne^{24}.

decay modes were obtained for the 1.99-, 3.87-, and 4.76-MeV levels, and Figure 13 illustrates the results. Spin assignments $J = 2$ and $J = 0$ or 1 are preferred for the 3.87- and 4.76-MeV levels, respectively. Since $T = 2$ for Ne^{24} and the neutron $d_{5/2}$ sub-shell is closed, one might expect that the low-lying states in Ne^{24} could be described by 2 protons in the $d_{5/2}$ and $2s_{1/2}$ orbits. This picture has been applied[11] to O^{18} with 2 neutrons in the $d_{5/2}$ and $2s_{1/2}$ orbits with reasonable success. There is a similarity between the location of the first few states in O^{18} and Ne^{24}, and reasonable correspondence is obtained with $J = 2$, 2 and 0 for the 1.99-, 3.87-, and 4.76-MeV levels, respectively. Identification of the 3.96- and 4.89-MeV levels would be useful.

TABLE II. Population Parameters[a] for

2^+ States in Even-Even Nuclei

Residual Nucleus	E_x (MeV)	P(0)	P(1)
O^{18}	1.99	0.69 ± 0.01	0.15 ± 0.01
	3.91	0.13 ± 0.05	0.43 ± 0.03
O^{20}	1.99	1.00 ± 0.02	0
Ne^{24}	1.99[b]	0.84 ± 0.03	0.08 ± 0.01
	3.87[b]	0.12 ± 0.03	0.43 ± 0.02
Mg^{28}	1.47	0.98 ± 0.02	0
	4.55	0.77 ± 0.04	0.10 ± 0.02
	4.87	0.89 ± 0.10	0.06 ± 0.04

(a) $P(0) + 2P(1) \equiv 1.0$

(b) The 2^+ assignment to the level is assumed.

$\underline{O}^{20}$

Four O^{20}, the spin of the first excited state has been
measured with the result J = 2. The shape of the distribution indicated that the state was populated mostly in the
m = 0 substate, as seems to be the case for all the first
2^+ states. Magnetic substate populations obtained for the
first and second 2^+ excited states of the nuclei studied
are summarized in Table II.

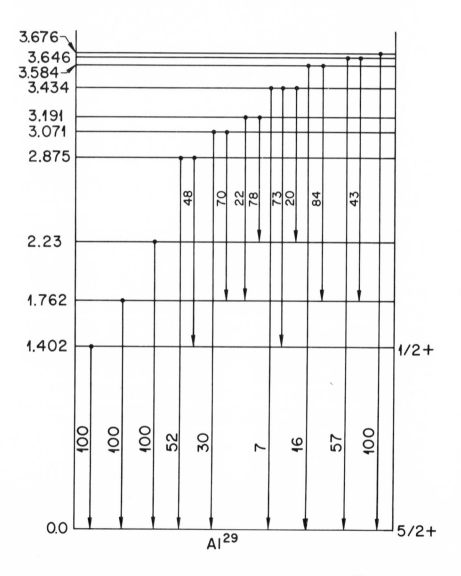

Fig. 14. Partial level scheme for Al^{29}.

Al^{29}

Al^{29} is being studied via the $Si^{30}(t,\alpha)Al^{29}$ and $Al^{27}(t,p)Al^{29}$ reaction. This is recent data, and only a little information has been deduced from the t,p data. A level scheme is illustrated in Figure 14. Isotropic angular distributions (to within 5%) have been obtained for the γ-rays from the first three excited states.

IV. OTHER WORK

Recalling the level scheme for Na^{25}, we note that the first excited state is at 90-keV. With the resolution of NaI(Tl) scintillation spectrometers, it is impossible to obtain the relative amounts of ground vs first excited state transitions, except in the case that no 90-keV radiation is observed in a given γ-ray pulse-height distribution, in which case an upper limit may be deduced for the first excited state transition. To get a better understanding of the γ-decay modes of the Na^{25} levels, a p-γ coincidence measurement was undertaken utilizing a Ge(Li) γ-ray spectrometer. Even with the high resolution of the γ-ray spectrometer it was necessary to add a charged particle coincidence requirement and obtain some charged particle pulse-height information in order to understand the γ-ray spectrum. γ-rays from the $Na^{23}(t,n)Mg^{25}$ reaction were especially troublesome in this respect. The $Na^{23}(t,p)Na^{25}$ reaction was used to populate the Na^{25} levels, and forward going reaction particles were detected in an annular counter. Particles were detected between (55 ± 15) . The Ge(Li) γ-ray spectrometer was located at 90°. Figure 15 illustrates the γ-ray distribution coincident with particles populating the 1068-keV level in Na^{25}, and shows clearly the branching of the 1068-keV level [1068 → 0 (10%) and 1068 → 90 (90%)]. Figure 16 illustrates the decay of the 2418-, 2204-, and 1068-keV levels. It is apparent from the figure that the 2418-keV level decays entirely via direct ground state transitions, while the 2204-keV level decays to the 90- and 1068-keV levels, as well as to the ground state. Note that this spectrum is already somewhat complex, and when decays from the other closely spaced levels near 4.5-MeV are included, one can see that interpretation of a single spectrum becomes very complicated.

Other recent work includes the measurement of nuclear lifetimes rising direct electronic techniques. The Na^{25} first excited state posseses a mean lifetime $t_m = (7.3 \pm 0.7)$

J. A. Becker

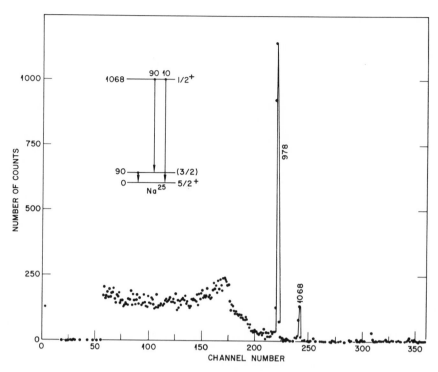

Fig. 15. Pulse–height distribution of γ–rays coincident with
reaction particles populating the 1068–keV state in Na^{25}.

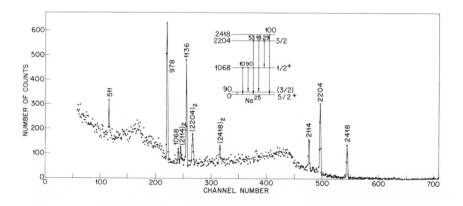

Fig. 16. Pulse–height distribution of γ–rays coincident with
reaction particles populating the 1068–, 2204–, and 2418–keV
levels in Na^{25}. Peaks in the spectrum are labelled in keV
indicating the full energy transition to which they correspond, while 2nd escape peaks are labelled by (full energy)$_2$.

$\times 10^{-9}$ sec. If the spin of this level is $3/2^+$ then this is
a retarded M1 transition with a strength $|M|^2 = 6 \times 10^{-3}$ Wu.
The corresponding transition in O^{19} has $|M|^2 = 2.6 \times 10^{-2}$
Wu. A similar measurement for the F^{21} first excited state
at 280-keV resulted in a value $t_m = (8.3 \pm 0.4) \times 10^{-9}$ sec.
Both measurements utilized the associated particle technique
to provide a $t = 0$ signal indicating formation of the first
excited state. This signal was obtained from a charged
particle spectrometer, and here again pulse-height selection
on the charged particle distribution was an experimental
requirement.

V. ACKNOWLEDGEMENTS

The work described above has been done in collaboration
with the following people, all of Lockheed: L. F. Chase,
Jr., D. Kohler, A. D. W. Jones, R. E. McDonald, A. R.
Poletti, R. W. Nightingale; and with E. K. Warburton
of Brookhaven National Laboratory. The necessary programming for the data acquisition system is the work of R. A.
Chalmers (Lockheed), who is also responsible for the
computer-man interface.

REFERENCES

1. L. F. Chase, Jr., Nuclear Research with Low Energy
    Accelerators, 1967, edited by J. B. Marion and D. M.
    Van Patter (Academic Press, New York, 1968).

2. P. M. Endt and C. van der Leun, Nuclear Physics 34,
    1 (1962); ibid., Nuclear Physics A105,1 (1967).

3. Much of the work on Q values and the location of
    energy levels has been done by Hinds, Middleton and
    collaborators.. Reaction particle angular distribu-
    tions are also reported in some cases.

4. A. E. Litherland and A. J. Ferguson, Can. J. Phys.
    39, 788 (1961). The method was reviewed by Dr. Prosser
    and at the 1966 symposium.

5. H. E. Gove and A. E. Litherland, Phys. Rev. 113,
    1078 (1959).

6. F. D. Lee, Ph. D. Thesis, University of Kansas (1966).

7. J. S. Lopes, O. Hausser, R. D. Gill and H. J. Rose, Nuclear Physics 89, 127 (1966).

8. L. F. Chase, Jr., D. A. Kohler, J. A. Becker and R. E. McDonald, Proceedings of the International Nuclear Physics Conference, 1966, Ed. R. L. Becker (Academic Press, New York, 1967).

9. A. R. Poletti and D. F. H. Start, Phys. Rev. 147, 800 (1966).

10. The procedure of the χ^2 fits to the data follows the method outlined by A. R. Poletti and E. K. Warburton, Phys. Rev. 137, B595 (1965).

11. I. Talmi and I. Unna, Nuclear Physics 30, 280 (1962).

12. R. Middleton and D. J. Pullen, Nuclear Physics 51, 77 (1964).

DISCUSSION

PRONKO: In your slide (Fig. 7) you show a state in Na^{23} at 5.53 MeV. Did you see that at all in your reactions?

BECKER: If we did not indicate the gamma ray decay mode of this state the level was populated weakly or not at all. I would have to look at the charged particle pulse-height distributions.

PRONKO: The reason I asked is that at Yale we have looked at Na^{23} with the (α, α') reaction and have seen this state decay to the 9/2 and the 7/2 states which leads us to believe that it may be 11/2 and a member of the ground state rotational band. We will know for sure when the angular correlations are analyzed.

I.B. EFFECTIVE INTERACTIONS IN NUCLEI
AND TWO-NUCLEON SCATTERING

Daniel S. Koltun
Department of Physics and Astronomy
University of Rochester

I.   INTRODUCTION

The idea of an effective interaction among nucleons
in a nucleus has essentially two main threads which are
somewhat intertwined in history. The first comes from
the study of low-lying levels of nuclei in terms of the
independent particle model -- the early Shell Model. The
fact that different levels assigned to a single Shell
Model configuration are not degenerate means that there
is a "residual interaction" among the nucleons which is
not accounted for in the average potential field which
determines the shell orbital structure. The second thread
comes from the study of two-nucleon scattering.

Early attempts were made to understand the residual
interaction in terms of the properties of potentials which
also could explain the low energy scattering of two nucleons,
and the binding of the deuteron. It was soon found to be
more fruitful to assume that the residual interaction was
a potential something like the free two-nucleon interaction,
but not necessarily identical with it. Thus one might assume no more than that the effective interaction was a two-
body potential, conserving parity and angular momentum.
Many calculations of spectra were done by assuming a simple
functional form, like Yukawa or Gaussian, and treating as
free parameters the strengths and ranges of the different
spin and isospin states -- the "exchange mixtures." And one
generally found that the parameters which were obtained
from attempts to fit the low-lying spectra of light nuclei
[1], affirmed that the effective potential was indeed
similar to the free two-nucleon potential in that it was
attractive in even-ℓ states, with a range of 1.5 fm or so,
with strengths of the order of 40 MeV, that is, consistent
with the binding of the deuteron. The exchange mixtures
found tended to favor repulsion in odd-ℓ states (Rosenfeld),
while "high energy" (e.g. 90 MeV) nucleon-nucleon scattering led to the Serber exchange mixture -- very weak odd-ℓ
interactions.

As the picture of the free two-nucleon interaction
developed further, it became clear that it was not identical
with the residual interaction, and in fact had features

which did not seem immediately compatible with the Shell
Model. In particular, the short-range repulsion apparently
required to explain the behaviour of scattering at 200-300
MeV, would seem to perturb violently a model built on independent particle motion.

It was, of course, the theory of Brueckner and many
others [2] which has built a theoretical bridge between
the two-nucleon problem and the low-lying states of nuclei.
And out of this many-body approach to nuclear dynamics comes
the method for defining and calculating the residual interaction in the Shell Model.

We shall discuss in this lecture several ways in which
the residual interaction can be related back to the two-
nucleon problem. A word about terminology: what we have
been calling the residual interaction in this section
refers in a general sense to whatever is used in Shell
Model spectroscopy, to split the levels of a given configuration. In the next section we shall define the effective
interaction, which plays this role in the formal theory.
This turns out, in general, to be a many-body operator,
which we shall denote by V. Then we shall talk specifically
about the interaction between two-valence particles with
an inert core: we then define a two-body effective interaction, V_2. It is assumed throughout that there is some
interaction between pairs of nucleons, independent of
the nucleus, which is responsible for nucleon-nucleon
scattering. This will be denoted by V, or V(r), although
we make no restriction to local, or momentum independent
interactions.

Most of the approaches we shall discuss start with some
specific assumption of the form of V(r). We shall also
discuss an approach in which elastic scattering information,
but not the explicit form of V(r), leads to very similar
results. This shows to what extent one really needs the
detailed features of V(r) in order to obtain V_2.

II.   EFFECTIVE INTERACTION[3]

Definition of the Shell Model Problem

In the many-body approach to the Shell Model, one
distinguishes between the actual solutions of the eigenvalue equation for the nucleus, and the equivalent Shell
Model matrix equations and solutions. To be specific,
consider a set of functions ϕ_i, which describe a set of
states degenerate in the independent particle model, that
is, states of one configuration (e.g. closed shell + j^n):

$$H_o \phi_i = E^o \phi_i, \qquad i = 1,\ldots,q. \tag{1}$$

Now consider a solution of the complete eigenvalue equation, with full interaction V:

$$(E_\lambda - H_o)\Psi_\lambda = V\Psi_\lambda . \tag{2}$$

We can expand Ψ_λ in terms of the states ϕ_i, and all the other eigenstates of H_o:

$$\Psi_\lambda = \sum_{i=1}^{q} a_i^\lambda \phi_i + \text{other states}. \tag{3}$$

The matrix elements of (2) with the ϕ_i gives

$$<\phi_i|E_\lambda - H_o | \Psi_\lambda > = (E_\lambda - E^o) a_i^\lambda = <\phi_i | V | \Psi_\lambda >. \tag{4}$$

We now <u>define</u> the effective interaction $V(E_\lambda)$ for the state $\chi_\lambda = \sum_{i=1}^{q} a_i^\lambda \phi_i$:

$$V(E_\lambda)\chi_\lambda \equiv V \Psi_\lambda \tag{5}$$

Then (4) becomes a secular matrix equation on the Shell Model basis functions only:

$$(E_\lambda - E^o) a_i^\lambda = \sum_{j=1}^{q} <\phi_i| V(E_\lambda) | \phi_j> a_j^\lambda. \tag{6}$$

Thus the residual interaction has been defined to be the effective interaction (5), which obeys the equation (degenerate Brillouin-Wigner)

$$V(E) = V + V \frac{Q_A}{E - H_o} V(E) \tag{7}$$

where Q_A is the projection operator which is zero in the shell model space $\{\phi_i\}$ and 1 otherwise.

Now the problem of getting the effective interaction from the interaction among nucleons is restated in terms of solving (7) for $V(E)$ in terms of V. This is a many-body problem, and in general, its solutions contain many-body components in the effective interaction. It is believed that nuclei are sufficiently dilute that the many-body effective potentials are smaller than the two-body effective potentials, and that the former can be calculated from the latter. This means that most effects in the Shell Model can still be traced to two-body interactions, as was assumed in the parametric models discussed above.

III. TWO-BODY EFFECTIVE INTERACTION

A simple example of the residual interaction problem

(6) is given by a nucleus whose shell model description
is two-valence nucleons outside a closed shell core, as
in ^{18}O or ^{42}Sc. The basis functions give the coupling
of the valence particles:

$$|\phi_i> = |n_1 \ell_1 j_1, n_2 \ell_2 j_2, JM >. \tag{8}$$

The effective interaction is given by a two-body matrix

$$<\phi_i | V (E) | \phi_j > = < j_1 j_2 JM | V (E) | j_1' j_2' JM> \tag{9}$$

which satisfies the equation (7), which we now write

$$< i| V (E) | j> = <i | V | j> + \sum_{k<q} \frac{<i|V|k><k|V(E)|j>}{E - E_k} \tag{10}$$

Equation (10) is still a many-particle equation; when E =
E_λ it is formally equivalent to the Schroedinger equation
(2) for the system. Thus, although the states i, j are
core plus two-valence-particle states, the intermediate
states k include those for which the two-valence particles
have been excited to higher shells, and also excitations
of the core: 3 particle - 1 hole states, 4p - 2h, and so on.

It is useful to try to separate the excitation of
the valence particles, which is closely related to the
strongest features of the free two-nucleon interaction,
from the excitations of the core, which are more a feature
of the low-lying states. To do this, we shall first
restrict the intermediate states k in (10) to excited two-
valence-particle states only, thus "freezing" the core:
no polarization. This makes (10) essentially a two-body
equation, which we may attempt to solve. We may express
this formally by changing the projection operator Q_A (7) to
Q_{2p} which selects only 2 particle + closed core states:

$$V_2(E) = V + V \frac{Q_{2p}}{E - H_o} V_2(E) \tag{11}$$

The full effective interaction (1) may be expressed in
terms of V_2

$$V(E) = V_2(E) + V_2(E) (\frac{Q_A - Q_{2p}}{E - H_o}) V (E) \tag{12}$$

Thus one may include the effects of core polarization
after calculating the "bare" effective interaction V_2.
Brown and Kuo [4] have calculated (12) by setting
$V \simeq V_2$ on the right, which gives the first perturbation
correction. They have included 3p - 1h and 4p - 2h
states in Q_A. The corrected V so calculated, has been
called the renormalized interaction. This method of solv-

ing for V by successive approximation avoids having to
solve directly the many-particle problem, but, of course,
it will not work well if V is not well approximated by V_2.

Note that both V and V_2 for the problem under discussion
are two-body effective interactions; this property need not
hold when the same methods are applied to several valence
particles.

IV. OBTAINING THE INTERACTION V_2

We may distinguish two approaches to extracting the
effective interaction V_2 from its definition equation (11):

1) If we consider V, the interaction between two
particles outside a nucleus, to be completely known, then
(11) may be treated as an integral equation, and solved
for $V_2(E)$ for some range of the parameter E, which is
appropriate to the matrix equation (6).

2) Alternatively, we may take the more restricted
view that what is actually known is two-nucleon scattering
data, to which a variety of model interactions V have been
fit. Then (11) cannot be "solved" but may be approximated
in ways we shall discuss.

I should like to think of the second approach as a way
of qualifying the results of the first: it provides a
way of determining to what extent V_2 depends only on the
two-nucleon scattering, or conversely, how much non-elastic
information is required for the two-nucleon system, in
order to get an accurate value for V_2.

We may begin the discussion of calculating V_2 in
either approach, on a common ground. Since the convenient
coordinate system for the free two-nucleon system is the
two-body relative and center-of-mass coordinates, it is
also convenient to separate the Shell Model basis states
accordingly. This can be done most simply for the harmonic oscillator Shell Model, which has therefore been a
popular choice. One uses the well-known transformations
of Talmi and Moshinsky [5]:

$$|n_1\ell_1,n_2\ell_2, \; \Lambda\rangle= \sum_{n\ell NL} |n\ell,NL, \; \Lambda\rangle\langle n\ell,NL,\Lambda|n_1\ell_1,n_2\ell_2\Lambda\rangle \; . \qquad (13)$$

This is a finite sum, and the coefficients are tabulated.
I have omitted spin at this point for notational simplicity.

Rewriting the basis function (13) does not mean that
equation (11) separates into uncoupled equations: the
Pauli operator Q_{2p} mixes states of different center-of-
mass quantum numbers, NL. This mixing has been estimated
to be small, however, and one usually considers only the
terms diagonal in NL:

$$\langle n'\ell', NL, \Lambda \mid V_2 (E) \mid n\ell, NL, \Lambda \rangle .\qquad(14)$$

With spin, one may, of course, have tensor mixing:

$$\ell' = \ell \text{ or } \ell \pm 2.$$

Now one must make some explicit choice of the intermediate states $\underline{k}$, and energies E_k, in (11):

$$\frac{Q_{2p}}{E - H_o} = \sum_{k>q} \frac{\mid k \rangle \langle k \mid}{E - E_k} .\qquad(15)$$

This is still an open problem for finite nuclei, but two choices have been made in practice:

1) Brown and Kuo have used plane wave states with E_k = kinetic energy, based on arguments used in calculation for infinite nuclear matter.

2) Others have taken $\underline{k}$ to be harmonic oscillator states, with the same H_o for the shell model basis states ϕ_i.

Brown and Kuo have followed the methods of Moszkowski and Scott [6] (at least for the even-ℓ states) in which the two-body potential is divided into short - and long-range parts:

$$V = V_s + V_\ell.$$

We then expand, to second order in V :

$$V_2 = V_s + V_\ell + V_\ell \frac{Q_{zp}}{E - H_o} V_\ell + \text{other terms,}\qquad(16)$$

The separation is arranged so that V_s, which is the solution to (11) with V_s only, is small or zero. Estimating the "other terms" to be small, the effective interaction in this approximation consists of the terms of first and second order in V_ℓ. For a central force, as for the S = 0 two-body states (e.g. $^1S_0$), the first-order term dominates, while for spin triplet states like $^3S_1$, the tensor force makes the second order term of (16) comparable with the first order term.

The approach based on oscillator states, which began with Eden, Emery, and Sampanthar [7], has generally begun by converting equation (11), in relative coordinates, into a wave-function equation, which is sometimes called the Bethe-Goldstone equation. Using the definition

$$V\Psi_{n\ell sj}(\underline{r}) = V_2 \phi_{n\ell sj}(\underline{r})\qquad(17)$$

one may obtain

$$(E-H_o-V(r)) \; \Psi_{n\ell sj}(r) = \phi_{n\ell sj}(r) \; (E-E_o \; -<\phi_{n\ell}|V|\Psi>)$$

$$- \sum_{n'} (P_{n'}-\delta_{n',n}) \phi_{n'\ell sj}(r)<\phi_{n'\ell}|V|\Psi > \quad (18)$$

The quantum numbers include the coupling of the two-body spin S to the relative orbital angular momentum ℓ: $\underline{\ell} + \underline{S} = \underline{j}$. This equation (18) looks like the Schroedinger equation with two inhomogeneous terms added. In fact, for the Schroedinger solution:

$$(E_{n\ell sj} - H_o - V) \; \Psi(\text{Sch.}) = 0 \quad (19)$$

we have the eigenvalue relation:

$$E_{n\ell sj} = E_o + <\phi_{n\ell} | V | \Psi (\text{Sch.})> \quad (20)$$

where E_o is the energy of the unperturbed oscillator state:

$$H_o \; \phi_{n\ell sj} = E_o(n\ell) \; \phi_{n\ell sj},$$

Thus, the first inhomogeneous term in (18) is proportional to the difference of the energy parameter E and the Schroedinger eigenvalue $E_{n\ell sj}$; we shall call this the spectral term.

The second inhomogeneous term is due to the exclusion of valence particles from the core, and shall be called the Pauli term. This term is approximate, as we have mentioned, in the sense that the terms which couple different NL have been dropped. The form of $P_{n'}$ derived by Grillot [8], and by Kallio and Day [9] is

$$P_{n'} = \sum_{n_1\ell_1 n_2\ell_2 \Lambda}^{\text{occupied}} \left\{ \frac{2 \Lambda + 1}{(2\ell+1)(2L+1)} \right\} \; |<n_1\ell_1,n_2\ell_2,\Lambda|n'\ell,NL,\Lambda>|^2. \quad (21)$$

For low values of n', $P_{n'} \cong 1$, and $P_{n'}$ decreases to zero with increasing n'.

Now, if the interaction V(r) is known, equation (18) may be solved for the functions $\Psi_{n\ell sj}(r)$, and for the matrix elements:

$$<n'\ell'sj | V_2 (E)| n\ell sj> = <\phi_{n'\ell'sj} |V|\Psi_{n\ell sj}> \quad (22)$$

which are our immediate interest. Note that the $\chi_{n\ell sj}$ depend on the parameter E, and on N,L.

Numerical solutions for this version of equation (18) have been obtained for some states, by Grillot and by Kallio and Day. Earlier work by Eden, Emery and Sampanthar,

and by Becker and MacKellar[10] is similar in approach,
but used a different approximation for the Pauli effect.
All of these people were interested in the binding energy
of O^{16}, and calculated all the effective interaction
matrix elements for two particles in the first s and p
shells.

    The Schroedinger approximation (19) to equation (18)
has also been solved numerically for some states by Talmi,
Dawson, and Walecka [11]. If this were a good approximation to the complete Bethe-Goldstone equation (18),
one could correct for the spectral and Pauli terms by perturbation theory. There would be no major advantage to
this approach if the interaction V(r) were known, since
the numerical solution of the inhomogeneous equation (18)
is apparently not essentially more difficult than that
of the homogeneous (Schroedinger)approximation.

    However, there is a significant advantage in treating
the Schroedinger equation first, if one does not know V(r)
explicitly, but does have the two-nucleon elastic scattering information. That is because it is possible to obtain
very good approximate values of the matrix elements of the
effective interaction (20) directly from the phase-shift
information [12]. It is also possible to use this method
to include the spectral and Pauli corrections, but to somewhat
less accuracy. We shall discuss this approach now.

    Connections between the effective interaction and two-
body scattering data have been discussed by several people.
I shall try to indicate the relation to the present approach,
a little later.

V. PHASE SHIFT METHOD [12]

    The Schroedinger equation (19) can be written out more
fully, removing the angular functions

$$\{E_{n\ell Sj} + \frac{1}{M}\frac{d^2}{dr^2} - \frac{\ell(\ell+1)}{Mr^2} - U(r) - V(r)\}\, u_{n\ell Sj}(r) = 0, \quad (23)$$

where we use the radial wave function $u_{n\ell Sj}(r)/r$ and $U(r)$ is
the potential part of H_o, in relative coordinates. We shall
consider the harmonic oscillator potential

$$U(r) = \frac{1}{4} M\omega r^2 \tag{24}$$

with M as the nucleon mass.

    We wish to solve (23) for the eigenvalues $E_{n\ell Sj}$, without
recourse to the explicit functional form of the two nucleon
potential V(r). In order to do this we shall have to assume
one general property of V(r): that it be short-ranged, compared to the distance over which the potential U(r) varies

significantly. We may see that this assumption is quite good
for the phenomenological potentials generally used to fit
the two-nucleon scattering data, of which the Hamada-
Johnston [13] is a well known example. Such potentials
generally have the longest range part given by a Yukawa
form of range $\mu^{-1} \simeq 1.4$ fm. The potential $U(r)$ (24) with
$\hbar\omega$ = 15 MeV, is only ~ 4 MeV at r = 1.4 fm, compared to
zero at the origin. This small energy variation is negligible compared to that of $V(r)$ within this range.

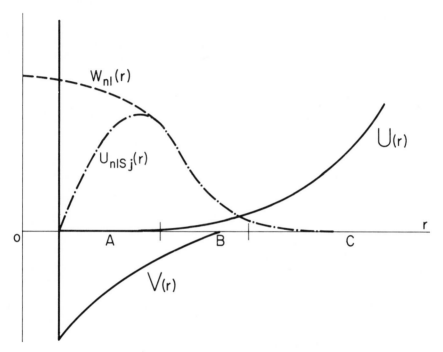

Fig. 1. This figure shows qualitatively, as a function of
relative coordinate r, the potentials (solid lines) and solutions (dot- dashed line) for the Schroedinger equation (23).
Within region A, the two-nucleon interaction $V(r)$ dominates,
while in region C, the external (oscillator) potential $U(r)$
dominates. The wave function matching is done in region B.
The dashed line shows the matched solutions continued into
A, from B.

     Now the central use of the flatness of $U(r)$ within the
range of $V(r)$ is, that the solutions of (23) within this
range are very similar to those with $U(r)$ identically
zero. These are, in fact, the solutions to the equation
for two-nucleon scattering by the potential $V(r)$, at a
relative energy $E = E_{n\ell Sj}$. In Figure 1, we are discussing
the region A. Now if we do not know the function $V(r)$,
neither do we know the solution $u_{n\ell Sj}(r)$ within A. However,

still within the flat region of $U(r)$, in which we do know
the solution to the scattering equation; it is of the form:

$$Z_{\ell Sj}(kr) \propto rj_\ell(kr) - rn_\ell(kr) \tan \delta_{\ell Sj} \quad (e), \qquad (25)$$

with

$$E = k^2/M.$$

Outside the range of $V(r)$, which includes both the
regions B, and C, beyond, the solutions of (23) are known:
they are the solutions of the harmonic oscillator problem
for the arbitrary energy E. They can be expressed in terms
of the confluent hypergeometric functions, which are known.
We shall denote these solutions, which are regular at
$r \to \infty$, by $\omega_{n\ell}(E,r)$.

Thus we conclude that the solution to the original
equation (23) must look both like the oscillator solution
$\omega_{n\ell}(E,r)$, and like the scattering solution $Z_{\ell Sj}(kr)$, in
the region B. So one may find the eigenvalue $E= E_{n\ell Sj}$ for
which these two functions do in fact coincide, up to normalization, by matching the logarithmic derivatives of
the two functions at some arbitrary point r_o, within B.
This solution can be done essentially by hand, requiring
only tables of the known functions, and of the appropriate
phase shifts, as a function of energy. So one has "solved"
the Schroedinger equation (23) for $E_{n\ell Sj}$, and thus (using
(20)) for the matrix elements of the effective interaction
in relative coordinates

$$\langle n\ell Sj \mid V_2(E_{n\ell Sj}) \mid n\ell Sj \rangle = E_{n\ell Sj} - E_o(n\ell) \equiv \Delta E_{n\ell Sj}, \qquad (26)$$

without the explicit form of $V(r)$, but with the scattering
phase shift $\delta_{\ell Sj}(E)$.

The solution is not very sensitive to the choice of
matching radius r_o; in fact it is consistent with the
present approximation to continue both the known functions
$\omega_{n\ell}(E,r)$ and $Z_{\ell Sj}(kr)$ to very short distances, well within
A. For example, one may take $r_o = 0$, for which the matching
can be done most easily [12] even though neither function is
a solution of (23) within region A. This follows from
the fact that, if $U(r)$ were identically zero within A and
B, then matching $\omega_{n\ell}$ and $Z_{\ell Sj}$ at one point r_o matches them
at all points in A and B. Then the small actual varia-
tion of the oscillator potential (24) over A and B does
not disturb this matching very much. At $r_o = 0$, the
matching condition becomes a relation between $\tan \delta(k)$
and gamma functions whose arguments contain E and ℓ. [12]

When the partial waves are coupled by tensor interactions, as for $^3S_1$ and $^3D_1$, the problem becomes one of matching simultaneously two interior to two exterior solutions for a single energy E. This is not substantially more difficult than the case of a single partial wave we have already discussed: one needs the eigenphase shifts δ_1 and δ_2, and the mixing parameter ε for the coupled waves. In this case, however, one obtains only the diagonal matrix elements (26), and not those of the form

$$<n_1, j + 1, S, j \mid V_2 \mid n, j-1, S, j>$$

Similarly, one does not obtain matrix elements off-diagonal in principle quantum number $\underline{n}$, but these are not required for particles within a single major shell.

As an example, we have compared the results of the phase shift method, with two other numerical methods for the Schroedinger equation (23). In Table I we listed the matrix elements (26) appropriate to two nucleons in the 0p shell, with $\hbar\omega \sim 15$ MeV, which gives the oscillator constant for ^{16}O to fit the mean square radius measured by electron scattering.

The phase shift method results quoted were calculated on a slide rule! Grillot's results [8] were obtained by numerical integration (on a computer) of equation (23) using the Hamada-Johnston potential [13] for V(r). Kim [14] used the same V(r), but followed a method suggested by Nigam, in which the wave equations are converted to large matrix equations, based on harmonic oscillator orbitals, whose origins are displaced to the hard-core radius. In order to make our comparison on the same ground, we used the phase shifts given by Hamada and Johnston for the phase-shift method.

Comparing the first two columns of Table I, it seems clear that the phase shift method is a very good approximation to direct numerical solution, and it is very much simpler. Kim's method does not agree well for the $^3S_1$ cases, but there is good reason to believe (from results not shown here) that his method converges very slowly in the presence of tensor interactions, although his matrices are 150 x 150!

One may now calculate the usual two-body effective interaction matrix elements

$$<j_1 j_2, J \mid V_2 \mid j_1 j_2, J>$$

by inverting the transformation (13) from $n\ell$, NL,Λ to $n_1\ell_1$, $n_2\ell_2$,Λ, with some Racah recoupling of the spins:

$$\ell + S = j, \quad j + \Lambda = J \quad \text{to } S + \Lambda = J.$$

Daniel S. Koltun

TABLE I

Schroedinger values of $\Delta E_{n\ell Sj}$ (Eqn. 26) (in MeV)
for 0p Shell

State ($n\ell$)	Phase Shift Meth. $\hbar\omega= 15$	Grillot $\hbar\omega=14.5$	Kim $\hbar\omega=15.27$
$^1S_0$ (0S)	-8.55	-8.16	-8.31
$^1S_0$ (1S)	-4.80	-4.39	-4.03
$^3P_0$	-1.59	-2.01	
$^3P_1$	1.73	1.86	
$^3P_2$	-1.46	-1.24	
$^1D_2$	-0.56	-0.61	
$^3S_1$ (0S)	-16.1	-15.91	-8.96
$^3S_1$ (1S)	-8.25	-7.84	-3.80
$^1P_1$	1.53	1.68	
$^3D_1$	1.86	2.11	
$^3D_2$	-2.35	-2.73	
$^3D_3$	-0.56	-1.07	

VI. CORRECTIONS AND COMPARISONS

We return to the Bethe-Goldstone equation (18) through
which we have defined the effective two-body interaction,
V_2. We have already discussed a method of calculating
the Schroedinger approximation to V_2 using the scattering
phase shifts. We shall now see to what extent we can calculate the spectral and Pauli corrections, to obtain an
improved approximation to V_2, still using the phase-shift
information alone. We should point out that in principle,
this improvement can be, at best, only approximate, since
both corrections require some knowledge of the wave-function

in the strongly interacting region, (A in Figure 1) and therefore, of the interaction $V(r)$ itself. This is not true for the Schroedinger equation: as we mentioned before, the phase-shift method gives the <u>exact solution</u> when $U(r)$ is <u>exactly constant</u> inside $V(r)$.

We first rewrite (18) in the more compact form

$$(E-H)\Psi_i = p\phi_i - \sum_j \phi_j (P_j - \delta_{ij}) < \phi_j | V | \Psi_i > \qquad (26)$$

where $H = H_o + V$, $H_o \phi_i = E_i^o \phi_i$,

P_i is the Pauli factor (21), and $p = E - E_o - < \phi_i | V | \Psi_i >$.

Let us first neglect the second (Pauli) term, and treat the first term by perturbation theory. The unperturbed solutions are the Schroedinger solutions:

$$(E_i^S - H)\Psi_i^S = 0.$$

Then, to first order in p:

$$\Psi_i = \Psi_i^S + p \sum_{k(\neq i)} \Psi_k^S \frac{<\Psi_k^S | \phi_i>}{E_i^S - E_k^S} \qquad (27)$$

But we may write the Schroedinger solution:

$$\Psi_i^S = \phi_k + \sum_{j(\neq k)} \phi_j \frac{<\phi_j | V | \Psi_k^S>}{E_k^S - E_j^o} , \quad \text{with} <\phi_k | \Psi_k^S> = 1. \qquad (28)$$

Then the spectral correction to the effective interaction (26) becomes

$$\Delta E(\text{spec.}) = <\phi_i | V | \Psi_i - \Psi_i^S> = p\sum_{k(\neq i)} \frac{<\Psi_i^S | V | \phi_k><\phi_i | V | \Psi_k^S>}{(E_k^S - E_i^o)(E_i^S - E_k^S)}. \qquad (29)$$

We may notice, by comparison with (28), that the correction term is approximately given by <u>p</u> multiplied by the probability

$$\sum_{k(\neq i)} |<\phi_k | \Psi_i^S>|^2 = <\Psi_i^S - \phi_i | \Psi_i^S - \phi_i> \qquad (30)$$

that the solution Ψ_i^S is not identical with the unperturbed oscillator state ϕ_i [15]. In the nuclear matter problem the analogous quantity, which has been called the volume of the "defect" or "wound", has been estimated to be 10-15%.

The Pauli term can be put in a similar form. If we now neglect the spectral term, and calculate to first order in the Pauli term:

$$\Psi_i = \Psi_i^S - \sum_{k(\neq i)} \sum_j \Psi_k^S \frac{<\phi_j|V|\Psi_i^S>}{E_i^S - E_k^S} <\Psi_k^S|\phi_j> (P_j - \delta_{ij}). \quad (31)$$

Again, using (28), the Pauli correction becomes

$$\Delta E(Pauli) = <\phi_i|V|\Psi_i - \Psi_i^S> = - \sum_{k(\neq i)} \frac{<\phi_i|V|\Psi_k^S><\phi_k|V|\Psi_i^S>}{E_i^S - E_k^S} \quad (32)$$

dropping terms of third order in V_2.

To evaluate (29) and (32), we need off-diagonal elements $<\phi_i|V|\Psi_k^S>$, which are not calculated in the phase-shift method. However, we believe that a reasonable estimate may be obtained by interpolating from the diagonal matrix elements, which can be calculated:

$$<\phi_i|V|\Psi_k^S> \simeq \frac{1}{2} \{<\phi_i|V|\Psi_i^S> + <\phi_k|V|\Psi_k^S> \} \quad (33)$$

We expect this to be valid for close values of i and k, since the diagonal elements change slowly with principle quantum number. This is presumably a consequence of the short range of $V(r)$. We rely on the denominators of (29) and (32) to damp the high-energy intermediate states, n'>>n, for which this estimate is probably poor.

Putting in numbers from Table I for the state n,ℓ = 0, s, (for which there is no Pauli term) we estimate roughly:

$$\Delta E(spec) \simeq 0.1 \cdot p \quad for \quad {}^3S_1$$

$$\Delta E(spec) \simeq 0.04 \ p \quad for \quad {}^1S_0.$$

For the 1S state, the shifts are reduced (for p < 0) by the Pauli term.

Now, what should we use for a value of p? This number is an energy, which expresses the fact that the energy of particles in occupied states, when calculated self-consistently, differs from the energy spectrum E_k^o we have used for the intermediate states. Both Grillot, and Brown and Kuo have chosen p $\simeq$ 100 MeV to bring down the single-particle energies from the positive value of 5/2 $\hbar\omega$ for 0p particles in an oscillator, to negative energies of -10 to -18 MeV per particle. This choice, although possibly valid for high intermediate states, probably over-suppresses the effects of the lowest unoccupied states.

For this large a value of p, the perturbation expression (29) should not be valid. However, an improved form may be derived:

$$\langle\phi_i|V|\Psi_i\rangle = \langle\phi_i|V|\Psi_i^S\rangle + p \sum_{k(\neq i)} \frac{\langle\Psi_i^S|V|\phi_k\rangle \langle\phi_i|V|\Psi_k^S\rangle}{(E_k^S - E_j^O)(E_i^S - E_k^S)} \tag{34}$$

$$\times \{ \frac{\langle\phi_i|V|\Psi_k\rangle}{\langle\phi_i|V|\Psi_k^S\rangle} \}$$

If we now make the "scaling" assumption, that

$$\frac{\langle\phi_i|V|\Psi_k\rangle}{\langle\phi_i|V|\Psi_k^S\rangle} \sim \frac{\langle\phi_i|V|\Psi_i\rangle}{\langle\phi_i|V|\Psi_i^S\rangle} \tag{35}$$

We may evaluate (34) from "known" quantities. What we have done, in effect, is replaced the ratio of the corrected, to Schroedinger, matrix elements

$$\frac{\Delta E}{\Delta E^S} \simeq 1 + p\chi \ , \ \text{by} \ \simeq \frac{1}{1-p\chi} \tag{36}$$

In Table II, we show our crude estimated based on (34) and (35), for the effective interaction matrix elements, using $p \simeq -100$ MeV. These are compared with the equation (26) numerically, and with the calculations of Kuo and Brown [4], mentioned previously. We list only the four S-states from Table I, for which the spectral and Pauli corrections are important.

TABLE II

$\Delta E_{n\ell Sj}$ in MeV, with Spectral and Pauli Corrections

	Corrected Phase Shift	Grillot & McManus	Kuo-Brown
$^1S_0(0S)$	-5.5	-6.61	-5.61
$^1S_0(1S)$	-3.6	-4.45	-4.53
$^3S_1(0S)$	-9.4	-7.77	-9.73
$^3S_1(1S)$	-5.9	-5.58	-8.44

I would like to draw several conclusions from this comparison:

1) Apparently one can make reasonable, if not very accurate, estimates of the effective interaction matrix elements, including spectral and Pauli effects with limited knowledge of V(r). We have used the phase shifts, and the short range to get the Schroedinger results, and an interpolation formula (33) (also based on short range for V(r)) for off-diagonal elements. Of course, the off-diagonal matrix elements calculated by Grillot or Brown and Kuo are also uncertain, in the sense that they are using a V(r) which is fit to elastic scattering data only (and the deuteron properties).

2) Different methods of calculating the same numbers, even with the same V(r), may give results differing by 20% or more.

3) All the results quoted in Table II depend on the choice of the value of $\underline{p}$, which essentially gives the gap between occupied and unoccupied single particle states. This is still an open problem for finite nuclei, which introduces some uncertainty into all the results.

It is then interesting to ask where the very short-range characteristics of the interaction V(r), such as the hard or soft repulsive cores, make their appearance. The Schroedinger calculation of V_2 depends only on the phase shifts, and for small nuclei, at energies well below those at which the S-wave phase shifts change sign. Presumably the major short-range effects appear in the spectral correction, which we have remarked, [15] is related to the volume of the wave-function distortion (30). This should depend on the short-range region of V(r). But apparently the effect is not too sensitive to the detailed structure of V(r), but only to some average property. Then we may fairly ask: to what extent do we need to know the detailed structure of V(r) at short distances?

It is also interesting to compare both the Schroedinger and the Bethe-Goldstone solutions with the effective interaction matrix elements which Cohen and Kurath [16] have fit empirically to the spectra of p-shell nuclei, A = 8-16. We have calculated some of the diagonal elements

$$<p^2 \; LSJT | V_2 | \; p^2 \; LSJT>$$

using the relative matrix elements of the Schroedinger phase-shift solutions of Table I, and Grillot's Bethe-Goldstone equations of Table II. These are compared in Table III with the elements in Table 8 of Cohen and Kurath [16].

TABLE III

Diagonal LSJT elements of V_2 in Op shell

JT	LS	Cohen & Kurath	Phase Shift (Schroedinger)	Grillot & McManus
10	01	-8.38	-12.2	-6.7
	21	-5.62	- 7.1	-3.2
	10	-0.29	+ 1.5	+2.0
20	21	-4.06	- 9.2	-5.1
30	21	-7.27	- 8.3	-3.9
01	00	-6.90	- 6.75	-5.5
	11	+3.82	+ 1.73	+2.1
21	20	-2.38	- 4.5	-3.6

There is some question about making a direct comparison of the theoretical V_2 with the empirical effective interaction, since the latter may include effects of polarization of the Os-shell core, which were neglected in V_2. Also, the variation in oscillator parameter which might be required for the different nuclei, has not been done -- the Cohen and Kurath matrix elements have absorbed this size variation.

We may notice that some compromise between the Schroedinger and the Bethe-Goldstone results would in general improve the agreement: this could be obtained, for example, by using a smaller spectral parameter p than was used for Table II. But neither calculation will give the Cohen-Kurath order of the T = 0, J = 2,3 states!

A calculation with Brown-Kuo matrix elements, of the spectra of the p-shell nuclei, has been reported by Halbert, Kim, and Kuo [17]. Both the size, and the $p_{3/2}$-$p_{1/2}$ splitting we varied for each nucleus. The theoretical spectra seem quite good.

VII. FURTHER REMARKS

The attempt to relate the effective interaction directly to the two-body scattering phase shifts goes back to the early work of Brueckner and his collaborators [18], who

noticed the similarity of the equation (11) for $V_2(E)$ with
the equation for the scattering reaction matrix:

$$K(E_k) = V + V \frac{P}{E_k - H_o} K(E_k), \tag{37}$$

(where P denotes the principal value) appropriate to the
standing wave solution of the Schroedinger equation for
two-body scattering, with $E_k = k^2/M$. The partial wave
matrix elements of K are given by

$$(k|K_\ell(E_k)|k) = -\frac{1}{Mk} \tan \delta (E_k) \tag{38}$$

An obvious first approximation for the effective interaction is

$$V_2(E) \simeq K(E).$$

This approximation gives only matrix elements diagonal
in momentum space. To apply this to a finite system, one
must either choose some average value of E_k, or make some
guess as to the form of the off-diagonal elements $(k'|K(E)|k)$.
Kallio [19] has actually done the former, using the
flatness of the oscillator potential at short distance as
a guide. He thus sets $E_k = (2n +\ell+ \frac{3}{2})\hbar\omega$ (oscillator energy
= kinetic energy near the origin) and obtains a formula
for the diagonal matrix elements of V_2:

$$\Delta E_{n\ell Sj} = \hbar\omega \, d_{n\ell} \tan \delta_\ell (E_k), \tag{39}$$

with

$$d_{n\ell} = \frac{2\Gamma(n+\ell+\frac{3}{2})}{\pi \, n!} \left(\frac{4}{4n+2\ell+3}\right)^{\frac{1}{2}(2\ell+1)}$$

This approximation can be shown to be a perturbation limit
of the Schroedinger phase-shift method of Section V, which
is valid for $|\tan \delta| << 1$.
Kahana and Tomusiack[20] have taken the second approach,
and made some specific assumptions about the form of K(E)
as an operator in configuration space. What they have
done, in fact, is replace the problem of obtaining the explicit form of the interaction V(r) from the phase shifts,
with that of obtaining the reaction matrix itself, for
momenta and energies which do not correspond to elastic
scattering. Having assumed a particular form, however,
they are able to include the effects of the spectral and
Pauli corrections. Their approach is then similar, in a
sense, to those which assume a known V(r).

A third method of using the phase shifts has been suggested by Elliott, Mavromatis, and Sanderson [21]. Their original approach assumed that V(r) is weak and local, so that perturbation theory may be used. This approach is discussed full in Professor Elliott's lecture.

ACKNOWLEDGMENTS

The author is happy to acknowledge useful conversations or correspondence with J. B. French, B. Brandow, S. Kahana, H. McManus, Y. E. Kim, and D. Grillot. The last three have also been most helpful with communications of unpublished work.

REFERENCES

1. See, for example, lectures by J. P. Elliott, in "Many Body Description of Nuclear Structure and Reaction," ed. C. Bloch (Varenna Course 36: Academic Press, New York and London, 1966).

2. See, for example, lectures by K. Brueckner, in "The Many Body Problem" (Wiley, New York, 1959). Two recent reviews are given by B. D. Day in Rev. Mod. Phys. $\underline{39}$, 719 (1967) and by B. H. Brandow, $\underline{ibid}$. p. 771.

3. This approach is given more fully in the review by Brandow, Ref. [2].

4. T. T. S. Kuo and G. E. Brown, Nucl. Phys. $\underline{85}$, 40 (1966), and T. T. S. Kuo, $\underline{ibid}$, A103, 71 $(\overline{1967})$.

5. A de Shalit and I. Talmi, "Nuclear Shell Theory" (Academic Press, New York and London, 1963); T. A. Brody and M. Moshinsky, "Tables of Transformation Brackets (Monografias de Instituto de Fisica, Mexico City, (1960).

6. B. L. Scott and S. A. Moszkowski, Ann. Phys. $\underline{14}$, 107 (1961).

7. R. J. Eden, V. J. Emery, and S. Sampanthàr, Proc. Roy. Soc. (London) $\underline{A253}$, 186 (1959).

8. D. Grillot and H. McManus, to be published; D. Grillot, thesis, Michigan State University, 1967 (unpublished).

9. A. Kallio and B. D. Day, Phys. Letters $\underline{25B}$, 72 (1967).

10. R. L. Becker and A. D. MacKellar, Phys. Letters 21, 201
     (1966).

11. J. F. Dawson, I. Talmi, and J. D. Walecka, Ann. Phys.
     18, 339 (1962).

12. D. S. Koltun, Phys. Rev. Letters 19, 910 (1967).

13. T. Hamada and I. D. Johnston, Nucl. Phys. 34, 382 (1962).

14. Y. E. Kim, Phys. Letters 19, 583 (1965).

15. This point has been stressed by B. Brandow.

16. S. Cohen and D. Kurath, Nucl. Phys. 73, 1 (1965).

17. E. C. Halbert, Y. E. Kim, and T. T. S. Kuo, Phys.
     Letters 20, 675 (1966).

18. K. A. Brueckner, C. A. Levinson, and H. M. Mahmoud,
     Phys. Rev. 95, 217 (1954).

19. A. Kallio, Phys. Letters 18, 51 (1965).

20. S. Kahana and E. Tomusiak, Nucl. Phys. 71, 402 (1965).

21. J. P. Elliott, H. A. Mavromatis, and E. A. Sanderson,
     Phys. Letters 24B, 358 (1967).

DISCUSSION

DAVIS: What you've done is reminiscent of carrying out a
dispersion theory analysis but over subvolumes of the
nucleus. Is this a fair but simplified statement?

KOLTUN: In a rough way I would say Elliott's model corresponds to it better than mine in a sense, at least Elliott's
original model in which there were integrals over energies.
It might in some sense be described as a dispersion model:
One has to know the phase shifts up to infinite energy in
order to obtain the results at finite energy. The present
method is a configuration space method and it uses what you
might call the accidental fact that the kind of potentials
you believe in are short range compared to the size of the
container, and that that allows the Schroedinger method to
be applied. It is not a dispersion method. But, Elliott's
is in some sense a dispersion method.

BARANGER: I have a couple of comments and one question.

KOLTUN: Will I get equal time?

SESSION CHAIRMAN (BARANGER): Yes, you will get equal time.

BARANGER: At the very beginning you contrasted the method
using harmonic oscillator intermediate states with the
method using plane wave intermediate states. I think it's
been established especially by the work of Kohler and
McCarthy, that the two give very, very similar results. The
difference between the two is less than 1 MeV. And if there
are differences between Kuo and Brown and somebody else like
Becker and MacKellar, it's not because of the choice of a
harmonic oscillator or plane wave intermediate states, but
it's because of other approximations in the method.

KOLTUN: I was just going to put this on again [shows Table
II] because I was going to say that I think because in part
it could reflect the difference. I don't know how much the
difference is. I don't know the actual work of MacKellar.

BARANGER: Just the choice of intermediate states makes
very little difference but the reason for the big differences
are due to other approximations.

KOLTUN: Tensor force I would think.

BARANGER: More than that. And that brings me to my second
comment. As you know there are two Kuo-Brown calculations.
There is Kuo-Brown and there is Kuo. In the first Kuo-
Brown, which is the one which has been mostly used because
it is the earliest, they completely throw out G_s which is
something that you said too, that they throw out the short-
range part. When Kuo later calculated this, he found that
it was not at all small. It could be a couple of MeVs. And
this is what accounts mostly for the difference between the
original Kuo-Brown and the other paper.

KOLTUN: If I could just comment, I think that one feature
of the phase-shift method which is a strength is that it
handles very well problems of tensor coupling because all
the tensor coupling is in the phase shifts. My impression
of Kuo-Brown is that its weakest point is higher orders of
the tensor force and therefore I think they have to work
hard in order to make up for that deficiency. They've
calculated to the second order in the tensor force. Third
order terms are estimated but not known, and so on. So,
even though the correction you mentioned is present, I'm
not convinced that there aren't further corrections.

BARANGER: Yes, well, the other people that have actually

solved the Bethe-Goldstone equation, namely Wong, Kohler and McCarthy, and Becker and MacKellar and Morris, have treated the tensor interaction exactly, and so they are not subject to your criticism.

KOLTUN: Their results don't all agree, though.

BARANGER: The reason they don't all agree is not this. The reason they don't all agree is because they have different assumptions concerning the particle spectrum, concerning the intermediate state spectrum. That's where the big difference is.

KOLTUN: In the gap?

BARANGER: Yes.

KOLTUN: Okay, well in the case of Grillot I didn't have time to describe this but his assumption is as close as you can get to Kuo-Brown, numerically, given that he is using oscillators and Kuo-Brown are using plane waves. Then if you argue that the difference between oscillators and plane waves doesn't matter, you still apparently have numerical differences. Of course I don't have the new Kuo set, I must admit.

BARANGER: Then you would expect Grillot to agree with Wong, because Wong uses plane waves but he does treat the tensor force very well, and so I would expect Grillot and Wong to come very close to each other.

KOLTUN: I don't know the answer.

PHILLIPS: I believe that Tang and Afnan at Minnesota have shown that certain properties of the very light nuclei such as energies, mean square radii, don't depend on whether the nucleon-nucleon potential has a soft core or hard core. Now this is not exactly the same calculation as yours, but the question is how sensitive are your calculations of the two-body matrix element. How dependent are they on the phase shifts?

KOLTUN: They do depend on the phase shift but they depend on the phase shifts at low energy. That's the strange result, you see, that you do not explicitly need very much of the high energy data in order to get the results. In the Schroedinger case you don't need it at all. You don't need the high energy data. So they only depend on the low energy phase shifts. Of course the phase shifts must be accurate but they're reasonably well established for the s-

states anyway. I might mention that this method can be
turned around and used as a variational principle in the
case of helium. One varies the $\hbar\omega$ size constant and one
gets what is essentially an upper limit of the binding
energy. One can't get the binding energy because one
doesn't have the wave function, therefore one cannot correct
for the kinetic energy quite properly. All one has here
basically is the potential energy shift. It's all right for
the shell model where you keep the size of the system fixed.
But the fact that the minima I get for helium are above but
not terribly above the known binding energies, would lead
me to believe a better method, that is a known force would
give that, and would not be terribly sensitive to the force.
So I agree with your results.

GOLDHAMMER: Have you in fact calculated an upper limit?

KOLTUN: I've done it. It's very crude. It isn't much of
a calculation but it isn't much of a limit. One gets very
reasonable numbers if one guesses what the corrections to
the kinetic energy are.

ELLIOTT: There is one thing that worries me a little when
one talks of effective forces, and this is that when you
come to calculate some physical property like the magnetic
moment or a transition probability one then needs to calculate an effective operator. Can you do this?

KOLTUN: The problem of calculating an effective operator
would be of the same difficulty and therefore the same
degree of approximateness in this method if you really stick
to phase shifts, as calculating the Pauli and the spectral
corrections to the Schroedinger equation, and it is of the
same order (the second order, in the effective interaction,
that is). Those are the first corrections which anybody has
calculated: Brown, Zannick, Mavromatis calculating magnetic
moments. One could do the same thing but one would have to
use the same crude approximations to extend it to off,
diagonal matrix elements of the effective interaction, from
information which is really only for the diagonal matrix
elements. So one could only do it to that order.

BARANGER: Now I can ask my question then. You can tell by
my French accent who I am.

I want to ask about that effective interaction calculation
again because that's very interesting. Apparently, by
solving the Schroedinger equation and not the Bethe-Goldstone
equation, you get the G-matrix for some special values of the
energy parameter. Now for a given matrix element do you get

the G-matrix for just one value of the energy, or for
several values of the energy?

KOLTUN: One get several using this linear extrapolation
method. There are two linear extrapolations; one is the
matrix element itself which has been extrapolated from on-
diagonal momenta or principal quantum numbers. But there is
a second extrapolation that is built into how one does a
perturbation theory.

BARANGER: Okay. But before you do any of these extrapolations you have only one value...

KOLTUN: The Schroedinger method gives one value of the G-
matrix.

BARANGER: So there is no way of plotting it on a piece of
paper and extrapolating it to the value of E that you want?

KOLTUN: No. I've tried to find tricks to do this by
varying $\hbar\omega$ which changes the E, but none of them is quite
consistent so I've abandoned that approach.

BARANGER: I understand that using the volume of the defect
wave function, then, you can extrapolate to other values of
E. But, the thing which amazes me is that nowhere in this
treatment do you use the properties of the nuclear force off
the energy shell, and therefore you are claiming that the
properties of nuclear matter or finite nuclei do not depend
on what the nuclear force does off the energy shell.

KOLTUN: That's in part my conclusion but with the following
caveat. One eventually has to face the problem of core
excitation and that requires reasonably good knowledge of
the off-diagonal matrix elements. Now what I say is that I
can give you matrix elements which crudely give that but not
very well because this averaging linear extrapolation is
crude. The second thing is this: Again I didn't have time
to describe my perturbation method. My perturbation method
is sort of a calculation of this defect by including only
low lying states, low lying in the sense of M´ the excited
intermediate states that one needs in the perturbation theory.
One does not get the same result as one would get if one
knew the wave function inside. It's only a crude approximation at that point as well to this defect volume. So, the
question is quite good. Where are the interesting short
range behaviors hidden? The answer, as far as I can tell,
is that the first thing you have to know are phase shifts,
that has most of the information. The next thing you have
to know is the volume of the defect. Let's say the first

has 90% very crudely speaking (let's say 80%); the next 10
or 15% I think comes from a knowledge of average properties
which do depend somewhat on the core but don't tell you
that the core is there or the volume of the defect.
Actually if you compare different potential models, the
bigger the core generally the bigger the volume of the defect
because it's roughly proportional to the core radius cubed
or something like that. So not very much information of the
short-range behavior is needed.

BARANGER: So you do use the size of the core when you
calculate the size of the defect?

KOLTUN: No, I don't know it. I calculate it a different
way, but I'm saying it's only a very crude approximation.
Basically what I've left out of my calculation of this
defect is excitations which go high in energy. Now I know
they contribute and I also know that my linear extrapolation
method isn't good for them; therefore, I've left out some
things, those high excitations do depend on the details of
the force but apparently they don't carry too much weight
in actually determining the numbers when you're finished.

BARANGER: Have you looked at some of the other problems
that are supposed to be useful to determine the off-shell
behavior like proton-proton bremssthralung? Can you say
that this is also determined only by the phase shifts?

KOLTUN: Well, no. If you're interested in the history, I
will say this. I got this method by trying to find an easy
way of generating correlated wave functions to use in pion
absorption problems which I have been working on and the
thing sort of backfired. Instead of getting the wave functions, I got wave function independent energy solutions.
It turns out also to be a useful way of getting correlated
wave functions. I do believe that nuclear correlations, the
short-range correlations, are of some importance in problems
of large momentum transfer like bremssthralung, inelastic
electron scattering and pi reactions with nuclei. But, in
almost every case that's been examined numerically, it has
been very hard to extract the unique behavior due to the
hard core, let's say. That is, it's there, but it's there
in some average sense just as in this theory it appears in
some average sense in the distortion volume. Almost every
case you can think of it has shown that problem. It's very
hard to find the hard core in nuclear physics.

II.A. NUCLEAR FORCES AND THE STRUCTURE OF LIGHT NUCLEI

J. P. Elliott
The University of Sussex
Brighton, England

Nuclear structure calculations may be divided into three broad categories, distinguished by the way in which the nucleon-nucleon interaction is treated, namely, (i) few parameters, (ii) many parameters, (iii) no parameters. In the first category go the intermediate coupling calculations with simple forces, for example those of Elliott and Flowers and Gillet, and also the pairing + quadrupole type of calculations of Kisslinger and Sorensen. All such calculations contain a few parameters, usually the strength of the force and its exchange character, which are chosen to fit some of the data in the many-body system being studied.

In the second category we have the Talmi-type calculations in which, for an initial choice of configuration, all the matrix elements of the interaction which occur are treated as free parameters. There are now so many parameters that a least-squares fitting procedure is necessary and, not surprisingly, one often obtains an accurate fit to the data.

In the third category are calculations with realistic forces. Here, realistic means that they have been fitted to the two-body data so that, once the calculation on the many-body system is begun, there are no free parameters left in the interaction. In my opinion it is only calculations in this third category which are capable of giving real insight into the structure of nuclei and I shall concentrate on them today. Calculations in the first two categories have the unsatisfactory feature that the adjustment of the interaction to fit the observations in the many-body system will hide the inadequacy of the wave functions being used. One is then forced to use effective charges and g-factors etc. to be fitted to the very data which the calculations are supposed to explain. With realistic forces, and provided one uses honest perturbation theory without adjustable energy denominators, any lack of agreement in the many-body systems is due either to an inadequate treatment of the many-body problem or to some uncertainty in the realistic force. It is possible that two potentials, while giving equally good fit to the known elastic nucleon-nucleon scattering data, may nevertheless give rather different results in a many-body system. For example, the Hamada-Johnston potential[1] which is singular but local and the Tabakin[2] potential which is non-singular but non-local are both fitted to the two-body data although the latter was not fitted accurately. In an attempt to remove or at least to clarify this possible uncertainty in the realistic potential we ask ourselves two questions,

(i)   What information about the interactions does one need,
to calculate the low energy properties of nuclei?   (ii)
What information about the interaction does one have from
the two-body data?   By low energy here we include essentially all the properties generally used in discussions
of nuclear structure, such as binding energies, spectra,
moments and transition probabilities.   The answer to the
second question is that we have the set of phase shifts
for channels with $\ell < 5$ at energies (Lab) below 350 MeV.
In view of this upper limit and the onset of relativistic
corrections and inelastic processes at such high energies
we are necessarily precluded from discussing high energy
features of nuclei.   The answer to the first question is
that, if we work with a complete set of harmonic oscillator wave functions in perturbation theory, then using a
Moshinsky transformation we need the set of relative
matrix elements $\langle n' |V|n \rangle$ in each spin-angular momentum
channel $s\ell j$.   In practice one finds that it is the smallest
n' and n which dominate the low energy properties of nuclei.
Furthermore in first order perturbation theory all matrix
elements have $n' = n$ and those off-diagonal in n enter
gradually as the order or the energy denominator increases.
Here, n is the oscillator radial quantum number denoting
the number of nodes in the wave function.
     We are therefore faced with the following problem –
given the phase shift, to deduce the set of matrix elements
$\langle n' |V|n \rangle$.   The usual technique for this is a two-stage
process, first deducing a potential which fits the phase
shift and then calculating the matrix elements.   I shall
describe a more direct process.   I should, at this point,
make some remarks about hard cores.   It is well known that
the phase shifts indicate that the potential becomes
repulsive at high energies i.e. at small distances and,
for convenience in the two-body problem, this repulsion
has often been represented by an infinitely hard core.
This is extremely inconvenient in the many-body problem
because it makes all the shell model matrix elements
infinite.   A sensible, finite answer can then be achieved
only by summing perturbation series to all orders.   This
is, in principle, possible using the technique of the
G-matrix but there are many uncertainties yet to be resolved in defining, deducing and dealing with the G-
matrix.   It seems to me that before one includes such a
catastrophic feature as a hard core one should be sure
that it is relevant to the properties one is calculating.
I am impressed by the fact that there is no evidence for
such a core in any nuclear structure properties.   It is
said that the core is necessary for an understanding of
nuclear saturation but this is such a delicate matter of
the balance of the central, non-central and exchange

properties of the interaction that I am unconvinced. It
is certainly true that the interaction must become repulsive at short distances, but the extreme repulsions in a
hard core represent very high energy phenomena in which
we are not interested. In other words, although there may
be very short-range correlations present in nuclei we
shall not insist that they are built in to our approximate
wave functions. We believe that there are many other more
important correlations to understand first. The very
short-range correlations will in principle be built in
gradually through high order perturbations. It was our
intention to proceed on these assumptions and, by calculating a variety of nuclear properties, to test them. The
program   is by no means complete but the results so far
are very promising.

    We first notice that if, in some channel, the poten-
tial is sufficiently weak to be treated in Born approximation, then

$$\tan\delta_\ell (k) = - \frac{mk}{\hbar^2} \int_0^\infty j_\ell(kr) \, V \, j_\ell(kr) \, r^2 dr. \qquad (1)$$

One therefore has, immediately from the phase shifts, the
set of diagonal matrix elements in Bessel wave functions.
It was pointed out by Kallio[3] that the oscillator radial
wave function $R_{n\ell}(r/b)$, where $b = \sqrt{\hbar/m\omega}$, has a very great
similarity to the Bessel function $j_\ell(kr)$, apart from the
normalization, if

$$k = (2n + \ell + \frac{3}{2})^{\frac{1}{2}} /b. \qquad (2)$$

In fact

$$R_{n\ell}(r/b) \sim \left\{ \frac{k^3 \Gamma(n + \ell + \frac{3}{2}) 2^{\ell+\frac{3}{2}}}{\pi n! (2n + \ell + \frac{3}{2})^{\ell+\frac{3}{2}}} \right\}^{\frac{1}{2}} \qquad (3)$$

and Fig. 1 shows the considerable accuracy of this relation
for small r. By using (3) in (1) we may then deduce the
diagonal oscillator matrix element $\langle n|V|n\rangle$ from the phase
shift in that channel at an energy given by (2). In this
it is necessary only that (3) is satisfied within the
range of the potential (1). A rather similar method
which does not rest on the approximation (3) but still
uses the Born approximation (1) was given by Mavromatis

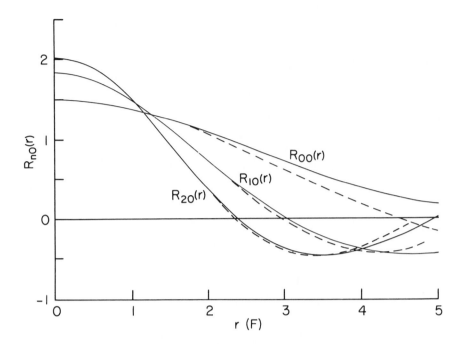

Fig. 1.   Comparison between oscillator and Bessel wave
functions, from Kallio, Ref. 3.

et al.   They used an expansion of the weighting function
$R_{n\ell}^2(r/b)$ as an integral of $j_\ell^2(kr)$ over k, thereby ob-
taining the matrix element $<n|V|n>$ as an integral over the
phase shifts, weighted with a function peaked near the
energy given by (2). From these simple arguments one sees
immediately that an upper limit on the energy of the known
phase shifts implies an upper limit on ℓ. For example with
b = 2fm and ℓ = 0, a laboratory energy <350 MeV implies
n < 7.
       Although this Born approximation treatment is instruc-
tive, it is quite inadequate in the s-states where the
potential is strong and is probably inaccurate in the p and
d-states. We therefore use the following improved method.
Write $V = V_0 + V_1$ where V_0 is called the auxiliary potential
and V_1 is supposed to be small enough to treat in Born
approximation. The generalization of (1) is then

$$\tan(\delta-\delta_0) = -\frac{mk}{\hbar^2} \int_0^\infty u_k(r)V_1 u_k(r)r^2 dr \qquad (4)$$

where u_k is the scattering radial wave function for the

52   J. P. Elliott

auxiliary potential at momentum k and δ_0 the corresponding
phase shift. We choose V_0 to be a cut-off oscillator

$$V_0 = -\frac{\hbar^2}{m} (\alpha - r^2/4b^4) \quad \text{in } r < a$$

$$= 0 \quad \quad \quad \text{in } r > a$$
(5)

with depth α and range a chosen roughly to fit the known
phase shift, thereby ensuring the smallness of V, and the
validity of the Born approximation for V_1. With this
choice of V_0, it follows that, in r < a, the wave function
u_k is a solution of the usual oscillator Schroedinger
equation but that, for arbitrary k, it contains increasing
as well as decreasing terms at infinity. However, for
specific energies, given by

$$k = \{(2n + \ell + \tfrac{3}{2})/b^2 - \alpha\}^{\frac{1}{2}}$$
(6)

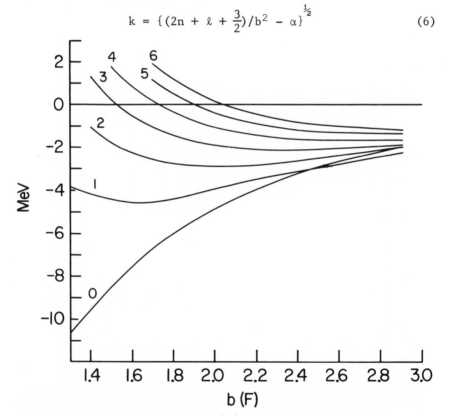

Fig. 2. Matrix elements $\langle n's_0|V|n's_0\rangle$ in MeV in the $^1S_0$
channel plotted against the parameter b in fermis. The
oscillator radial quantum number, n is to the left of each
curve.

where n is an integer we have $u_k = A R_{n\ell}(r/b)$, i.e. apart from normalization, u_k is just an eigenfunction of the infinite oscillator. If we neglect the very small long-range correction due to the departure of u_k from $R_{n\ell}$ in the outer region (and this neglect may be justified) we may deduce from (4) the matrix elements $\langle n|V_1|n\rangle$. Knowing V_o

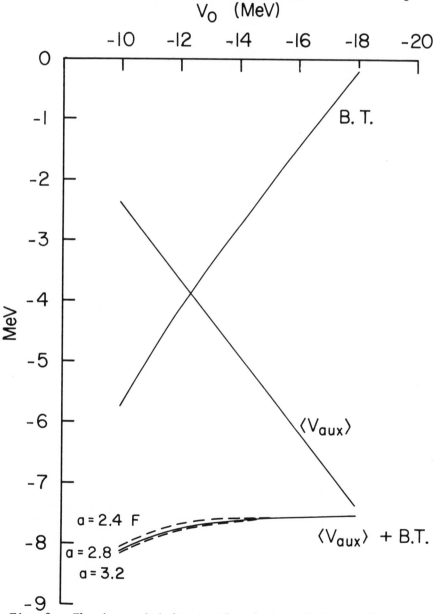

Fig. 3. The insensitivity to the choice of the auxiliary potential.

from (5), we have the required $\langle n|V|n\rangle$. Results for the $^1S_0$
channel are shown in Fig. 2, and Fig. 3 demonstrates the insensitivity of the final result to the choice of auxiliary

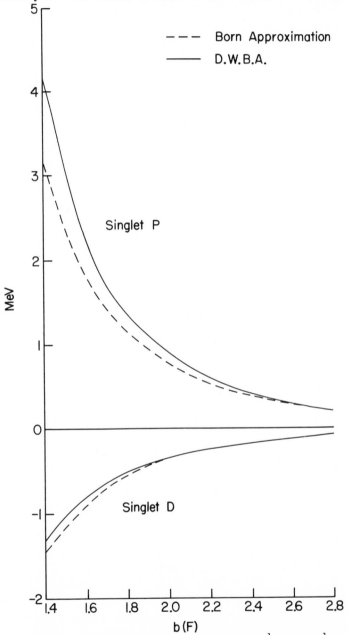

Fig. 4.   The $n = 0$ matrix elements for the $^1P_1$ and $^1D_2$
channels showing the connections to the simple Born approxi-
approximation treatment.

potential. One sees the Born term adequately compensating
for the changes in V_0.

Fig. 4 shows the difference between the matrix elements
calculated with the simple Born approximation and with the
auxiliary potential method for $\ell = 1$ and $\ell = 2$. It is small,
but significant for small b with $\ell = 1$. The splitting of
the triplet-P is shown in Fig. 5 for n = 0. From this we
may analyze the central, spin-orbit and tensor contributions.
A little Racah algebra shows that

Central contribution $\propto$ $<^3P_0>+3<^3P_1>+5<^3P_2>$

Spin-Orbit   " $\propto 2 <^3P_0>+3<^3P_1>-5<^3P_2>$ (7)

Tensor   " $\propto 2 <^3P_0>-3<^3P_1>+<^3P_2>.$

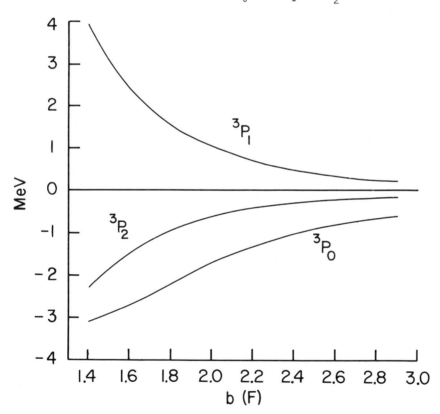

Fig. 5. The splitting of the ^3P channels for n = 0.

Fig. 6 shows how very small is the central contribution
while the spin-orbit contribution increases rapidly at
small b, consistent with it being a short-range effect. As
percentages, one finds for lowest energies, i.e. at n = 0

with large b, -23%, 15% and 108% respectively while, at the
high energy end, the figures are 15%, 50% and 35%. This
shows the dominance of the tensor force at low energies and
the increasing importance of the spin-orbit force as the
energy increases.

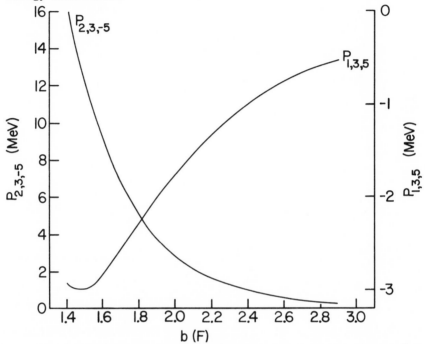

Fig. 6.   The central and spin orbit contributions in the ^{3}P
channels.

It is interesting to ask whether our matrix elements for
different n (see Fig. 1) are independent. If the relation
were satisfied, then the wave functions for different n would
be related. We therefore plot, in Fig. 7, the function

$$f_\ell(\beta) = \frac{(2n + \ell + \frac{3}{2})^{+\frac{3}{2}} n!}{\beta^3 \Gamma(n + \ell + \frac{3}{2})} \langle n|V|n \rangle \qquad (8)$$

against $\beta = (2n + \ell + \frac{3}{2})^{\frac{1}{2}}/b$. If the relation (3) is satisfied, then $f_\ell(\beta)$ will be independent of n. The figure shows
this to be true except for the small b values with n = 0.
The relation is less good for higher ℓ values.

In principle, we may deduce the off-diagonal matrix
elements using the identity

$$b \frac{\partial}{\partial b} R_{n\ell} = \sqrt{(n+1)(n+\ell+\frac{3}{2})}\, R_{n+1\,\ell} - \sqrt{n(n+\ell+\frac{1}{2})}\, R_{n-1\,\ell}$$

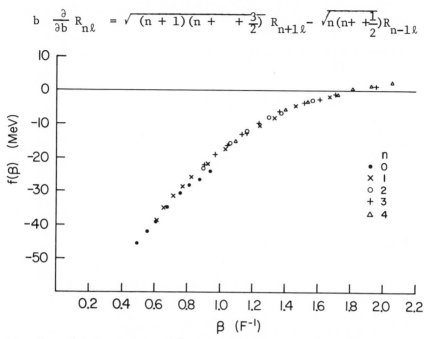

Fig. 7. The function $f(\beta)$, illustrating the relation
between matrix elements in the same channel (the $^1S_0$) for
different n.

which implies that

$$\frac{1}{2}b \frac{\partial}{\partial b} \langle n|V|n\rangle = \sqrt{(n+1)(n+\ell+\frac{3}{2})} \langle n+1|V|n\rangle$$

$$-\sqrt{n(n+\ell+\frac{1}{2})} \langle n|V|n-1\rangle$$

Thus, starting from n = 0, we may deduce the elements
$\langle n'|V|n\rangle$ with $(n' - n) = 1$ by differentiating the diagonal
matrix elements treated as functions of b. Successive
differentiations lead to matrix elements with $(n' - n) > 1$.
In practice this procedure gives decreasing accuracy with
increasing $(n' - n)$. The first differentiation, corresponding to $(n' - n) = 1$ is accurate, but for $(n' - n) > 1$ we
use a simpler method but one which requires the assumption
that the potential is momentum independent. With this
assumption, the oscillator wave functions yield the
relation

$$\langle n'|V|n\rangle = 2(n'-n-1)\langle n'-1|V|n\rangle + \sqrt{(n+1)(n+\tfrac{3}{2})}\,\langle n'-1|V|n+1\rangle$$

$$+ \sqrt{n(n+\tfrac{1}{2})}\,\langle n'-1|V|n-1\rangle - \sqrt{(n'-1)(n'-\tfrac{1}{2}+\ell)}\,\langle n'-2|V|n\rangle$$

One benefit of extracting matrix elements directly from the phase shifts is that one is made aware of one's genuine ignorance about the potential. Thus we saw earlier the high energy limit on n and now we see inaccuracies entering with increasing (n' – n) which reflects a lack of information about the 'off-energy-shell' properties. We notice however that these two limitations do not appear to be severe for nuclear structure calculations. In the first place, although for heavier nuclei the mean value of n increases, the nuclear size demands that b also increases. These two effects just about cancel each other out as far as the relevant energy is concerned, see (2) or (6). Secondly n' – n > 1 enters only with the mixing of $4\hbar\omega$ excitations.

Let us now test these matrix elements by using them in nuclear structure calculations.

(i) Closed shell binding energies. This is surely the most difficult quantity to calculate accurately since it involves the interaction of all nucleons in the nucleus. The first order contribution to the energy may, however, be calculated very simply and this already provides a test. If the matrix elements are correct, the first order energy must be an upper bound to the energy. If the matrix elements describe, on the other hand, a non-saturating force, the first order energy will tend to give a binding energy increasing too rapidly with A and exceeding the experimental values for large A. We find the following values for the N = Z closed shell nuclei

A	4	16	40	80
First Order B.E.	7	34	145	408
B.E./A	1.8	2.1	3.8	5.1

These values are satisfactory. Although they fall short of the experimental value of about 8 MeV, the difference could easily come from higher order terms. Such calculations are under way.

(ii) Single-particle energies. These will be somewhat less delicate to calculate than the binding energies and they involve the interaction of a chosen particle with the remainder, rather than the interaction between all parts. We find

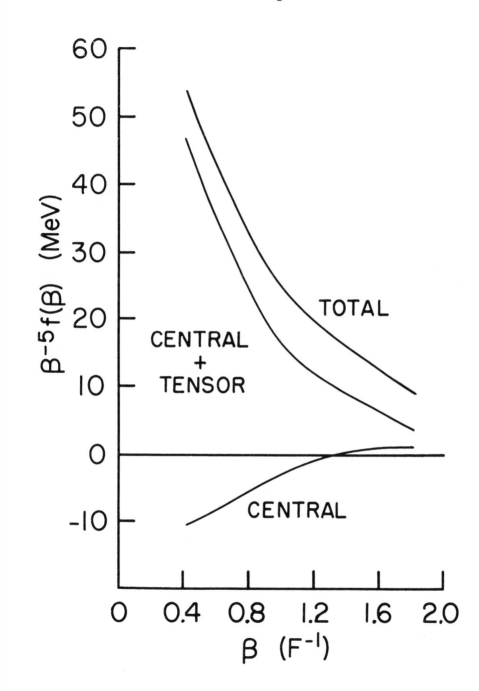

Fig. 8.   The central, spin-orbit and tensor decomposition of
the $n = 0$ $^3P_1$ matrix element.

the following first order values

b	1.4	1.6	1.8	Exp
He - He	10.4	7.8	6.3	1.0
O - O	-	1.3	0.6	-4.2
O $(s_{1/2}-d_{5/2})$		2.7	0.8	0.9

They show agreement in the ℓ-splitting, but require an additional 5 MeV of binding from higher orders.
(iii) Spin-orbit splittings. For a single particle or hole plus a closed shell the first order spin-orbit splitting is due entirely to the spin-orbit (k = 1) force, both central and tensor forces contribution nothing. In fact, the splitting for light nuclei is dominated by the ^3P splitting shown in Fig. 5. The calculated first order splittings are shown in Fig. 9 and compared with the experimental data in Table I. One sees good overall agreement from the simple theory. It is meaningless to ask for detailed agreement for a variety of reasons. Apart from higher order contributions there is high sensitivity to the uncertain b-value and also the question whether the upper member of a doublet, lying high in the spectrum, can be described as a single particle level with any accuracy. The large higher order corrections to the closed shell and single particle energies will, being scalar, leave the splitting unaffected.

Table I

Spin Orbit splittings, compared with experiment

Nucleus	Orbit	b(fm)	Δ(MeV) Calc	Δ(MeV) Exp
He^5	0p	$1.6 \pm .05$	4.1 ∓ 0.6	~ 4
N^{15}, O^{15}	$0p^{-1}$	$1.7 \pm .05$	5.0 ∓ 0.7	6.3
F^{17}, O^{17}	0d	$1.75 \pm .05$	5.6 ∓ 0.8	5.1
K^{39}, Ca^{39}	$0d^{-1}$	$1.95 \pm .05$	4.9 ∓ 0.6	~ 6
Sc^{41}, Ca^{41}	0f	$1.95 \pm .05$	5.7 ∓ 0.7	6.4
	1p	$1.95 \pm .05$	2.2 ∓ 0.2	~ 2

(iv) Spectra. Here, we are concerned with the spectrum for simple two-particle or particle-hole systems to further test the matrix elements and the perturbation treatment but avoid the complexities of many-particle configurations. Results

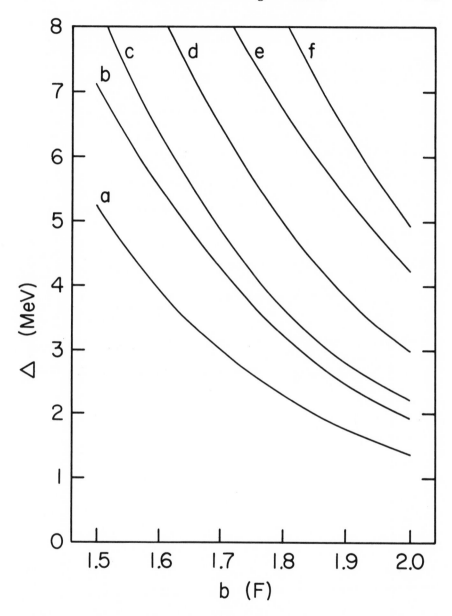

Fig. 9.   The spin orbit splitting, $\Delta = E_{(j=\ell-1/2)} - E_{(j=\ell+1/2)}$
The curve labels are: a) $He^5(0p)$, b) $Ca^{41}(1p)$,
c) $O^{15}(0p^{-1})$, d) $O^{17}(0d)$, e) $Ca^{39}(0d^{-1})$ and f) $Ca^{41}(0f)$.

are shown in the figures 10 to 15. In O^{18}, the three calculations give almost identical results. The pattern of
calculated levels is in agreement with the experimental data

but connections from higher configurations are clearly important to depress the 0^+ ground state and open up the 0 - 2
spacing. A similar, but exaggerated picture is seen for
Ca^{42}. One sees again the absence of a calculated low-lying
excited 0^+ state from the lowest configuration consistent
with suggestions that there is a collective state from
higher configurations lying at low energy in this nucleus.
In Li^6 the comparison suggests that the inclusion of higher
configurations must depress the T = 0 states more than those
with T = 1. This is to be expected in these light nuclei

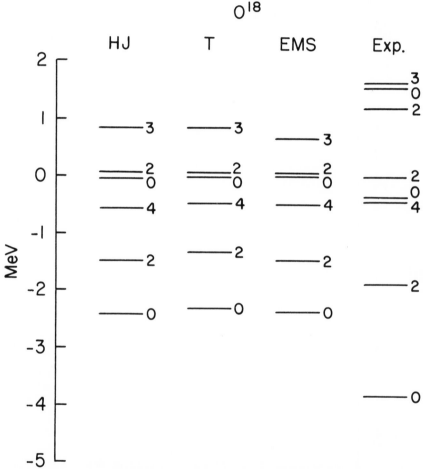

Fig. 10. The spectrum of O^{18}. The diagrams are denoted by:
    HJ - Hamada-Johnston potential as interpreted by
         Kuo-Brown
     T - Talakin Potential
    EMS - Phase-shift method described in this talk.
    Exp - Observed

due to the strong tensor force coupling the $^{13}S_1$ and $^{13}D_1$ channels. The odd-parity levels of He^4, the simplest parti-cle-hole system, again have the correct pattern of levels in the calculated spectrum with a need for a larger connection to the T = 0 levels as in Li^6. The excitation energy of these odd-parity levels relative to the He ground state is also given correctly, through being sensitive to b.

Our conclusion from these first order calculations, with matrix elements deduced directly from the phase shifts, is

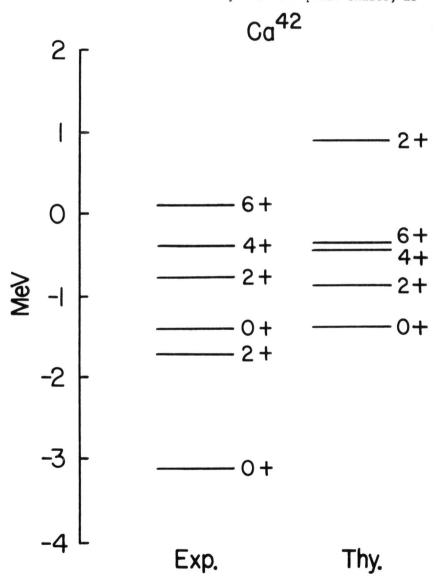

Fig. 11. The spectrum of Ca^{42}. Here b = 2.0 fermis.

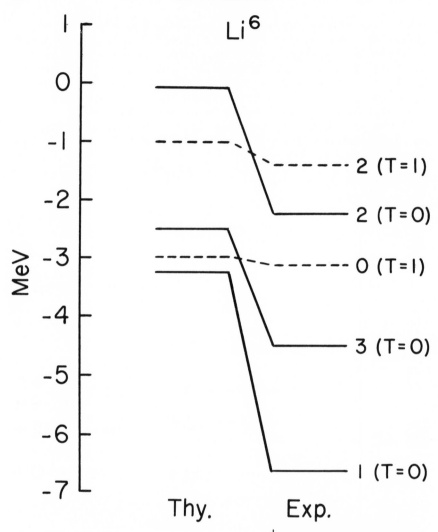

Fig. 12. The spectrum of Li^6. The 0^+ (T=1) level is drawn
          at the observed energy. Here b = 1.6 fermis.

that all the results are very reasonable. We do not pre-
tend that accurate results may be obtained in first order,
but the indication is that the inclusion of second order
terms will go a long way towards achieving this aim. At
no point have we met with any conflict due to our exclusion
of a hard core.

      Finally, let me give a second interpretation of the
calculations I have described. The first interpretation is
that the difference $V_1 = V - V_0$ between the real and the
auxileary potentials may be treated in Born approximation.
In effect, this says that we disregard any singular or near-

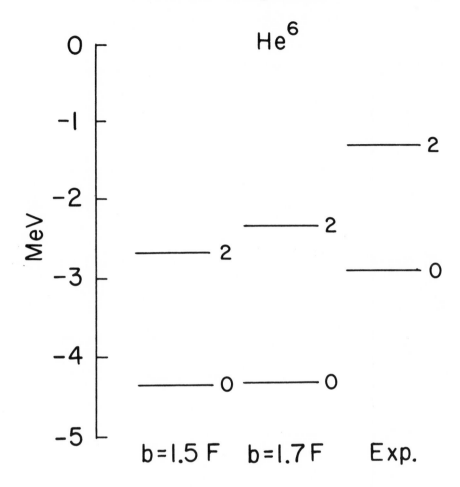

Fig. 13.   The spectrum of He^6 relative to He^4 and He^5.

singular behavior. The second interpretation is that the
matrix elements we have derived are those of a G-matrix
satisfying $Gu_k = V\psi_k$ where ψ_k is the exact scattering wave
function. G will then contain those correlation effects
due to the inadequacy of u_k at small distance. This G-
matrix would differ markedly from that of Kuo and Brown
which includes corrections from much lower energy. It seems
to me that the difference between these two interpretations
will be significant, from a practical point of view, only
when high energy phenomena or high orders of perturbation
theory are being discussed.
      Finally, let us compare our matrix elements with other
realistic matrix elements, those of Tabakin and the G-matrix
elements of Kuo and Brown. Table II shows the T = 1 matrix
elements in which the only notable difference is the larger

J. P. Elliott

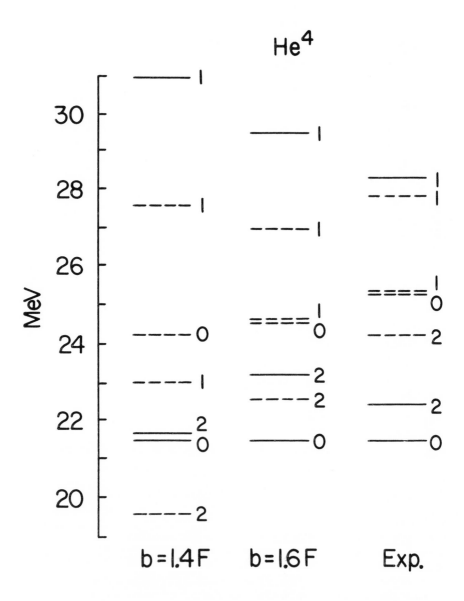

Fig. 14. The spectrum of He⁴, odd-parity levels. The
0⁻(T=0) level is drawn at the observed energy.

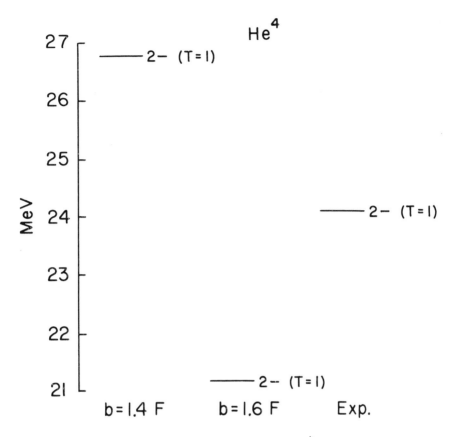

Fig. 15.   The excitation energy of the He^4 odd-parity levels
relative to the ground state.

$^3P_1$ matrix element of Tabakin. These numbers correspond to
b = 1.7 fm.   Table III shows the T = 0 matrix elements in
which the large Tabakin value is due to his poor phase shift
fit.   It is ironic that the $^3S_1$ matrix element, which is one
of the most important for structure calculations is the least
well known.   This is because of the $^3S_1$ - $^3D_1$ coupling which
must be unravelled. The experimental situation for the
mixing parameter ε is shown, in Fig. 16, to be very uncertain
and Tabakin's fit to the Breit YLAM phase shift is very crude.
The $^3S_1$ G-matrix of Brown and Kuo owes 60% of its strength
to second order tensor contributions. The central force
contribution must therefore be much less than that of
Tabakin or ourselves. These questions are crucial for
binding energy calculations, a 1 MeV change in the $^3S_1$ matrix
element leading to a 70 MeV change in the energy of Ca^{40} for
example!

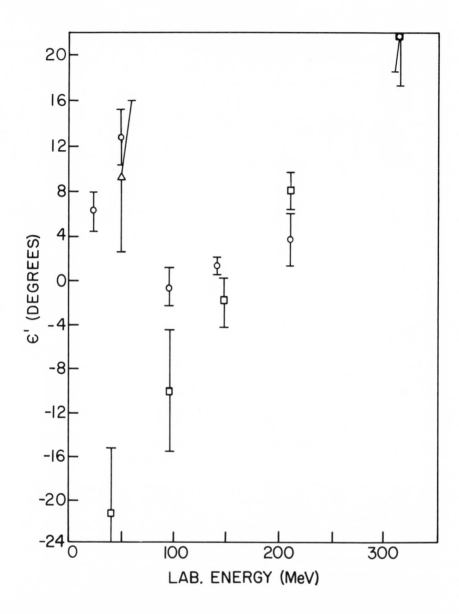

Fig. 16.   The experimental values of the mixing parameter
  E in degrees plotted against the energy in the laboratory.

Table II

Orbital	n	HJ	T	EMS
$^1S_0$	0	-6.3	-6.1	-6.5
$^1S_0$	1	-4.1	-4.3	-4.6
$^3P_0$	0	-1.7	-2.3	-2.4
$^3P_1$	0	2.0	2.5	1.8
$^3P_1$	0	-0.9	-0.9	-1.1
$^1D_2$	0	-0.5	-0.5	-0.6

Table III

Orbital	HJ	T+	T	EMS
$^3S_1$	-9.1	-8.7	-7.2	-6.3
$^3D_1$	1.1	4.0	4.8	2.0
$^3D_1$	-2.3	-2.0	-2.0	-2.7
$^3D_1$	-0.0	-0.7	-0.7	-0.2
$^1P_1$	1.8	1.2	1.7	1.5

ACKNOWLEDGEMENTS

This talk describes work carried out by H. A. Mavromatis, E. A. Sanderson, A. Jackson, B. Singh and myself.

REFERENCES

1. T. Hamada and I. D. Johnston, Nuclear Physics 34, 382 (1962).

2. F. Tabakin, Ann. Phys. 30, 51 (1964).

3. A. Kallio, Phys. Letters 18, 51 (1965).

4. J. P. Elliott, H. A. Mavromatis and E. A. Sanderson, Phys. Letters 24B, 358 (1967).

5. T. T. S. Kuo and G. E. Brown, Nuclear Physics 85, 40 (1966).

DISCUSSION

DE LLANO: I would like to ask Professor Elliott, does your
n label on the matrix elements stand for n e, S and j?

ELLIOTT: The n label is the conventional number of nodes in
the radial wave function. The calculations are done
separately in each channel S, L, J.

DE LLANO: So the non-diagonality that you discussed refers
only to different n's but the same ℓ's?

ELLIOTT: Yes.

DE LLANO: So what would you mean by higher order terms or
second order calculations?

ELLIOTT: The mixing of excited configurations by perturbation theory or some more accurate technique. This would
involve relative matrix elements with $n' - n = 1, 2, 3$ etc.

DE LLANO: And different ℓ's?

ELLIOTT: The coupling between ℓ's is only involved in a
few channels, in particular the $^3S_1$ which couples with the
triplet $^3D_1$ and the triplet $^3P_2$ which couples with the $^3F_2$.
And in fact, in these cases we put tensor mixing in the
auxiliary potential. We did not treat the mixing here in
the simple Born approximation.

DE LLANO: And could you tell me if the calculation of the
odd-parity He^4 levels is a particle-hole calculation?

ELLIOTT: Yes, this is, if you like, the simplest particle-
hole nucleus. It's sometimes called a supermultiplet
calculation but it's nothing more than a particle-hole
system. For the ground state of He^4 the simplest picture
is $(s)^4$ and if you want odd-parity levels you must excite
to s^3p. You simply write down all states in this configuration (because the 's are so small, there are very few of
them) and on the slide you saw them all. The actual matrix
elements in this case are almost trivial combinations of the
relative matrix elements. So this is a nucleus where one
is almost looking directly at the relative matrix elements.

RIPKA: People who do nuclear matter calculations often
stress that the difference between the potential acting
between free nucleons and those in nuclear matter contains
a density dependent component of the force. I would like to
ask you whether one does get any density dependence out of

the matrix elements you calculate?

ELLIOTT: There is no density dependence as we calculate them. The density dependence will have to come out from the structure calculations. All I've described are the relative matrix elements. Now I imagine the density dependence will come in when you improve your model wave functions as you go to higher order corrections.

RIPKA: So that would be what you would call a higher order effect?

ELLIOTT: I think so, yes.

KOLTUN: Just one comment on the question of whether it's worth separating higher order effects. Well, I would like to state it is just the traditional Brueckner view which has been promulgated by the G-matrix people over the years and which I think still makes sense is that there are two kinds of correlations. One does not change very much from nucleus to nucleus. The other one can be quite different in neighboring nuclei. This distinction, if you like, of high momentum or low momentum or short range and long range and so on, may therefore be useful to keep certain high order terms which are not very sensitive to which nucleus you're in, that is the high tensor effect, the hard-core effect, etc. and that may be the only real argument for the G-matrix.

ELLIOTT: The question is what do you mean by high?

KOLTUN: Well in Brown and Kuo, for example, it is very explicit what is meant by high. I mean they use a closure method or they argue very close to the closure method. They really aren't talking about states 200 MeV up.

ELLIOTT: But this simply isn't true, is it, because there the tensor force comes in in second order and this is a comparatively low energy, mixing of $2\hbar\omega$ and $4\hbar\omega$ states in quite a strong way.

KOLTUN: They don't include that in their so-called bare effective interaction, the low states, only the high ones. The Pauli principle keeps you out of the low ones, essentially, or diminishes them and their way of calculating it explicitly leaves out the low states. They are put back in later. Their later terms would agree with your later terms.

HANNA: Have you looked at transition strengths in any of this work and in particular in He^4?

ELLIOTT: No.

HANNA: Actually I think it's quite straightforward in He because if you look at the El strength you locate the two upper T = 1, 1- levels, and experimentally the El strength appears to reside in the lower of these two. The El strength is connected pretty much with the singlet-triplet character of the levels. It depends really on how much singlet character you have in each level.

ELLIOTT: Yes, let me just say that these first order calculations I've shown were rushed out in a couple of weeks just to see whether the matrix elements were giving sense or not. It's clear that once you have the wave functions you can then calculate all the transition probabilities. This just simply was not done. But, I think this probably has been done by Barrett with the Tabakin potential.

HANNA: Yes, Barrett has certainly calculated them, and was able to get the strengths approximately right.

II. B. GAMMA DECAY OF ANALOGUE STATES IN THE 2s-1d SHELL

P. M. Endt
Fysisch Laboratorium der Rijksuniversiteit
Utrecht, The Netherlands

I. INTRODUCTION

At the time of the Dayton conference, two years ago, we had just seen the first examples of a new class of strong M1 transitions, with strengths of several Weisskopf units, which deexcite analogue states in odd-A nuclides in the s-d shell. The decay proceeds to a state with the same spin and parity, which later was termed the anti-analogue state. The explanation sounded simple: if a proton in an orbit (ℓ,j) is coupled to an even-even core with $T = T_0$, one obtains two states both with $J = j$ and with $T_< = T_0 + \frac{1}{2}$, the analogue state, and $T_< = T_0 - \frac{1}{2}$, the anti-analogue state, respectively. States which are so much alike are connected by large M1 matrix elements.

In the first section of my present talk I want to show that this explanation is often wrong, that the situation is much more complicated, that the occurrence of these strong M1 transitions is something like a freak of nature, and, finally, the understanding of these freaks requires a reasoning which is different from nuclide to nuclide.

The same problems are also encountered in even-even nuclides, and in the second section I would like to describe an attempt to understand the decay of analogue and anti-analogue states in Ar^{38}, one of the most thoroughly investigated nuclides in the s-d shell.

The third section is devoted to Doppler shift attenuation (DSA) measurements, which during the last year have fast become the most important source of information on γ-ray transition probabilities of bound (and even of some unbound) states.

II. ANALOGUE STATE γ DECAY IN ODD-A NUCLIDES

Let us start by sticking to the simple picture outlined in the introduction. The transition probability between $T_< = T_0 + \frac{1}{2}$ and $T_< = T_0 - \frac{1}{2}$ states then reduces to the expression

$$|M|^2 = (g_p - g_n)2j(j + 1)f(T_0),$$

where g_p and g_n are the Schmidt g factors of the proton and neutron, respectively, in the orbit (ℓ,j). The function

$f(T_0) \times 10^2$ has the values 2.94, 2.11 and 1.61 W.u. for
$T_0 = 1, 2$ and 3, respectively. In table 1, $|M|^2$ is tabulated (for $T_0 = 1$) for different orbits.

Table I

Strengths (in Weisskopf units) of different
$T = 3/2 \rightarrow 1/2$ M1 analogue→anti-analogue transitions as a function of ℓ and j (from ref. 1).

j	s	p	d	f
$\ell + \tfrac{1}{2}$	1.95	1.59	1.85	2.24
$\ell - \tfrac{1}{2}$	---	0.07	0.05	0.01

Quite remarkable is the large difference (up to a factor
of 200) between the "parallel", $j = \ell + \tfrac{1}{2}$, and the "anti-
parallel", $j = \ell - \tfrac{1}{2}$, cases. Apparently, strong transitions
can only occur between two $s_{1/2}$, $p_{3/2}$, $d_{5/2}$ or $f_{7/2}$ states,
but not between $p_{1/2}$, $d_{3/2}$ or $f_{5/2}$ states.

A famous example is the 9.40→4.43 MeV $7/2 \rightarrow 7/2^-$ transition in P^{31}, which, experimentally, has a strength of
0.5 W.U. This is rather smaller than the 2.2 W.u. expected,
which leads us to question the simple presentation given
above.

If we assume a $(2s_{1/2})^2{}_{01}$ configuration for the core,
Si^{30}, our analogue and anti-analogue states have
$(s^2{}_{01}\ f)_{7/2\ 3/2}$ and $(s^2{}_{01}\ f)_{7/2\ 1/2}$, respectively, where
the two lower indices refer to J and T. But there should be
a second low-lying $7/2^-$ state, with the configuration
$(s^2{}_{10}\ f)_{7/2\ 1/2}$. In P^{30}, the 0^+, $T = 1$, and 1^+, $T = 0$,
states are only 680 keV apart, such that we also expect the
two $7/2^-$, $T = \tfrac{1}{2}$, states in P^{31} at not too different excitation energies. The strength of the $(s^2{}_{01}\ f)_{7/2\ 3/2} \rightarrow$
$(s^2{}_{01}\ f)_{7/2\ 1/2}$ transition can also be computed without too
much difficulty. The M1 operator now only operates on the
core part of the wave function, and because the $s_{1/2}$ orbit
belongs to the group leading to large matrix elements, one
finds that the transition should also be strong, 1.95 W.u.
This is in conflict with experiment, because not two but
only one strong $7/2 \rightarrow 7/2^-$ transition is observed.

Experimentally, the position of this second low-lying
$7/2^-$ state in P^{31} is unknown, but one can make a good guess
from a three-particle shell-model calculation in which Si^{28}
is taken as an inert core. This has been done by Maripuu[1])

who computed the necessary two-body matrix elements with the
modified surface delta interaction (MSDI), and who obtained
the six parameters in the calculation from a least-squares
fit to 33 states in the A = 29-34 region. The two $7/2^-$,
T = ½, configurations in P^{31} will mix, of course, and it
turns out that the lower of the two, at E_x = 4.4 MeV, con-
tains 72% $(s^2_{01}$ $f)_{7/2\ 1/2}$ and 28% of the $(s_{10}\ f)_{7/2\ 1/2}$ configuration. The upper state is predicted at E_x = 6.2 MeV
(see Fig. 1). One can again compute M1 transition probabilities for these mixed configurations, which yields the remarkable result that almost all the combined strength,
4.0 W.u., should go to the lower state and very little,
0.1 W.u., to the upper. From this calculation one can thus
understand why there is only one strong transition, but the
disagreement between observed and predicted strengths, 0.5
and 4.0 W.u., respectively, has only increased. Our conclusion must be that Si^{30} has a much more complicated structure than just $s_{1/2}^2$. It certainly contains large fractions
of the $d^2_{3/2}$ and $d^{-2}_{5/2}s^4_{1/2}$ configurations, as has been shown
by recent elaborate shell-model calculations[2]).

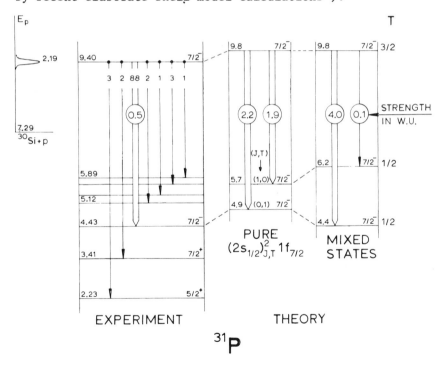

Fig. 1. Shell-model calculations, both for pure and for
mixed states, of the γ decay of the 9.40 MeV $J^\pi = 7/2^-$ state
in P^{31}, as compared to experiment (from ref. 1).

Another prize example is the 10.24 3.11 MeV, $7/2^- \rightarrow 7/2^-$, $T = 5/2 \rightarrow 3/2$, transition in Cl^{37}, with a strength of 1.7 ± 0.3 W.u. The corresponding resonance is the strongest (p,γ) resonance known. In this case, the analogue state is assumed to have the d^4_{02} $f)_{7/2\ 5/2}$ configuration, with d and f referring to the $1d_{3/2}$ and $1f_{7/2}$ orbits, respectively, and there are four lower states with $J^\pi = 7/2^-$, $T = 3/2$, where the $f_{7/2}$ particle is coupled to d^4_{02}, d^4_{11}, d^4_{21} and d^4_{31} core configurations, respectively. The analogue should only strongly decay to the $(d^4_{02}\ f)_{7/2\ 3/2}$ configuration, the anti-analogue proper. The M1 transitions in which the core changes from d^4_{02} to d^4_{21} or d^4_{31} are forbidden because the spin change is larger than one. The transition with a $d^4_{02} \rightarrow d^4_{11}$ core change would be allowed, but the matrix element is negligibly small because the M1 operator only operates on the $d_{3/2}$ particle (see Table I). One thus concludes that the analogue state should decay through four $7/2^-\ 7/2^-$ M1 transitions with matrix elements proportional to the squared amplitudes of the $(d^4_{02}\ f)_{7/2\ 3/2}$ admixtures into the four (mixed) states. The mixing has been discussed by Bansal[3]), who predicts $7/2^-$ states at E_x = 2.60, 4.85, 5.30 and 5.90 MeV, with 60, 8, 9 and 23% of the relevant configuration. Taking into account the E_γ^3 factor, one computes branchings of 87, 4, 3 and 6% for the decay of the analogue state. This is not incompatible with experiment, where $\geq$ 80% was found to go to the only known $7/2^-$ state, at E_x = 3.11 MeV, and $\leq$ 13% to unknown higher levels. Actually, in Cl^{37} things behave more or less according to our simple picture. The four states do not mix very strongly, most of the strength goes into the lowest component, and the E_γ^3 factor further reduces the branching to the three higher states.

III.   GAMMA DECAY OF ANALOGUE
AND ANTI-ANALOGUE STATES IN Ar^{38}

A large amount of information has been accumulated during the past two years on the bound and unbound states of Ar^{38}, mainly with the $Cl^{37}(p,\alpha)Ar^{34}$ reaction [4]), but also with the $Cl^{37}(p,\alpha)S^{34}$ [5]) and $Cl^{37}(p,p)Cl^{37}$ [6]) reactions. The excitation energies of analogue states and of many bound states are known with errors varying between 0.1 and 2.0 keV, their spins and parities were determined from double and triple angular correlation measurements, respectively, the branchings of these states have been measured, and finally DSA measurements provided the mean lives of the $J^\pi = 5^-$, 3^- and 4^- levels in Cl^{38} at $E_x = 0.67$, 0.76

and 1.31 MeV, respectively. The analogue of the
$J^\pi = 2^-$ Cl^{38} ground state has probably been seen as a resonance in the $Cl^{37}(p,\gamma)Ar^{38}$ reaction at $E_p = 427$ keV, but

the resonance is too weak to be investigated with any success. These four lowest states in Cl^{38} together form the
$d^{-3}_{3/2}$ $f_{7/2}$, $T = 2$, quadruplet, of which the energies al-

ready twelve years ago were shown to be linearly related to
the energies of the $d^{-1}_{3/2}$ $f_{7/2}$ quadruplet in K^{40}.

The 5^- analogue in Ar^{38} is split into two components,
observed as $Cl^{37}(p,\gamma)Ar^{38}$ resonances at $E_p = 1\ 089$ and

$1\ 094$ keV, with almost identical γ decay, the 3^- analogue
is split into components, centered at $E_p = 1\ 140$ keV, and

the 4^- analogue is single, at $E_p = 1\ 732$ keV. These ana-

logue resonances almost exclusively decay by M1 transitions
to bound states with odd parity, e.g. 100% for the two 5^-
resonances and 99% for the 4^- resonance. The second remarkable characteristic is that the resonances decay very
strongly to bound states with the same spin, e.g. 91, 97
and 68% for the two 5^- resonances and the 4^- resonance,
respectively. This was termed "Erné's J→J rule". The same
two rules hold for the decay of odd-parity bound states.
They decay, wherever possible, to lower odd-parity states
with a strong preference of J→J over J→J+1 or J→J-1. The
strength of the stronger M1 transitions is some $0.2-0.5$ W.u.
There is little doubt that these bound odd-parity states
together form something like the anti-analogue state, only
of a much more complicated nature than in odd-A nuclides.
In the $d^{-3}_{3/2}$ $f_{7/2}$, $T = 1$, configuration there are 24 states,
of which one has $J^\pi = 0^-$, two 1^-, four 2^-, five 3^-, five 4^-,
four 5^-, two 6^- and one 7^-. It soon became clear, however,
that in any more serious calculation one also has to take
into account at least the $d^{-3}_{3/2}$ $p_{3/2}$ configuration, not only

in the anti-analogue but also in the analogue state. In the
$Cl^{37}(d,p)Cl^{38}$ reaction, e.g., an appreciable $\ell_n = 1$ contri-

bution is observed for the transition to the 0.76 MeV 3^-
level, and many strong $\ell_n = 1$ transitions are observed to

states at only slightly higher excitation energies.
Such shell-model calculations were recently performed by
Engelbertink[7]), along very much the same lines as those indicated for P^{31} in the previous section. Only, because of
the larger configuration space, the Ar^{38} calculation is of
a rather higher degree of sophistication. Still, it is not
a really large calculation (the largest matrix to be diagonalized is 9 by 9, as compared e.g. to the Oak Ridge shell-

model program which diagonalizes matrices up to 500 x 500. The smaller size programs have the advantage that it is still easy to trace which component in a wave function is the main contributor to a particular transition probability. Ten slightly different sets of parameters were tried, ac-

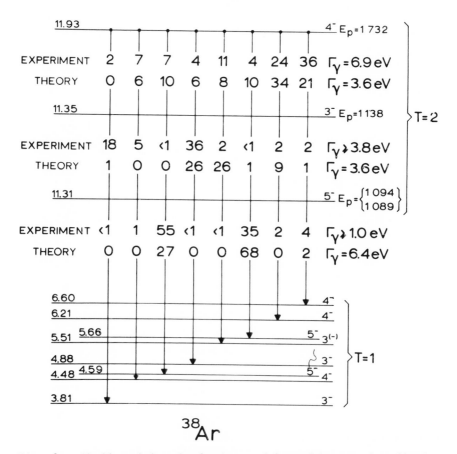

Fig. 2. Shell-model calculations of branchings and radiation widths for the γ decay of analogue states in Ar^{38}, as compared to experiment. The experimental Γ_γ values for the 5$^-$ and 3$^-$ analogues represent the sums of the Γ_γ values for the components into which these states are split. The branching indicated for the 5$^-$ analogue is the average of those for the E_p = 1 089 and 1 094 keV resonances. For the 3$^-$ analogue the branching of the strongest component is indicated (from ref. 7).

cording to different groups of levels taken along in the
least-squares fitting procedure. The wave functions thus
obtained were used for the calculation of M1 and E2 transition probabilities.

The results for the decay of the analogue states, as
computed with parameter set No. 8, are compared to experiment in Fig. 2. On the whole one should say that the calculations don't do too badly, especially for the 5⁻ and 4⁻
analogues. The theory correctly predicts which transitions
should be strong and which weak. The largest disagreements,
by an order of magnitude, are found for the decay of the 3⁻
analogue to the 3.81 and 5.51 MeV 3⁻ levels. The other
parameter sets are not doing much better. They give slightly better results for some transitions and slightly worse
for others.

The results for the decay of bound odd-parity states are
presented in Figs. 3, 4 and 5. Some calculated mean lives
are pretty good, with the 6.60 MeV 4⁻ and the 4.88 MeV 3⁻
levels as exceptions.

The calculations have been extended to include the lowest
three even-parity states in Ar^{38} (Fig. 6), for which the
configurations $s^4_{1/2} d^6_{3/2}$, $s^3_{1/2} d^7_{3/2}$ and $s^2_{1/2} d^8_{3/2}$
(taken with reference to Si^{28} as an inert core) were considered. The wave functions thus found will also be used
to compute transition probabilities for the few E1, M2
and E3 transitions which have been observed, and log ft
values for the β decays of Cl^{38} and K^{38}.

One aspect of the calculations should be mentioned here,
which is very much in line with what was said in the pre-
ceding section on Cl^{37}. In the analogue states the $d^{-3}_{3/2}$
part of the wave functions is coupled to maximum isospin,
$(d^{-3}_{3/2})_{3/2\ 3/2}$. The strong M1 transitions deexciting the
analogue states occur to levels which have a large component of this same configuration. The reasoning is the same
as before. If the $d^{-3}_{3/2}$ part of the wave function is coupled differently for the initial and final states, the M1
operator operates on the $d_{3/2}$ particle, which gives a very
small contribution to the transition probability (see table
1).

The J→J rule is easily explained. One 6-j symbol occurs
in all transition probabilities, as already remarked by
Erne[4]), which is large for J→J and small for J→J+1 transitions.

One might conclude that apparently this theoretical work
offers a nice overall picture of what is going on, but that,
again, the configuration space is probably not yet large
enough to give a detailed agreement.

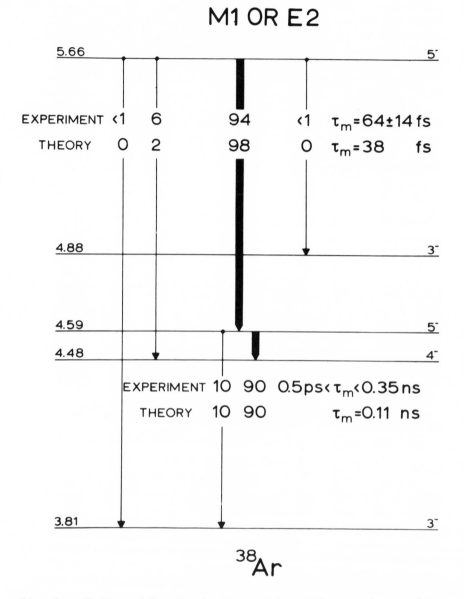

Fig. 3. Shell-model calculations of branchings and mean lives for the γ decay of 5⁻ bound states in Ar[38] (from ref. 7).

IV. PROTON CAPTURE DSA MEASUREMENTS

One of the most welcome benefits of the Ge(Li) detector has become the possibility to obtain nuclear lifetimes from Doppler shift attenuation measurements. In this section I would like to describe some DSA measurements on γ radiation

following proton capture, to discuss the region of lifetimes
to which the method is applicable, and to compare different
reactions as to their usefulness for DSA measurements.

In Utrecht, lifetimes were obtained of many levels in
Al^{26}, P^{31}, Ar^{38} and Ca^{40}. The P^{31} data, obtained with the
$Si^{30}(p,\gamma)P^{31}$ reaction[8]) will be discussed below in some
more detail.

With a 20 cm^3 Ge(Li) detector γ-ray spectra were taken
at 46 resonances in the E_p = 0.5-2.3 MeV region. This large

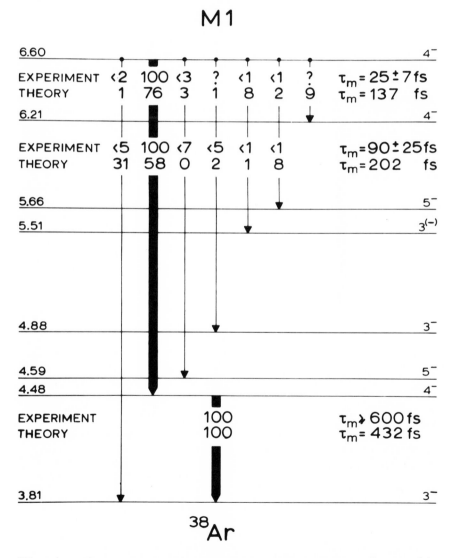

Fig. 4.   Shell-model calculations of branchings and mean lives
for the γ decay of 4^- bound states in Ar^{38} (from ref. 7).

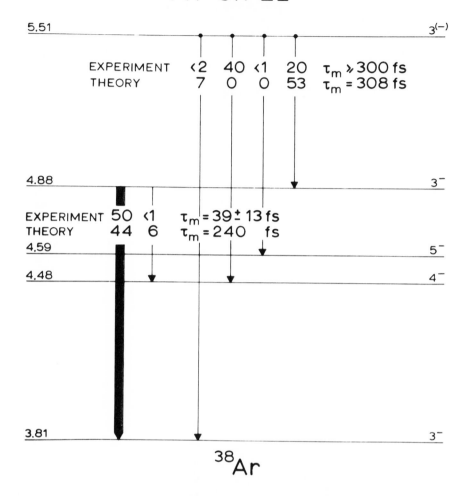

M1 OR E2

Fig. 5. Shell-model calculations of branchings and mean lives for the γ decay of 3⁻ bound states in Ar³⁸ (from ref. 7).

number guarantees that always some resonances can be found which excite a particular lower level of interest. The analysis of the spectra provided the branchings of resonances and of 34 bound states up to E_x = 7.2 MeV, their accurate excitation energies (errors from 0.12 to 3.0 keV), and the reaction Q value, Q = 7 297.4 ± 1.2 keV, which is 10.2 ± 4.0 keV higher than the value from the 1964 mass table.

Gamma-ray Doppler shifts were obtained from spectra taken at θ = 0° and 140°, at 13 different resonances. The full shift, for an infinitely short-lived state, then amounts to $\Delta E_\gamma / E_\gamma$ = 3.2 x 10⁻³ at E_p = 1.5 MeV. For a

γ ray deexciting a level with mean life τ_m, the shift is a fraction $F(\tau_m)$ of the full shift, where F also depends on the target material and on E_p. For a calculation of $F(\tau_m)$, see e.g. ref. 4.

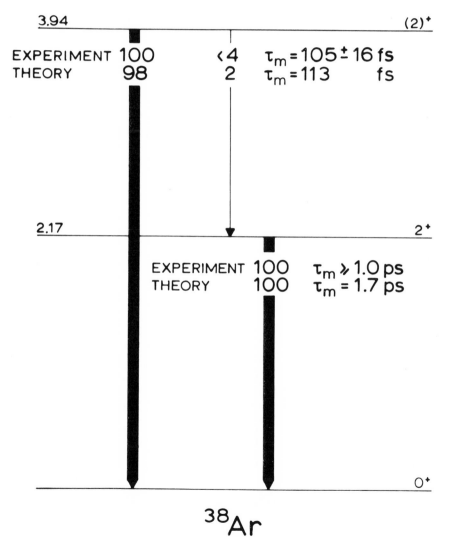

Fig. 6. Shell-model calculations of branchings and mean lives for the γ decay of 2^+ bound states in Ar^{38} (from ref. 7).

There are several checks on such measurements. Primary
lines should show the full shift (because the resonances are
very short lived), and one may use radioactive sources to
obtain unshifted calibration lines. Consistent results·
should be obtained at different resonances which excite the
same lower level, and for different γ rays which deexcite
one particular level. An example of measured shifts is
shown in Fig. 7.

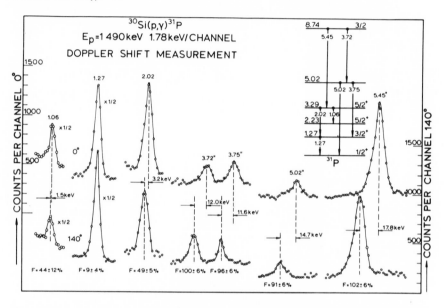

Fig. 7. Doppler shifts of some γ-ray transitions measured
at the E_p = 1 490 keV Si^{30}(p,γ)P^{31} resonance. The primary
γ rays are fully shifted. The shifts of the E = 5.02 and
·3.75 MeV γ rays are identical within the epxerimental error;
same for the E = 2.02 and 1.06 MeV γ rays. The shift of
the E = 1.27 MeV γ ray as measured at this resonance is
unsuitable for a lifetime determination, because the 1.27
MeV level is excited both directly and through several cascades, of which two are shown in the insert (from ref. 8).

The DSA measurements in P^{31} yielded the mean lives of
17 bound states, including all levels below E_x = 5.1 MeV.
Only for two of these, upper limits had to be given, because the measured shift was equal to the full shift within
the experimental error. The other 15 mean lives are all
in the region τ_m = 10 fs - 1 ps.

A curious case is the 5.01 MeV level which from the DSA
measurements was proven to be a doublet. Some indication
of this had already been obtained from the decay. At all

four resonances where it is excited more than 10%, it is
seen to decay to the ground state (γ_o) and first excited
state (γ_1), but at two resonances the intensity ratio was
measured as $\gamma_o/\gamma_1 = 2.1 \pm 0.3$ and 2.1 ± 1.0, and at the
two others as 0.78 ± 0.10 and 0.61 ± 0.08, respectively.
The excitation energies measured at the two groups of
resonances were equal, 5 014.9 $\pm$ 1.0 and 5 015.2 $\pm$ 0.8 keV,
respectively. The mean lives, however, are vastly different, 67 $\pm$ 11 and 10 $\pm$ 7 fs, respectively, such that there
are definitely two different levels.

All this went to show that (p,γ) DSA measurements are a
highly successful method to provide nuclear lifetimes. Apparently, a large fraction of levels in the s-d shell has
lifetimes within a fraction of 10 equal to the slowing-
down time of the recoiling ion, about 0.1 ps. The method
is easy, because if one sticks to not too high proton energies, say E_p < 2 MeV, lines are unbroadened, such that
one only has to measure the shift, and one does not have
to fit complicated line shapes as observed for most other
reactions producing γ radiation. Of course, the shifts are
quite small, at best just a little larger than the line
width, but because the line shapes are identical at the two
angles, it is possible to measure the shifts, with good
statistics, with a precision of about 2% of the width.

A drawback of (p,γ) DSA measurements is that the energy
of the recoil is quite low. Consequently, the range of the
ion is small, a few $\mu g/cm^2$, such that it is impossible to
get the ion out of the target material. At high recoil energies, the possibility to have the ions slow down in different target materials provides a valuable check on slowing-down theories (which are most dubious at low energy).
It also provides a way to extend the range of DSA measurements to longer mean lives, τ_m > 1 ps, because the slowing-
down time can be increased by having the ion slow down in
light material, such as carbon or air.

Apparently, DSA measurements with (p,γ) reactions on the
one hand, and with heavy-ion reactions, (d,pγ) and (α,pγ) on
the other, are supplementary. The former reaction is most
useful for short mean lives, τ_m < 1 ps, the latter are best
for longer lifetimes. Measurements of lifetimes in the
intermediate overlapping region offer possibilities to check
the slowing-down theory, as do measurements with other reactions, like Coulomb excitation, inelastic electron scattering, or resonance fluorescence.

REFERENCES

1. S. Maripuu, Utrecht University, Nucl. Phys. submitted.
2. E. Halbert, J. B. McGrory, B. H. Wildenthal and P. W. M. Glaudemans, Oak Ridge National Laboratory and Utrecht University, unpublished.
3. R. K. Bansal, Phys. Rev. 153, 1084 (1967).
4. F. C. Erné, W. A. M. Veltman and J. A. J. M. Wintermans, Nucl. Phys. 88, 1 (1966); G. A. P. Engelbertink, H. Lindeman and M. J. N. Jacobs, Nucl. Phys. A107 305 (1968).
5. B. Bosnjakovic, J. A. van Best and J. Bouwmeester, Nucl. Phys. A94, 625 (1967).
6. B. Bosnjakovic and W. Bruynesteyn, Utrecht University, Nucl. Phys., submitted.
7. G. A. P. Engelbertink, Utrecht University, unpublished.
8. A. C. Wolff, M. A. Meyer and P. M. Endt, Nucl. Phys. A107, 332 (1968).

DISCUSSION

RIPKA: Concerning the M1 transitions which you mentioned at the beginning of your talk, I wonder whether the theory wouldn't agree more with experiment if you used instead of the magnetic moment operator itself the one which would be renormalized by particle-hole excitations from the $d_{5/2}$ to $d_{3/2}$ states? The reason is that this works extremely well, for example, for the magnetic moment of S^{33} and it makes a significant difference.

ENDT: Yes, one can use effective moments.

RIPKA: Do you know whether this improves the agreement between theory and experiment?

ENDT: It makes all numbers smaller which means that it improves the agreement for P^{31} but it makes it worse for Cl^{37} where the agreement is already pretty good. So we would much rather keep working with the actual g values and not go over to effective g values, but instead take on more configurations which actually amounts to something like taking effective g values. I mean if you would take all configuration space you wouldn't have to use any effective g factors at all. So, we would rather go on taking on more configurations, as many as the program allows and see if we can get agreement that way.

GEDCKE: In a case like P^{31} where the core is presumably pretty well distorted, what effect does that have on the calculated transition probability?

ENDT: I just couldn't say. I don't think that it's so spherical but it's not a really distorted nucleus like the rare earth nuclei, but certainly you have to take into account other configurations.

GEDCKE: It seems to me there there must be some effect to coupling the core into your excited states.

ENDT: There definitely is.

KURATH: Don't you feel that the situation in the upper end of the 2s-1d shell is rather unique in that you have a strong $f_{7/2}$ M1 transition on a weak background of $d_{3/2}$ M1 transitions?   Then one can easily understand such features as the preference for gamma decay of such a $T_>$ resonance to a $T_<$ state of the same J. In most regions the situation would be much more complex.

ENDT: The j→j transitions are rather more general it seems to me. Transition probabilities are proportional to a 6-J symbol which is large for j→j and small for j→j±1 transitions.

II. b. T = 2 Levels in Ne^{20}, Mg^{24}, and S^{32} as Compound-Nucleus Resonances*

S. S. Hanna, F. Riess, W. J. O'Connel, K. A. Snover
H. M. Kuan, D. W. Heikkinen, G. L. Latshaw
E. Adelberger, and A. V. Nero.
Department of Physics, Stanford University
(Presented by S. S. Hanna)

The T = 2 resonances in T_z = 0 nuclei are observed by means of the isospin cascade T = 2 → 1 → 0 in (p,γγ) reactions. For the lowest T = 2 levels, the spin cascade is J^π = 0$^+$ → 1$^+$ 0$^+$ which produces the γ-γ correlation 1 + cos^{2}θ. These resonances are also observed in the reactions (p,p$_0$), p,p$_1$)... (p,α$_0$), (p,α$_1$)... and (p,n$_0$), (p,n$_1$)... In general the T = 2 → 1, T_z = 0 transitions are gamma ray analogs of observed T_z = 2 → 1 beta transitions.

The lowest T = 2 level in Ne^{20} is observed as a resonance in F^{19}(p,γγ)Ne^{20}. As shown in Fig. 1. The T = 2 state cascades through a 1$^+$, T = 1 level for which all particle channels are closed. The resonance was located by observing the yield of the second γ ray of higher energy. The primary transition is the gamma analog of the beta transition from the ground state of O^{20} to the analog 1$^+$, level of F^{20}. The γ spectrum on resonance is shown in Fig. 1. The 11.2 MeV γ ray is resonant at E_p = 4.090 ± 0.005 MeV (Fig. 1) or E_x = 16.728 ± 0.005 MeV in Ne^{20}. The insert in Fig. 1 shows the angular distribution of the 11.2-MeV γ ray relative to the proton beam. Isotropy is consistent with J = 0 for the T = 2 state. Alpha-particle transitions to excited states in O^{16} can be detected by observing the de-excitation γ rays. No resonance was observed for the 6.14 MeV γ ray (Fig. 1) or the unresolved 7.0 MeV doublet. The particle groups from the reaction were observed at angles of 168°, 148°, 123° and 87°. The T = 2 state appears as a sharp anomaly in the elastic scattering at all angles. The curves are consistent with ℓ = 0, J^π = 0$^+$, Γ ≤ 2 keV, and Γ_p/Γ 0.1. No prominent resonances were observed in α$_3$, α$_4$, p$_3$, p$_4$ and p$_5$. However, the unresolved group α$_1$ + α$_2$ showed a striking anomaly at the backward angles. At 154° the α$_2$ group was resolved and showed that the anomaly can be attributed principally to the transition to the 3$^-$ level of O^{16}. This result is very surprising since ℓ = 3 and ΔT = 2 for this transition. However, the anomaly vanishes at angles less than 148° and was not observed in the total cross section (Fig. 1). Thus, it seems the ℓ = 3 wave interferes strongly with "background" of the reaction but has a very small intensity. The α$_0$ group shows similar but less pronounced anomalies. From the γ-ray

* Supported in part by the National Science Foundation

data it is estimated that $\Gamma_p \Gamma_\gamma / \Gamma \simeq 0.5$ eV. Thus $\Gamma_\gamma \simeq 5$ eV. The Weisskopf estimate is 3.4 eV.

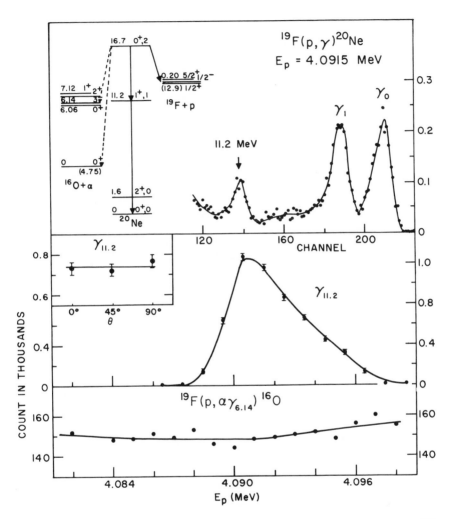

Fig. 1. The determination of the lowest T = 2 level in Ne^{20} from the F^{19}(p,γ)Ne^{20} reaction.

The second T = 2 level in Ne^{20} was observed in F^{19}(p,p$_0$) (p,α$_0$), (p,α$_1$) and (p,α$_2$) at E$_p$ = 5.880 ± 0.005 MeV, E$_x$ = 18.427 MeV, with Γ_{lab} = 11 ± 3 keV, and $\Gamma_p / \Gamma \simeq 0.2$ (for J$^\pi$ = 2$^+$). In F^{19}(p,γ)Ne^{20} the gamma rays γ$_0$, γ$_1$, γ$_2$, γ$_3$, γ$_4$, and γ$_5$ are not resonant but the resonance is observed for a 10.6-MeV γ ray, identified as the second γ ray of a cascade through a T = 1 level at E$_x$ = 12.26 MeV to the 2$^+$, 1.63-MeV level. The resonance curves gives $\Gamma_p \Gamma_\gamma / \Gamma \simeq 0.055$ eV. Hence,

$\Gamma_p/\Gamma \simeq 0.3$ eV. The $F^{19}(p,n)Ne^{20}$ total cross section was measured by observing the activation of Ne^{20} and the resonance was not observed. However, strong anomalies were observed at backward angles in the differential cross section with a pulsed-beam, time of flight spectrometer.

The lowest T = 2 level in Mg^{24} was observed by similar observations. A more complex γ-decay scheme was obtained as shown in Fig. 2. The $0 \to 1 \to 0$ spin sequence was confirmed by γ-γ correlation measurements. The resonance was also observed in $Na^{23}(p,p_0)Na^{23}$.

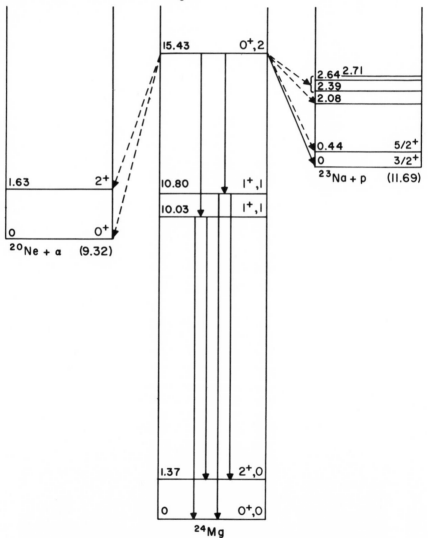

Fig. 2. A partial decay scheme of Mg^{24}.

The lowest T = 2 level in S^{32} appears in $P^{31}(p,\gamma\gamma)S^{32}$ and $P^{31}(p,p_0)P^{31}$. In this case the γ cascade is through a 1^+, T = 1 level at $\simeq 7.2$ MeV.

III. A.   THE MIRROR NUCLEI Mg^{25} AND Al^{25}

A. E. Litherland
University of Toronto
Canada

I.   INTRODUCTION

^{25}Mg and ^{25}Al are at present two of the most thoroughly studied mirror nuclei. The first eighteen energy levels in each nucleus have adequate spin and parity assignments and much gamma-ray decay and particle reduced-width data is available. ^{25}Mg and ^{25}Al are also unique because they are the only adequately studied mirror pair of nuclei that exhibit well developed rotational bands in their level schemes.

The rotational bands in ^{25}Mg and ^{25}Al were discovered about 13 years ago (1) and the most up-to-date summary of the published information is given in the 1967 compilation of Endt and Van der Leun (2). Figures 1 and 2 show the rotational band grouping of some of the energy levels of ^{25}Mg and ^{25}Al. In these figures the energies of the excited levels E_J are plotted against $J(J+1)$ and the levels in the same band are joined by a solid line. In Fig. 1 two 11/2+ levels are included in the two lowest rotational bands. These correspond in excitation energy to two intense alpha particle groups observed (3) in the $^{27}Al(d,\alpha)^{25}Mg$ reaction where the yield is roughly proportional to $(2J+1)$. The zig-zag of the lowest $K=\frac{1}{2}$ band in ^{25}Mg is associated with a non-zero decoupling parameter (4) and in ^{25}Al there are additional perturbations due to Thomas (5) – Ehrman (6) shifts.

There are two main advantages in studying the nuclear spectroscopy of a pair of mirror nuclei and these advantages exist because of the well known charge symmetry of nuclear forces. Apart from the relatively minor electromagnetic effects due to replacing a neutron by a proton the level schemes of ^{25}Mg and ^{25}Al should be identical. The main effect of the electromagnetic interaction is to make the binding energy of the proton in ^{25}Al only 2.268 MeV compared with the 7.329 MeV binding energy of the neutron in ^{25}Mg. This basic difference permits the ^{25}Al levels above 2.268 MeV to be studied by resonance reactions. In Fig. 2 the proton binding energy is shown for the break-up of ^{25}Al into $^{24}Mg + p$ and in addition for the breakup of ^{25}Al into $^{24}Mg^* + p$.

The first advantage that this situation confers is that proton widths, Γ_p, and gamma-ray widths, Γ_γ, can be determined either by directly measuring the widths of resonances or by measuring the absolute cross sections for the "thick" target resonant nuclear reactions (7). This is

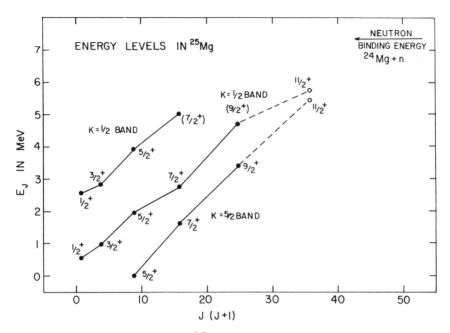

Fig. 1. The energy of Mg^{25} levels, E_J, is plotted against
$J(J+1)$ where J is the angular momentum of the levels. Levels
believed to be members of three rotational bands are joined
together.

in contrast with the situation in ^{25}Mg where neutron reduced
widths, θ_n^2, and gamma-ray widths of bound levels have to
be determined respectively from deuteron stripping reaction
studies and by direct lifetime measurements of the nuclear
energy levels. The proton reduced widths θ_p^2, obtained
from the measured values of Γ_p, are expected to be closely
similar to the values of θ_n^2 in the mirror nuclei. The
gamma-ray reduced widths $|M|^2$ are also expected to be
similar in the mirror nuclei. Consequently, the results of
experiments on ^{25}Mg levels can often give clues relevant
to possible experiments on ^{25}Al and vice versa. It will be
evident later in this contribution that sometimes experiments
on ^{25}Mg can provide a key piece of evidence in the study of
A=25 levels and sometimes experiments with ^{25}Al are more
revealing.

    In addition to the complementary information that the
study of a mirror pair produces, the small differences in
the properties of the levels of ^{25}Mg and ^{25}Al can, in
principle, be used to probe more deeply into the structure
of these nuclei. For example the Thomas (5) - Ehrman (6)
energy shifts of the mirror levels give information on reduced particle widths for particle emission to excited
nuclear levels which are unobtainable by other methods.
Also in principle the assumed nuclear wavefunctions can be

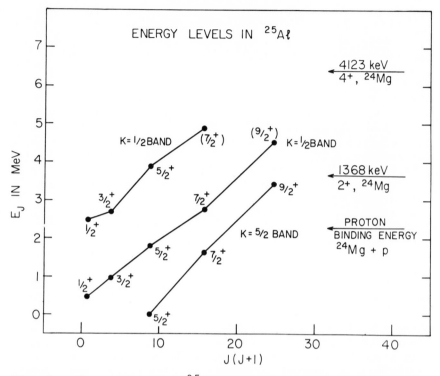

Fig. 2. The energy of Al²⁵ levels, E_J, is plotted against
J(J+1) where J is the angular momentum of the levels. Levels
believed to be members of three rotational bands are joined
together.

tested further if it becomes possible to separate the
Thomas-Ehrman Coulomb shifts from the magnetic shifts due
to replacing a neutron by a proton. This second advantage
has not yet been significantly exploited and this contribution will be concerned mainly with the exploitation
of the experimental advantages of studying a mirror pair.

II. RECENT EXPERIMENTAL STUDIES OF ²⁵Mg and ²⁵Al

II. 1. Introduction

The mirror pair ²⁵Mg and ²⁵Al are being studied at present in a collaboration between nuclear physicists of the
University of Toronto and the Chalk River Nuclear
Laboratories. At Chalk River a series of experiments (8)
on the high resolution study of the gamma rays from the
reaction ²⁵Mg(p,p')²⁵Mg have produced estimates of lifetimes
of ²⁵Mg levels below 4057 keV and in addition branching
ratio estimates have been made. In this contribution I will
refer to these results frequently but I will concentrate

largely upon the data taken at Toronto.

The studies at Toronto on ^{25}Al use an ancient 3MV Van de Graaff accelerator as the source of up to 30 μA of protons. These protons are used to form excited levels in ^{25}Al by the resonant capture reaction ^{24}Mg(p,γ)^{25}Al. The gamma-ray detection equipment, unlike the accelerator, is however modern and includes a 40 cm^3 Ge(Li) counter with a-bout 3.5 keV resolution (FWHM) at 1.33 MeV gamma-ray energy. Under carefully controlled conditions this counter also has a resolution of 8 keV at 10 MeV gamma-ray energy. The gamma-ray spectra are recorded in a dual 3200-channel Victoreen SCIPP 6400 pulse-height analyser.

It is now well known that the large high-resolution Ge(Li) gamma-ray counters have revolutionized nuclear spectroscopy with small Van de Graaffs. This is because, in addition to being able to resolve complex gamma-ray spectra, it is now possible to study the attenuation of the small Doppler shifts (9) following low energy proton or alpha-particle capture and so deduce nuclear lifetimes in the range from about 3 ps down to about 3 fs. An additional advantage of the high resolution of the Ge(Li) counter is the much improved signal to noise which permits the detection of weak gamma-ray transitions in the presence of the background that is always present. In this contribution I will be giving examples of all these advantages in radiative capture gamma-ray studies with Ge(Li) spectrometers.

II.2. Total and Particle Widths of the 9/2$^+$ levels

in ^{25}Al at 3422 and 4038 keV

The original work on these two levels was done ten or more years ago with NaI(Tl) gamma-ray spectrometers (1,10) and the work left several questions unanswered. For example the interpretation of the original data left un-answered the question as to which of the two 9/2+ levels was to be associated with the K=5/2 rotational band based upon the 5/2+ ground level. Also neither level had the properties expected of the expected 9/2+, K=½ member of the rotational band based upon the ½+, 451-keV level in ^{25}Al. These problems have now been resolved satisfactorily by new measurements on the two previously known 9/2+ levels and the recent discovery of a third 9/2+ level at 4507 keV in ^{25}Al. Both of the rotational bands referred to are shown in Figure 2.

The 9/2+ level in ^{25}Al at 3422 keV is also the g-wave resonance at 1.20 MeV in the reaction ^{24}Mg(p,γ)^{25}Al and it was originally realized that Γ_p could be much less than Γ_γ.

This point is important because if the 9/2+, 3422-keV level in ^{25}Al is a rotational level of a K=5/2 band based upon the 5/2+ ground level of ^{25}Al then the E2 transitions within the band should be strongly enhanced. If $\Gamma_p \ll \Gamma_\gamma$ then the small value of $\Gamma_p\Gamma_\gamma/\Gamma$ of 5 meV indicates that Γ_p and not Γ_γ is equal to 5 meV. The original work on ^{25}Al did not determine which of Γ_p or Γ_γ was larger and consequently the enhancement of the E2 transitions from the 9/2+, 3422-keV level in ^{25}Al could not be determined.

The Chalk River work (8) on the lifetime of the 9/2+, 3400-keV level in ^{25}Mg first suggested that $\Gamma_p \ll \Gamma_\gamma$ because in ^{25}Mg the level is bound and can decay only by gamma-ray emission. The observed lifetime given in column 2 of Table 1 was short compared with the value in ^{25}Al deduced from the measurement of $\Gamma_p\Gamma_\gamma/\Gamma$. The partial lifetime in ^{25}Al assuming $\Gamma_p \gg \Gamma_\gamma$ is called lifetime A and is given in column 5 of Table 1. This difference suggests strongly, but of course does not prove, that $\Gamma_p \ll \Gamma_\gamma$.

Table 1

Comparison of Lifetimes in ^{25}Mg and ^{25}Aℓ

Energy keV	Lifetime fs	J^π	Energy keV	Lifetime A fs	Lifetime B fs
3400	33 ± 19	9/2+	3422	120 ± 24	10 ± 6
4057	53 ± 10	9/2+	4038	1100 ± 200	22 ± 6

Lifetime A = h $\Gamma/2\pi$ Γ_p Γ_γ Partial Lifetime from Radiative Capture Yield

Lifetime B = h/2π Γ Doppler Shift Attenuation

The lifetime of the 9/2+, 3422-keV level in ^{25}Al has now been measured (11) by the Doppler shift attenuation method (DSAM) and the result is given in column 6 of Table 1. A Ge(Li) counter gamma-ray pulse spectrum is given in Figure 3. There are only three gamma rays observed from the capturing level and these are shown in the inset. To facilitate the accurate measurement of the Doppler shifts the 1274.5-keV gamma ray from a ^{22}Na source and a Tennelec precision pulse generator were used to encompass the 1611, 1811-keV cascade gamma-ray peaks. The total absorption peak of the 3422-keV gamma ray can be seen in Figure 3 superimposed on the double escape peak of the gamma ray from the first-excited level of ^{12}C from the contaminant reaction ^{15}N(p$\alpha\gamma$)^{12}C.

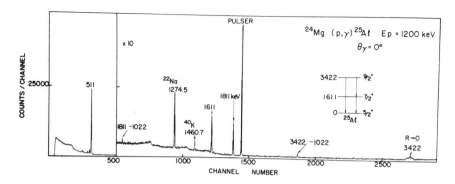

Fig. 3. The pulse spectrum of gamma rays from a Ge(Li) counter at the 9/2+, 1.20-MeV resonance in the reaction Mg^{24}(p,γ)Al^{25}.

More details of the results of the Doppler shift measurement of the 3422-keV level are given in Table 2. It is quite clear that the lifetime of 10 ± 6 fs is near the lower limit of measurement by the DSAM. However the authors of the work (11) feel that it is in one respect more reliable than the ^{25}Mg measurement. This is because the initial velocity of the excited ^{25}Al nuclei is known precisely whereas the unknown angular distribution of the inelastic protons (8) in the ^{25}Mg(pp'γ)^{25}Mg reaction causes an uncertainty in the average initial velocity of the excited ^{25}Mg nuclei which is most serious for the measurement of the shorter lifetimes.

The second line of Table 2 gives the results of an attempt to measure the attenuation of the Doppler shift, $F(\tau)$, a function of the nuclear lifetime, for the 7/2-, 1.490-MeV resonance which is known to be very fast (2). The value of $F(\tau) = 1.00 \pm 0.02$ gives an indication of the confidence to be placed upon the value of $F(\tau) = 0.95 \pm 0.02$ for the 9/2+, 3422-keV level.

The ^{25}Al level at 4038 keV has also almost certainly a spin-parity of 9/2+ (10,12) and has similar properties to the 9/2+, 3422-keV level. The 4038-keV level in ^{25}Al which is also the 1.842-MeV resonance in ^{25}Mg(p,γ) Al has also been studied recently at Toronto (12) and its lifetime determined by the DSAM. Measurements at Chalk River (8) on the 4057-keV mirror level in ^{25}Mg also given in column 2 Table 1 indicate that, if mirror levels have similar lifetimes, $\Gamma_p \ll \Gamma$ for the 4038-keV level in ^{25}Al.

A Ge(Li) gamma-ray spectrum taken at this very weak, $\Gamma_p\Gamma_\gamma/\Gamma = 0.6$ meV, 1.842-MeV resonance, Figure 4, shows only three resonant gamma rays from ^{25}Al. The rest are from a variety of contaminants. The 1368-keV gamma ray, however, is from the inelastic scattering from ^{24}Mg by a broad

Table 2

Doppler Shift Attenuation Measurement of the Resonance
Widths of the 3422-keV Level in ^{25}Al

Ep(keV)	Ex(keV)	J^{π}	$F(\tau)$	τ(fs)	Γ(MeV)	θ_p^2
1200	3422	9/2+	0.95 ± 0.02	10 ± 6	66	$(5 \pm 1 \times 10^{-4}$
1490	3702	7/2−	1.00 ± 0.02		3×10^{5} *	

*Measured by Proton Elastic Scattering

resonance that underlies the sharp 1.842-MeV resonance.
Figure 5 shows that the decay scheme of the 4038-keV level
is remarkably simple.

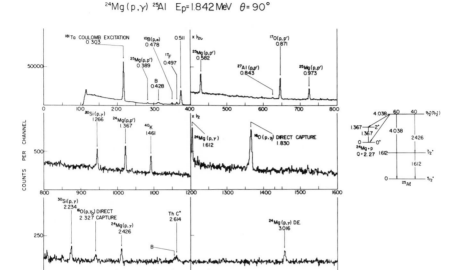

Fig. 4. The pulse spectrum of gamma rays from a Ge(Li)
counter at the (9/2+), 1.842-MeV resonance in the reaction
Mg^{24}(p,γ)Al^{25}.

Doppler shift attenuation measurements (12) give a lifetime of 22 ± 6 fs for the 4038-keV level and the similar
lifetime for the mirror level at 4057-keV in ^{25}Mg, given in
Table 1, indicates that $\Gamma_p < \Gamma_\gamma$.

The measured values of $\Gamma_p\Gamma_\gamma/\Gamma$ and Γ in ^{25}Al and the lifetimes of the mirror levels in ^{25}Mg permit the reduced g-wave
proton widths for the two 9/2+ resonances in ^{25}Al to be calculated. These values are given in the last column of
Table 2 and in Table 3. Both values of Θ_p^2 were obtained
with the help of the barrier penetrability graphs given by
Gove (7). The reduced particle widths for the 4038-keV
level in ^{25}Al are also summarized in Table 3 where it can
be noted that Θ_p^2 and $\Theta_p^2{}'$ are both small. From the absence
of a resonant yield of the 1368-keV gamma ray it is possible
to deduce that $\Gamma_p/\Gamma_\gamma < 0.1$.

The results shown in Table 3 are important because the
reduced inelastic scattering width Θ_2^2 is so small. The
value of Θ_2^2 is expected to be much larger for the 9/2+,
K=5/2 level because the ground level rotational band in
^{24}Mg provides the parent levels for the K=5/2 band in ^{25}Al.
The small value of Θ_2^2 is one piece of evidence that suggests that the 9/2+, 4038-keV level in ^{25}Al does not have

K=5/2.   Inelastic scattering from the 9/2+, 3422-keV level
in ^{25}Al is not possible as it is below the threshold.   However gamma-ray M1 and E2 strengths provide extra clues
which help further in the assignment of K=5/2 to the 9/2+,
3422-keV level.

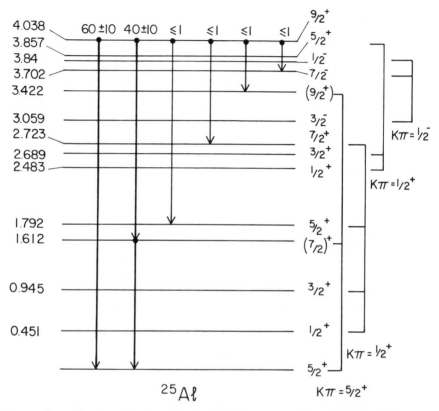

Fig. 5.   The gamma-ray decay scheme of the 4.038-MeV level
in Al^{25}.

II.3.   Gamma-ray Transition Strengths from the two

lowest 9/2+ levels in ^{25}Al

The branching ratios, mixing ratios and lifetime data
on the two 9/2+ levels in ^{25}Al at 3422 and 4038 keV permit
the M1 and E2 transition strengths to be derived.   These
strengths are given in Table 4.   It is immediately apparent that both the M1 and E2 strengths are greater for
the 3422-keV level than the 4038-keV level.   Also as shown
in the first two rows in Table 5 there is good agreement
between theory (13) and experiment if the K value of the

3422-keV level is assumed to be 5/2. A tentative assignment of K=9/2 for the 4038-keV level is in reasonable agreement with experiment as shown in the second two rows. The
last two rows are included to support the suggestion that
the 2+, 4233-keV K=2 level (14) in ^{24}Mg is the parent
level of the 9/2+, 4038-keV K=9/2 level   in ^{25}Al. The
large K value for the 4038-keV level ^{25}Al gives a natural
explanation for the very small values of θ^2 given in Table
3. This is because the emission of a d-wave proton from a
K=9/2 resonance to the 2+, K=0 first excited level of ^{24}Mg
is K=forbidden.

Table 3

Properties of the (9/2+), 4038-keV Level in ^{25}Al

Channel	ℓ	θ_ℓ^2 (expt.)
P	4	$(2.35 \pm 0.5) \times 10^{-6}$
P'	2	$< 2.7 \times 10^{-3}$

From Experiment

^{24}Mg$(p,\gamma)^{25}$Al radiative capture	$\dfrac{\Gamma_p \Gamma_\gamma}{\Gamma} = 0.6$ MeV
	$\Gamma_p'/\Gamma_\gamma < 0.1$
Doppler Shift	$h/2\pi\Gamma = 22 \pm 6$ fs
4057-keV analog level in ^{25}Mg	$h/2\pi\Gamma = 53 \pm 10$ fs

II.4. Properties of the new level at 4507-keV in ^{25}Al

The measured particle widths and gamma-ray decay data
of the 9/2+, 4038-keV level in ^{25}Al tend to rule it out as
a member of the K=1/2 band based upon the 1/2+, 451-keV
first excited level (15). A new level at 4507-keV has
now been located (16) in ^{25}Al and this level has many of
the properties of the missing 9/2+, K=1/2 level in ^{25}Al.
The new level is shown in Figure 6 as a new resonance at
E_p = 2.330 MeV in the inelastic scattering of protons by
^{24}Mg. The yield curve shown in the upper part of Figure 6
shows the region between the two well known resonances at
2.010 and 2.400 MeV in the same reaction. The yield curve
was obtained by setting a narrow window on the total absorption peak in the pulse spectrum of the 1367-keV gamma
ray from ^{24}Mg. A 40 cm^3 Ge(Li) counter was used for the

Table 4

Measured M1 and E2 Transition Strengths From Two 9/2+ Levels in ^{25}Al

Transition keV	J_f^π	$\|M\|^2$(Wu) E2	$\|M\|^2$(Wu) M1
3422 → 0	5/2+	3.4 ± 2.1	
3422 → 1612	7/2+	15 ± 9	(+) (5 ± 3) × 10^{-1}
1612 → 0	7/2+ → 5/2+	$22^{+5.5}_{-4.5}$	(+) (1.8 ± 0.5) × 10^{-1}
4038 → 0	5/2+	4.7 ± 1.5	
4038 → 1612	7/2+	5.3 ± 2.6	(+) (3.4 ± 1.1) × 10^{-1}

Note: The signs of the M1:E2 amplitude mixing ratios are in brackets.

Table 5

Comparison of E2 Strengths with Collective Model

Transition keV		K_i, K_f	$|M|^2$(Wu) Theory	$|M|^2$(Wu) Expt.
^{25}Al	3422 → 0	5/2,5/2	6.2*	3.4 ± 2.1
^{25}Al	3422 → 1612	5/2,5/2	18.7*	15 ± 9
^{25}Al	4038 → 0	9/2,5/2	3.67†	4.7 ± 1.5
^{25}Al	4038 → 1612	9/2,5/2	1.77†	5.3 ± 2.6
^{24}Mg	4233 → 0	2.0	1.2	1.06 ± 0.1
^{24}Mg	4233 → 1368	2.0	1.75†	1.97 ± 0.1

†Theory normalized to 1.22 Wu for the 4233 → 0 E2 transition.

*Theory normalized to 22 Wu for the 1612 → 0 E2 transition.

A. E. Litherland

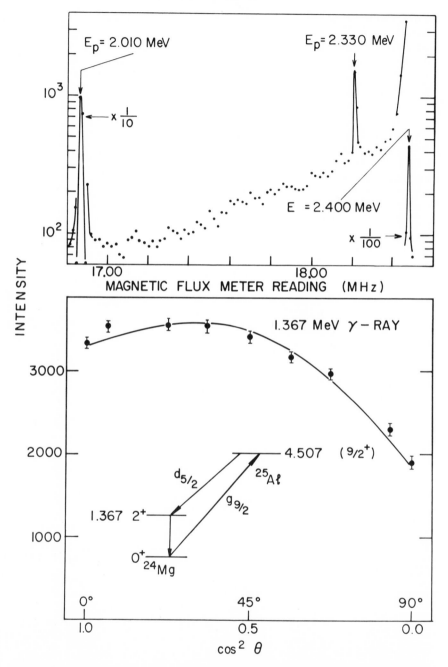

Fig. 6.   The yield curve of the 1367-keV gamma ray from the
$Mg^{24}(pp'\gamma)Mg^{24}$ reaction is shown in the upper portion of the
figure.   The angular distribution of the 1367-keV gamma ray
at the 2.330-MeV resonance is shown in the lower portion of
the figure.

yield curve and the use of the narrow window increased the
signal to noise significantly. The new resonance can be
located in data taken during 1955 at Chalk River but it
was not considered significant then because of peculiar
background subtraction difficulties in the region of the
resonance. The superior signal to noise of the Ge(Li)
counter makes the resonance easy to locate and a detailed
angular distribution is shown in the lower part of Figure 6.
The solid line is the theory for a 9/2+ assignment to the
resonance. As the inelastic protons have an energy of
only 972 keV, the neglect of ℓ higher than 2 seems very
reasonable. If ℓ is assumed to be   < 2 then there are no
adjustable parameters for an assignment of 9/2+. The
measured value of $(2J+1)\Gamma_p\Gamma_{p'}/\Gamma$ was 16 ± 2eV and (2J+1)
$\Gamma_p\Gamma_\gamma/\Gamma$ was observed to be < 1 meV. If the reasonable
assumption is made that Γ_γ = 10 meV then it is clear that
in this case $\Gamma_p < \Gamma_{p'}$. The experimental values of θ^2 are
shown in Table 6.

Table 6

Properties of the (9/2+), 4507-keV Level in ^{25}Al

Channel	ℓ	θ_ℓ^2(expt)	θ_ℓ^2(theory)
p	4	1.5×10^{-3}	5.6×10^{-3}
p'	2	> 0.085*	0.23

*Assuming $\Gamma_\gamma \sim$ 10 MeV

If the 4507-keV level is assumed to be the 9/2+, K=1/2
level of the band based on the 1/2+, 451-keV level then
θ_4^2 and θ_2^2 can be calculated with the help of the expressions
given by Nilsson (13). For θ_4^2 to be greater than zero an
admixture in the proton wavefunction from the N=4 harmonic
oscillator shell is required and the value shown was calculated by perturbation theory θ_2^2 can be deduced from the
Nilsson wavefunctions and equation 6 of Litherland et al.
(4).

The angular distribution shown in Figure 5 is unfortunately not unique and 7/2+ and 5/2+ assignments are
possible provided the inelastic proton has a suitable mixture of j and ℓ values.

There are, however, some additional clues from the
nucleus ^{25}Mg. The most likely candidate for the mirror
level in ^{25}Mg is at 4704 keV. The 4704-keV level was
observed to decay mainly by a transition to the 5/2+,
1960-keV level as expected for the 9/2+, K=1/2 level. Also

the 4704-keV level is probably excited quite strongly in
the ^{27}Al(d,α)^{25}Mg reactions (3). The alpha particle group
leading to the unresolved 4704, 4712-keV doublet in ^{25}Mg is
intense and as the yield of alpha particles in the above
reaction has been observed to be roughly proportional to
2J+1 it seems reasonable that the lower member of the
doublet may have a high spin. The other member has probably a spin-parity of 5/2+ (8).

A further study of both the 4704-keV level in ^{25}Mg and
the 4507-keV level in ^{25}Al would clearly be highly desirable.
The large 197 keV shift between the levels in the mirror
nuclei ^{25}Mg and ^{25}Al is presumably a Thomas-Ehrman shift
due to the large reduced widths for inelastic scattering.
In this respect the level would be similar to the 5/2+ and
1/2+ levels of the same band. This observation illustrates
the point made earlier that additional information can be
obtained by studying mirror nuclei. The Thomas-Ehrman
shift information however has not yet been exploited to obtain quantitative information on reduced particle widths.

II.5. The spin, parity and lifetime of the 2723-keV

level in ^{25}Al

The spins and parities of the 3422, 4038, 4507-keV
levels in ^{25}Al are almost certainly 9/2+ but the resolution
of the ambiguities that still exist in these spin-parity
assignments will require more difficult experiments to be
carried out in the future (17). The spin of the important
2723-keV level in ^{25}Al has however been determined (11) un-
ambiguously by studying the gamma rays from the 7/2-,
1.490-MeV resonance (2) in the reaction ^{24}Mg(p,γ)^{25}Al. The
2723-keV level is the fourth member of a rotational band
based upon the 1/2+, 451-keV first excited level in ^{25}Al
and confirmation of the expected spin (18) of 7/2 is welcome. The latest decay scheme of the 7/2-, 1.490-MeV resonance is shown in Figure 7. Apart from the weak transition from the resonance to the 2723-keV level the other
gamma rays have been observed previously. In Figure 8 a
979-keV gamma ray is shown to be resonant. The 945-keV
gamma ray is the ground level transition from the second
excited level at 945 keV. The 979-keV gamma ray is weak
but can be observed with the help of a 40 cm^3 high-resolution
Ge(Li) gamma-ray detector. The angular distribution of
the 979-keV gamma ray, which is identified to be a primary
transition from the resonance level to the 2723-keV level,
is shown in Figure 9. The measured points agree well with
the theory for spin of 7/2 for both resonance level and
the 2723-keV level and rule out spins of both 9/2 and 5/2
for the 2723-keV level. It is worth noting that the value
of ωγ for the 979-keV gamma ray is only 1 meV.

DECAY OF THE 3.702 MeV LEVEL
IN ²⁵Al

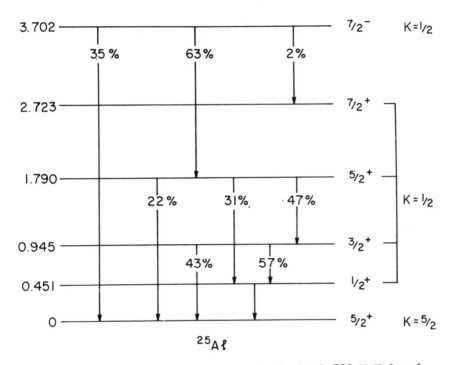

Fig. 7. The gamma-ray decay scheme of the 3.702-MeV level
in Al²⁵.

The suggested assignment of even parity to the 2723-keV
level is strongly supported by the measured lifetime (11)
of 450 ± ¹⁰⁰₈₀ fs and the observed prominent quadrupole decay
to the 3/2+, 945-keV second excited level of ²⁵Al. Odd
parity for the 2723-keV level would imply a strongly enhanced M2 transition. The lifetime of the 7/2+,2723-keV
level   because of the weak, 2%, branching ratio,   was
measured at the 5/2+, 1.660-MeV resonance in the
²⁴Mg(p,γ)²⁵Al reaction. The lifetime of the 5/2+, 1790-keV
level in ²⁵Al was however measured (11) at the 1.490-MeV
resonance and was found to be 800⁺⁴⁰⁰₋₂₀₀ fs.
    A spin of 7/2 for the 2.738-keV level in the mirror
nucleus ²⁵Mg has recently been determined by McCallum and
Sowerby (19) and a preliminary account has been published.
The lifetime of the 2738-keV level in ²⁵Mg has been
measured by Sharpey-Schafer et al (8) to be 288 ± 20 fs.

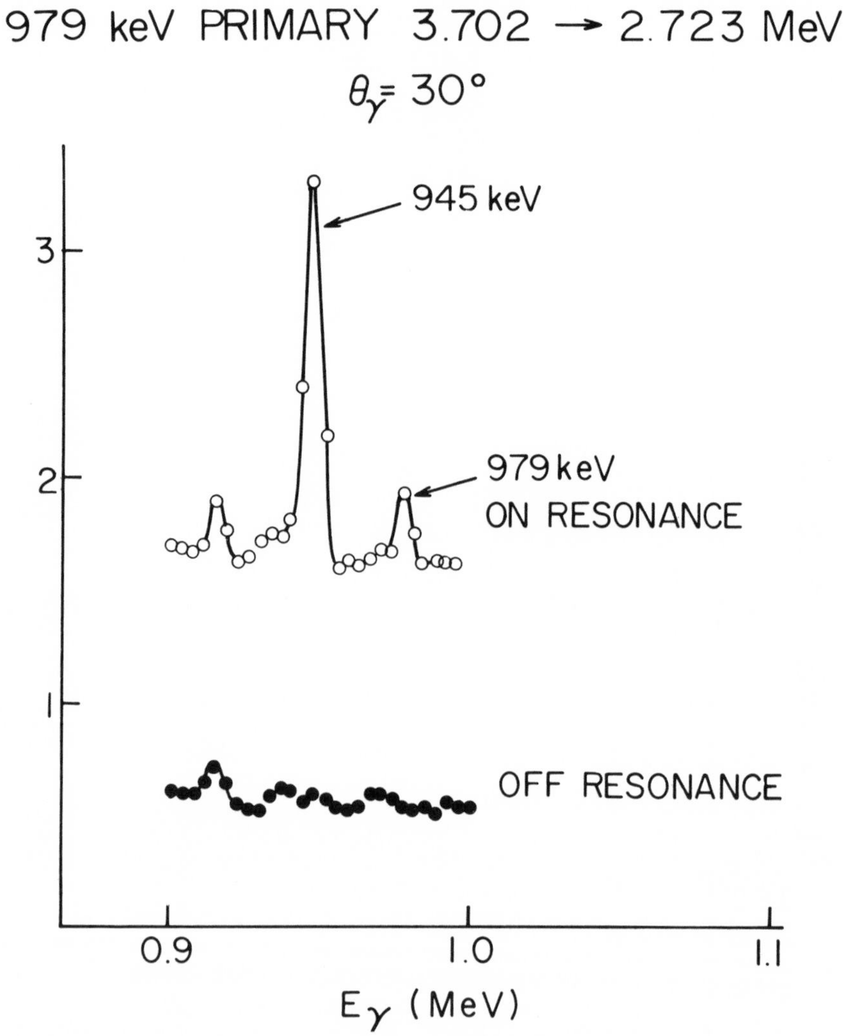

Fig. 8. Evidence for the presence of a 979-keV gamma ray from the 3.702-MeV level in Al[25].

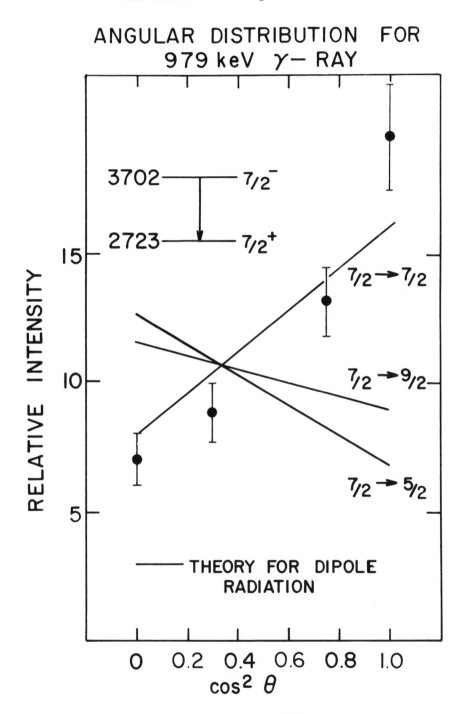

Fig. 9.   Angular distribution of the 979-keV gamma ray at the 1.490-MeV resonance (3.702-MeV level) in Mg^{24}(p,γ)Al^{25}.

II.6.   E2 Enhancements in ^{25}Al

Figure 10 summarizes the present situation with regards to the E2 enhancements in Weisskopf units (20) of the gamma ray transitions among the two lowest rotational bands in ^{25}Al. The present situation in ^{25}Mg is similar and has been discussed by Sharpey-Schafer et al (8).

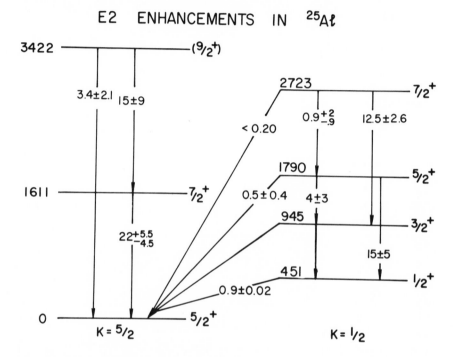

Fig. 10.   E2 Enchancements within the two lowest rotational bands in Al^{25} together with E2 enhancements between the rotational bands.

There are two striking features of the E2 strengths in Figure 10. The first feature is that the E2 transitions from the K=½ band to the K=5/2 band are in general weak compared with the transitions within the K=½ and the K=5/2 bands. This is to be expected if the rotational bands are to be taken seriously and is a situation in marked contrast with ^{27}Al^2. Secondly, the observed cascade E2 transitions in the K=½ band are weaker than the observed cross-over E2 transitions. This is actually expected on the basis of the collective model (15) as the strengths are proportional to vector coupling coefficients which are small (8) for the cascade transitions shown in Figure 10. An increase in the accuracy of the lifetime measurements would clearly provide a more detailed check of the predictions of the collective model. An increase in accuracy is experimentally possible but the accuracy of the measurement of long, 0.1 ps to 1 ps, lifetimes by the DSAM at present depends upon the accuracy of the approximate theoretical treatment (21) of the scattering of the low-velocity recoiling nuclei during the the slowing down process. Further work on this problem is desirable.

II.7. Evidence in favour of the third rotational

band in ^{25}Al

The lower two rotational bands in ^{25}Al shown in Figure 2 have the enhanced E2 transition strengths for gamma-ray transitions within the bands shown in Figure 10. The third band shown in Figure 2, however, has until recently had no enhanced E2 strengths within the band and one aim of an experiment by Dworkin et al.(22) was to try to locate the E2 transition from the 5/2+, 3858-keV level to the lowest 1/2+ member of the band at 2483-keV.

The 5/2+, 3858-keV level is also the 1.660-MeV resonance in the reaction ^{24}Mg(pγ)^{25}Al and has already been studied (18) with low resolution NaI(Tl) spectrometers. The main features of the decay scheme deduced by Gove et al. (18) are correct but the branching ratios, which were deduced from coincidence measurements, are not accurate. A more correct decay scheme deduced by Dworkin et al. (22) is shown in Figure 11. Besides changes in the branching ratios two additional primary transitions have been observed. The 1368-keV gamma ray from inelastic scattering is definitely present and in addition a very weak 1375-keV transition seems to be fairly well established. The 3407-keV transition to the first excited state seems to be < 1.7% compared with the previous value of 5%. The 8% feed to the 7/2+, 2723-keV level was used by Anyas-Weiss et al. (11) to study the lifetime of the 2723-keV level by the Doppler shift attenuation method.

The complex Ge(Li) gamma-ray pulse spectrum shown in Figure 12 illustrates some of the problems in studying the gamma rays from the 3858-keV level with a NaI(Tl) spectrometer. Contributions from ^{12}C, ^{28}Si and ^{16}O target contaminants can be seen and it is probably the partly resonant ^{12}C and ^{28}Si contributions that are responsible for the apparent 5% transition to the first excited level in the work of Gove et al. (18).

The region near 1368-keV gamma-ray energy is shown expanded in Figure 13. The 1368-keV gamma ray from the ^{24}Mg(pp'γ)^{24}Mg reaction is resonant. Another gamma ray at 1375 keV also appears to be resonant and, if it is, then it can be identified with the E2 primary transition from the resonance to the 1/2+, 2483-keV level in ^{25}Al. The

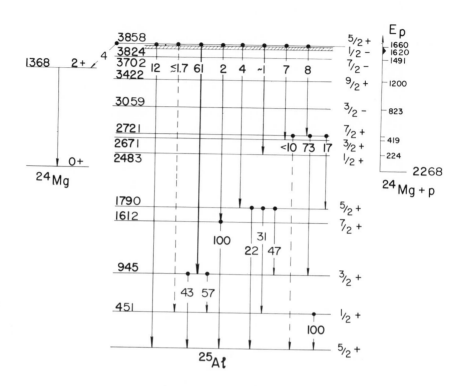

Fig. 11. The gamma-ray decay scheme of the 3858-keV level in
Al²⁵ which is the 1.660-MeV resonance in Mg²⁴(p,γ)Al²⁵.

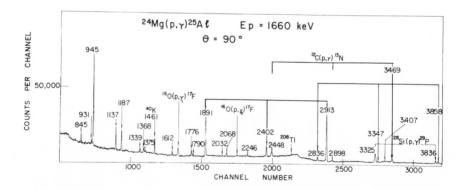

Fig. 12. The pulse spectrum of gamma rays from a Ge(Li)
counter at the 5/2+, 1.66 MeV resonance in the reaction
Mg²⁴(p,γ)Al²⁵.

GAMMA RAYS IN THE E$_\gamma$ = 1368 keV REGION FROM THE
REACTION ^{24}Mg (p,γ) ^{25}Al AT θ = 30°

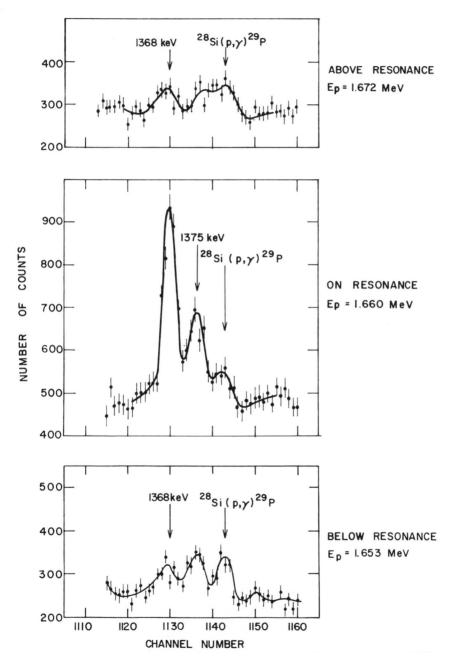

Fig. 13. Pulse spectra of gamma rays in the region of 1368
keV at the 5/2+, 1.66-MeV resonance and also above and below
the resonance.

branching ratio of 1% and measured value of $\Gamma_p\Gamma_\gamma/\Gamma = 45 \pm 9$ meV for the resonance ($\Gamma_p \gg \Gamma_\gamma$ in this case (2))gives an E2 enhancement of about 25 Wu. The error on this value is uncertain because the branching ratio of 1% is a preliminary one at present. However, such an enhancement strongly supports the idea of a third rotational band in ^{25}Al. Further experiments with better targets are planned to establish firmly this E2 primary.

II.8.   Comparison of the energy levels of

^{25}Mg and ^{25}Al

The spin and parity information for the energy levels of ^{25}Mg and ^{25}Al can be combined with the radiative and particle widths to make the comparison of the positions of the energy levels shown in Figure 14. Eighteen levels can now be paired in ^{25}Mg and ^{25}Al with reasonable certainty and it is apparent that there is much hitherto unused information in the energy shifts between ^{25}Mg and ^{25}Al.

The large Thomas-Ehrman shifts of the negative parity levels are to be expected because of the large known (2) reduced particle widths for these levels.

There are however some anomalies in the energy shifts. A striking anomaly is evident for the $K=\frac{1}{2}$ band based upon the 1/2+, 451-keV first excited level of ^{25}Al. The 1/2+, 5/2+ and 9/2+ levels show a large shift but the 3/2+ and 7/2+ levels do not. Another anomaly which is immediately apparent is the shift upwards of the 9/2+, 3422-keV level in ^{25}Al from the mirror 9/2+, 3400-keV level. Such a small discrepancy could result either from the Thomas-Ehrman shift for the 5/2+ ground level being greater than that for the 9/2+, 3422-keV level or from a magnetic interaction.

3.   ALPHA-PARTICLE RADIATIVE CAPTURE REACTIONS

In addition to the detailed study of the $T=\frac{1}{2}$ levels of the A=25 system, the members of the Van de Graaff group at the University of Toronto are studying other capture reactions.

For some time now a detailed study of the ^{14}N$(\alpha,\gamma)^{18}$F reaction has been carried out by Charlesworth et al. (23). A logical extension to this study was the ^{15}N$(\alpha,\gamma)^{19}$F reaction (24) which exploits the excellent Ti^{15}N targets prepared by Charlesworth and Aitken. These targets, when directly water-cooled, can survive alpha-particle currents in excess of 50 µA for several hours. With these large currents alpha-particle capture reactions are not difficult to study with a 40 cm^3 Ge(Li) counter.

Several new resonances in the ^{15}N$(\alpha,\gamma)^{19}$F reaction have recently been located by Aitken et al. (24) and a yield curve is shown in Figure 15. The resonances at 1681, 1852 and 1883 keV have previously been studied by Price (25) and Tolbert (26).

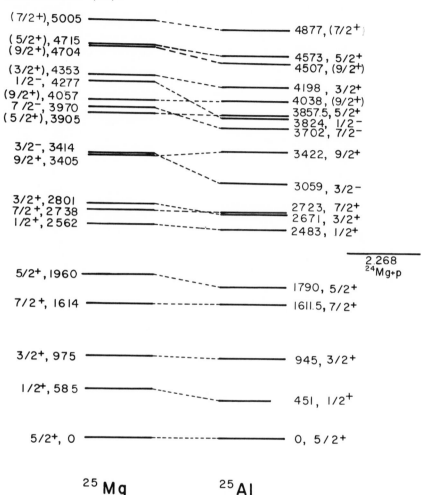

Fig. 14. The energy level spectra of the mirror nuclei Mg^{25} and Al^{25} are compared.

New resonances appear starting at 1790 keV and many more appear at higher bombarding energies. The $^{13}C(\alpha,n)O^{16}$ reaction is the principle contaminant reaction in the yield curve. The energies of the new resonances are listed in Figure 15. The new resonances actually correspond closely to other levels in ^{19}F found using the $^{20}Ne(t,\alpha)^{19}F$ reaction (27) and the $^{19}F(pp')^{19}F$ reaction (28). In fact all the new resonances in $^{15}N(\alpha,\gamma)^{19}F$ correspond to levels previously observed by these reactions and this point is illustrated in Figure 16.

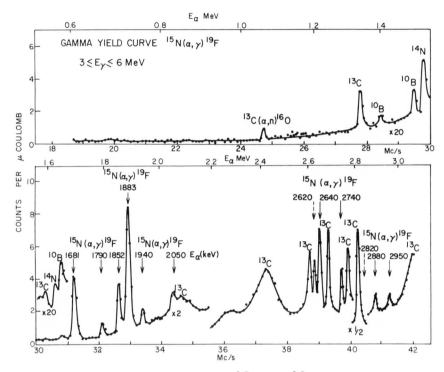

Fig. 15. A yield curve of the $N^{15}(\alpha,\gamma)F^{19}$ reaction resonances in the reaction are labelled by four figure numbers and contaminants by symbols.

A detailed study of these resonances is underway (24) and some recent results are shown in Figure 17. The gamma-ray spectrum at the 1.79-MeV resonance is shown together with a decay scheme in the insert. Transitions are observed to the 5/2-, 1.35 and 3/2- 1.46-MeV levels and in addition two low-energy primaries and their secondaries are observed. These primaries feed the two levels at 4.00 and 4.04 MeV and angular distributions of these primaries together with the primaries to the 5/2-, 1.35 and 3/2-, 1.46-MeV levels show that the resonance has spin-parity of 7/2- and the 4.00 and 4.04-MeV levels have spin-parities of 7/2- and 9/2- respectively. A preliminary analysis of the branching and multipole mixing ratios (24) suggests that the resonance has K=3/2 and the other low-lying negative parity levels have K=½.

In conclusion, I would like to present the preliminary results of some work which was partly inspired by the talk by Cor Van der Leun at the first Kansas Conference (29) in 1964. A useful unpublished yield curve on the $^{23}Na(\alpha,\gamma)^{27}Al$ reaction was included in the Conference proceedings and the statement made that the reaction seems to populate the high spin levels in ^{27}Al.

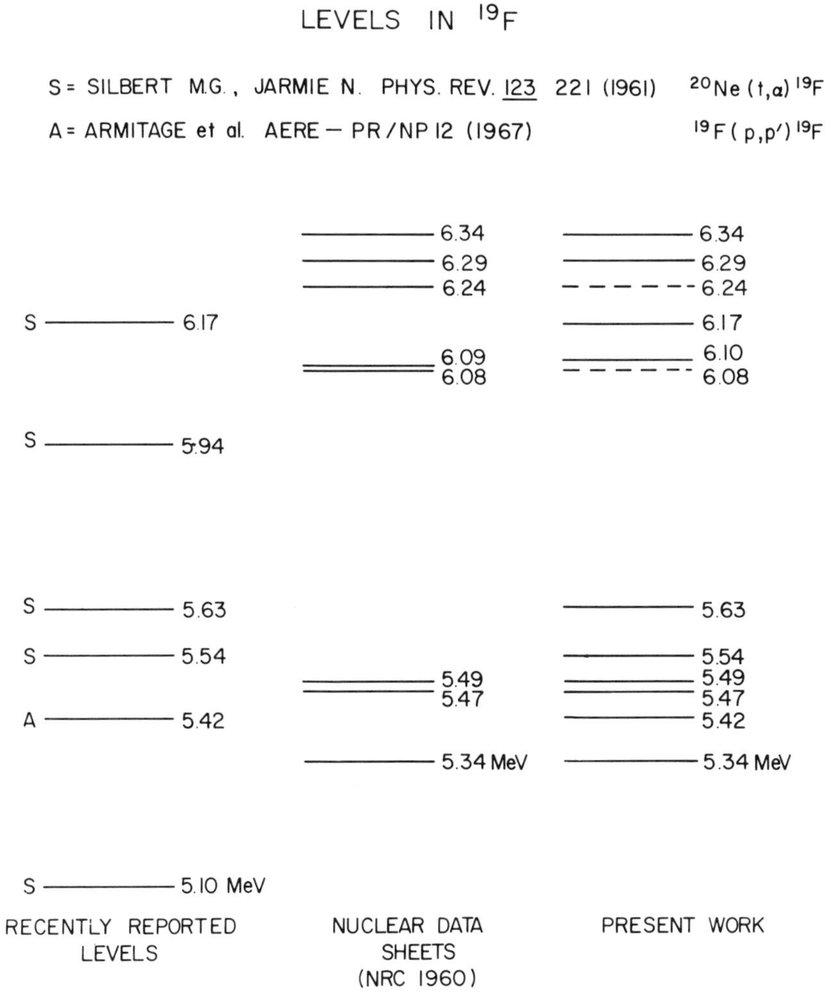

LEVELS IN ^{19}F

S = SILBERT M.G., JARMIE N. PHYS. REV. 123 221 (1961) ^{20}Ne (t,a) ^{19}F

A = ARMITAGE et al. AERE − PR / NP 12 (1967) ^{19}F (p,p') ^{19}F

	6.34	6.34
	6.29	6.29
	6.24	6.24
S — 6.17		6.17
	6.09	6.10
	6.08	6.08
S — 5.94		
S — 5.63		5.63
S — 5.54		5.54
	5.49	5.49
	5.47	5.47
A — 5.42		5.42
	5.34 MeV	5.34 MeV
S — 5.10 MeV		

RECENTLY REPORTED   NUCLEAR DATA   PRESENT WORK
LEVELS   SHEETS
(NRC 1960)

Fig. 16. The correspondence between the resonances, observed in N$^{15}(\alpha,\gamma)$F^{19} and F$^{1.9}$ levels observed in other reactions.

Recent work (30) at the University of Toronto and the Chalk River Nuclear Laboratories (31) on the ^{26}Mg$(p,\gamma)^{27}$Al reaction has established that the spin-parity of the 4509-keV level in ^{27}Al is 11/2+. Figure 18 shows a partial decay scheme at the resonance used to study the 11/2+ in the ^{26}Mg$(p,\gamma)^{27}$Al reaction (30) and also a partial decay scheme of the level at 12404 keV in ^{27}Al excited by the ^{23}Na$(\alpha,\gamma)^{27}$Al reaction (32). The 11/2+, 4509-keV level is populated strongly in the alpha-particle capture reaction at E_α = 2.704 MeV. Other transitions are observed at the resonance and we are hopeful that other high spin levels in ^{27}Al will be located in the near future.

A. E. Litherland

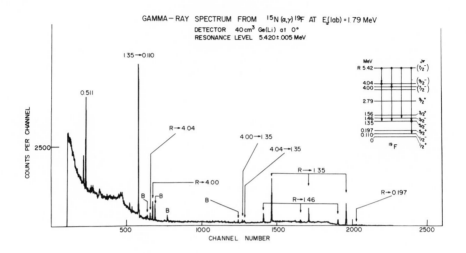

Fig. 17. The gamma-ray pulse spectrum from a Ge(Li) counter at the 1.79 MeV resonance in the reaction $N^{15}(\alpha,\gamma)F^{19}$.

ACKNOWLEDGMENTS

I would like to acknowledge the invaluable assistance of the University of Toronto Van De Graaff group in the preparation of this contribution. The work was also supported in part by a grant from the National Research Council of Canada and the Van de Graaff was provided by the Ontario Cancer Institute. The 40 cm Ge(Li) counter was supplied by the RCA Victor Company, Montreal.

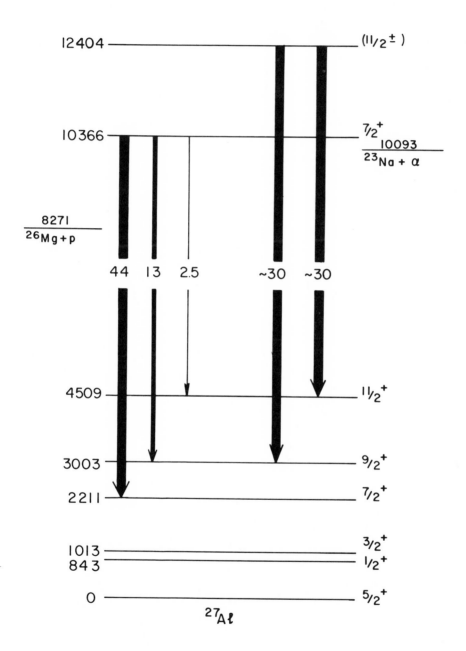

Fig. 18. Partial decay schemes of the 2 MeV resonance in Mg²⁶(p,γ)Al²⁷ and the 2.704-MeV resonance in Na²³(αγ)Al²⁷.

REFERENCES

1. A.E. Litherland, E.B. Paul, G.A. Bartholomew and
    H.E. Gove, Phys. Rev. 102, 208 (1956).

2. P.M. Endt and C. Van der Leun, Nucl. Phys. A105,
    68 (1967).

3. S. Hinds, R. Middleton,   and A.E. Litherland,
    Proceedings of the Rutherford Jubilee Conference
    (Manchester), edited by J.B. Birks (1961) p305.

4. A.E. Litherland, H. McManus, E.B. Paul, D.A. Bromley
    and H.E. Gove, Can. J. Phys. 36,378 (1958).

5. R.G. Thomas, Phys. Rev. 88, 1109 (1952).

6. J.B. Ehrman, Phys. Rev. 81, 412 (1951).

7. H.E. Gove, Resonance Reactions, Experimental, Nuclear
    Reactions, Vol. 1 pp 271-275, North Holland Publishing
    Company.

8. J.F. Sharpey-Schafer, R.W. Ollerhead, A.J. Ferguson
    and A.E. Litherland to be submitted to Can. J. Phys.
    1968.

9. L.E. Carlson and R.E. Azuma, Phys. Letters, 24B, 462
    (1967).

10. A.E. Litherland, H.E. Gove and A.J. Ferguson, Phys.
    Rev. 114, 1312 (1959).

11. N. Anyas-Weiss and A.E. Litherland, Bull. Amer. Phys.
    Soc. 13 (1968) 85.

12. H. Ropke, N. Anyas-Weiss and A.E.Litherland, to be sub-
    mitted to Can. J. Phys. 1968.

13. S.G. Nilsson, Kgl. Danske Videnskab. Selskab, Mat.-fys.
    Medd. 29, No. 16. (1955).

14. T.K. Alexander et al. International Nuclear Physics
    Conference, Gatlinburg, page 367 (1966) Academic Press.

15. B.R. Mottelson and S.G. Nilsson, Matt. Fys. Skr. Dan.
    Vid. Selsk. 1, No. 8, 16 (1959).

16. H. Ropke, N. Anyas-Weiss and A.E. Litherland, to be
    submitted to Phys. Letts. 1968.

17. H.E. Gove and A.E. Litherland, "Gamma Rays from Un-
    bound Nuclear States Formed by Charged Particle Cap-
    ture", Chapter II C2 in "Nuclear Spectroscopy A"
    edited by F. Agzenberg-Selove Academic Press.

18. H.E. Gove, A.E. Litherland, E. Almquist and D.A.
    Bromley, Phys. Rev. 111, 608 (1958).

19. G.J. McCallum and B.D. Sowerby, Physics Letters, 25B,
    109 (1967).

20. D.H. Wilkinson "Analysis of Gamma Decay Data", Chapter
    V.F. in "Nuclear Spectroscopy B" edited by F.
    Ajzenberg-Selove Academic Press.

21. A.E. Blaugrund, Nucl. Phys. 88, 501 (1966).

22. P.B. Dworkin, N. Anyas-Weiss and A.E. Litherland,
    private communication.

23. A.M. Charlesworth, R.E. Azuma, K. Cassel and J.A.
    Kuehner, Bull. Amer. Phys. Soc. 12, 53 (1967).

24. J.H. Aitken, R.E. Azuma and A.E. Litherland, private
    communication.

25. P.C. Price, Proc. Phys. Soc. A70, 661 (1957).

26. D.D. Tolbert and F.W. Prosser, Bull. Amer. Phys. Soc.
    12, 1033 (1967).

27. M.G. Silbert and N. Jarmie, Phys. Rev. 123, 221 (1961).

28. Armitage AERE - PR/NP12 (1967) unpublished.

29. C. Van der Leun, Proc. Kansas Symp. on the Structure
    of Low-Medium Mass Nuclei, Kansas (1964) p. 109.

30. H. Ropke and S.T. Lam. Can. J. PHys. to be published.

31. O. Hausser, D. Pelte and J.F. Sharpey-Schafer, Can.
    J. Phys. to be published.

32. H. Ropke, N. Anyas-Weiss and A.E. Litherland, un-
    published.

DISCUSSION

ENDT: In the $N^{15}(\alpha,\gamma)F^{19}$ reaction you excite a few resonances. Are they all proton unstable?

LITERLAND: No, they are all proton stable.

ENDT: The situation is different from the resonances in Al^{27}, is it not? They are all proton unstable.

LITHERLAND: Yes.

ENDT: I saw a very nice strong 0.48 MeV peak just below your annihilation peak in the germanium spectrum. You did not assign it. We always see it. It's some sort of a background peak. I don't know what it is.

LITHERLAND: We are not at all sure where quite a number of the peaks seen in the germanium spectra come from. They certainly are not resonant and so they must be from contaminants. We see gamma rays from Hg (p,p') or Coulomb excitation of the Hg target contamination which is presumably from a nearby mercury pump. We also see silicon contamination from a silicon oil containing diffusion pump. I don't have any clues where these other contaminants are from.

ENDT: It's just always there [the 0.48 line], constant as anything.

LITHERLAND: Yes, it seems to be always there. It is another one of the many unsolved contaminant problems.

ENDT: Then, your nice alpha gamma work on Na^{23}. We have recently done a little bit on $Al^{27}(\alpha,\gamma)P^{31}$ and just find the same thing which you mentioned that your resonances are just the very high spin resonances because the low spin resonances would be proton unstable. And, the only sharp ones which you see are the high spin resonances and they decay to a whole host of high spin states, let's say in P^{31} this would be between 5 and 7 MeV or so and it's quite hard to make out what they really are, but they should be 9/2 and 11/2 or something like that. It's the same thing. It's a wonderful way to find the very high spin states.

LITHERLAND: Yes, and in connection with that comment, the $Ne^{21}(\alpha,\gamma)Mg^{25}$ reaction might be very good for studying the high spin problems in A = 25.

PRONKO: Since you have mentioned Ne^{21}, I thought that I might take this opportunity to mention our latest results on this nucleus. It looks as though we might have found the 11/2 state as well as the 13/2 state for the K = 3/2 ground state rotational band.

ENDT: It was F^{19}?

PRONKO: No, this is Ne^{21} which was populated by the $O^{18}(\alpha,n)$ Ne^{21} reaction and is work performed at Freiburg.

DAVIDSON: What band was that?

PRONKO: This is the K = 3/2 ground state rotational band.

DAVIDSON: The 11/2 and the 13/2 states?

PRONKO: Yes, a state at 4.43 MeV has been measured to be 11/2 or 7/2 and decays to the 9/2 and 7/2 states. Branching ratio and lifetime measurements support the interpretation that this state is the fifth member of the ground state rotational band. More recently a state has been found at 6.4 MeV which decays to the 11/2 and 9/2 states and is a prime candidate for the sixth member of this ground state rotational band. This whole rotational band seems to obey a J(J+1) relation very closely.

LITHERLAND: Has the mirror nucleus Na^{21} been studied in detail recently?

PRONKO: Na^{21} is more difficult to study and less is known about it. This is because most of the states of interest are proton unstable and must be studied by $Ne^{20}(p,\gamma)Na^{21}$ techniques.

III. a. Gamma Decay of States in Al^{25}

R. C. Bearse
Argonne National Laboratory

At Argonne, D. H. Youngblood, R. E. Segel, G. C. Morrison and I have made some measurements of the gamma-ray decay of the Al^{25} states that are the T = 3/2 analogs of the ground state and first excited states of Na^{25}. The approximate positions of these T = 3/2 states were known from the study[1] of delayed protons following β decay of Si^{25}. These states were located and populated via the isospin-forbidden reaction Mg^{24}(p,γ)Al^{25}. The states are at excitation energies of

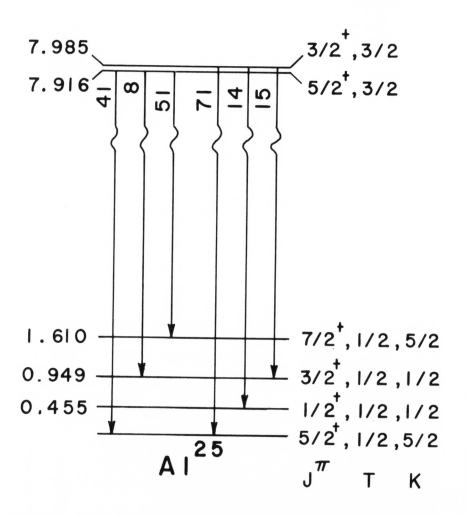

Fig. 1. A partial decay scheme of Al^{25}.

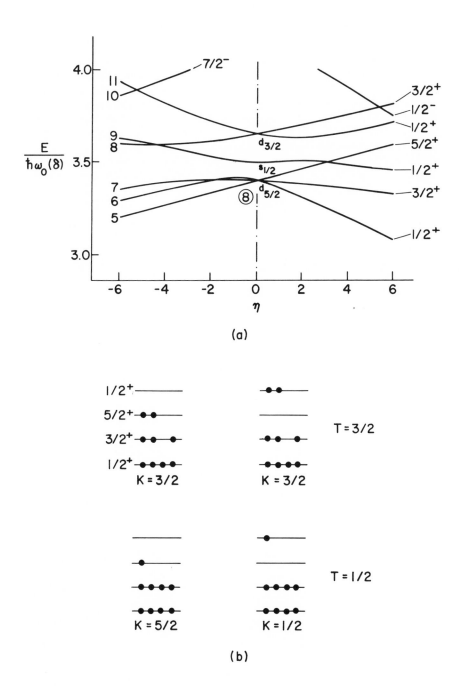

Fig. 2. a) The Nilsson diagram for the 2s-1d shell, b) A schematic representation of the wave functions involved in the γ decays.

7.916 ± 0.006 and 7.985 ± 0.006 MeV, respectively, and their
70-keV energy separation is similar to the 90-keV separation
of the parent states in Na^{25}. Gamma-ray decay spectra were
taken on each resonance and between resonances with a Ge(Li)
detector. A rough angular distribution of the ground-state
transition was also determined for each resonance. Figure 1
shows the observed branching ratios after correction for
detector efficiency and angular distribution. The spins and
parities[2] of the parent states in Na^{25} are 5/2+ and 3/2+
and these then must be the spins and parities of the analog
states in Al^{25}, though their order may be reversed. The
angular-distribution measurements require that the upper
resonance be the 3/2+ state, and consequently the lower
resonance must be the 5/2+ state. The gamma-ray decay
schemes also require these assignments. The anisotropy
measurements require nearly pure M1 ground-state transitions
from both resonances with an E2 admixture of at most 6%.

As the low-lying states of Al^{25} and Mg^{25} seem well explained by the Nilsson model, it is interesting to see if the
analog states can also be explained in this way. If we assume
that the deformation of Na^{25} is similar to that of Al^{25}, the
Nilsson picture (Fig. 2a) would predict low-lying bands with
K = 3/2, K = 5/2, and K = 1/2. The J = 5/2 members of each
of these bands will be quite close together in energy and
ΔK = 1 mixing would be expected with a resultant change in
the positions of the J = 5/2 states. A sufficient lowering
of one of the J = 5/2 states to an energy below the 3/2+
member of the K = 3/2 band is plausible. The 3/2+ state
would thus be expected to be practically pure K = 3/2+, and
the 5/2+ state would have admixtures of K = 5/2+ to its
predominantly K = 3/2+ configuration. Figure 2b is a
schematic representation of the wave functions of the states
involved in the gamma-ray transitions. It is easily seen
that an M1 transition can connect the T = 3/2, K = 3/2 configuration shown at the upper left to the T = 1/2, K = 5/2
states, but cannot connect it to the T = 1/2, K = 1/2 states.
Similar diagrams for the T = 3/2, K = 5/2 and T = 3/2, K = 1/2
configurations show that M1 transitions are not possible to
the low-lying T = 1/2 states of either band. However, if the
T = 3/2, K = 3/2 states are assumed to have an admixture of
the configuration shown at the upper right (with paired
neutrons in the K = 1/2 orbit), then gamma-ray decay to the
T = 1/2, K = 1/2 states is allowed. A small admixture of
this latter configuration then would explain the weak decays
seen to the members of the low-lying K = 1/2 band. The
ratios of the reduced transition probabilities for gamma rays
to different members of the same K band have been compared
with the ratios of the squares of Clebsch-Gordan coefficients
connecting these states. For the case of the lower resonance,
the expected ratio of the reduced transition probabilities

to the ground state and 3rd excited state (both K = 5/2) is 0.4. The measured value is 0.41. The decay of the upper resonance allows comparison of the transitions to the first and second excited states (both K = 1/2). The expected ratio is 1.2 and the measured ratio is 0.8, which is satisfactory if it is remembered that a large experimental error is involved in determining the yield of these weak transitions.

Further evidence in favor of the Nilsson picture is the failure of the analog of the 2nd excited state of Na to manifest itself in the Mg^{24}(p,γ) reaction. This is expected because it must be a member of the K = 5/2 or K = 1/2 band and hence is not allowed to decay to the low-lying T = 1/2 states by strong M1 radiation.

One apparent discrepancy with the model is that the ratio of the transition probabilities of the decays from the two resonances to the ground state is not in agreement with the prediction. Such a comparison requires a determination of the absolute transition probability which requires a knowledge of Γ_{p0}/Γ for each resonance. Although this value is known for the lower resonance, only an estimate is available for the upper resonance. We hope that a more exact determination of Γ_{p0}/Γ for the upper resonance will remove the discrepancy.

REFERENCES

1. R. McPherson, in <u>Isobaric Spin in Nuclear Physics,</u> Pro ceedings of the Conference, Tallahassee, Florida, 17-19 March 1966, edited by John D. Fox and Donald Robson (Academic Press, Inc., New York, 1966), pp. 162-172 and references cited therein.

2. R. Middleton, private communication to G. C. Morrison.

III. B. SHELL-MODEL CALCULATIONS IN THE 2s-1d SHELL

E. C. Halbert
Oak Ridge National Laboratory
Oak Ridge, Tennessee

INTRODUCTION

The work I'll describe today has been very much a joint effort. I'm just a delegate. The other principals in this effort are -- in alphabetical order -- P. W. M. Glaudemans,[*] J. B. McGrory,[**] and B. H. Wildenthal.[***]

The work comprises several separate projects. They all deal with even-parity states for nuclei within the mass region 17-through-39, and they all attempt a many-particle shell-model description of these states. All our projects follow the conventional shell-model pattern. We choose a restricted space of shell-model wave functions, and then we diagonalize a model Hamiltonian in that space. The low-lying eigenvalues are interpreted as energy levels, and the eigenvectors as nuclear wave functions.

In some projects we use the full space of all states formed from 2s-1d particles outside a closed 16-particle core; and in other projects we truncate this space. We've always used a model Hamiltonian made up of one- and two-body operators. In some projects we use "realistic" interactions derived from the Hamada-Johnston potential, which fits nucleon-nucleon scattering data; and in other projects we use model Hamiltonians derived from least-squares fits to energy-level data.

The realistic interactions which we have used were calculated by Kuo and Brown (1), or by Kuo (2), or from Kuo's computer codes (3). These interactions are derived from the hard-core Hamada-Johnston potential (4) by reaction-matrix techniques. The main contribution to such a realistic interaction is the "bare" reaction matrix, G_{bare}. This is an effective energy-operator; it incorporates into our shell-model matrix elements the effects of rather short-range nucleon-nucleon correlations. In other words, by

---

[*] Rice University, Houston, Texas, and Oak Ridge National Laboratory. Present address: Physisch Laboratorium, Utrecht, Netherlands.

[**] Oak Ridge National Laboratory.

[***] AEC Postdoctoral Fellow, with Oak Ridge National Laboratory; also Rice University, Houston, Texas.

using the bare G-matrix as an effective interaction, we make
up for the fact that our restricted shell-model basis omits
high-lying states (that is, high-lying on a harmonic oscillator model). Then there are renormalization corrections to
G_{bare}. These corrections are designed to make up for the
fact that our shell-model basis omits some low-lying configurations. For example, these renormalizations introduce
some perturbative effects of breaking up the 16-particle
core. The s-d-shell interactions which Kuo and Kuo-Brown
have calculated are designed for use in shell-model calculations which use the entire function space for s-d-shell
particles outside a closed mass-16 core. Or, to state it
more accurately, the Kuo and Kuo-Brown interactions are not
designed for calculations which truncate this space. That
explains in part why we turn to other (least-squares) kinds
of interactions for those mass regions in the s-d shell
where we can't handle the full vector space of all s-d-shell
functions.

We are of course always interested in comparisons between shell-model results from the realistic interactions,
and shell-model results from interactions based more directly on nuclear-structure data. In this connection, I'd
like to remind you about some of the very general sources
of uncertainty in reaction-matrix calculations of realistic
effective interactions. Obviously one might derive
different effective shell-model interactions by starting
with different scattering potentials, say a soft-core potential instead of Hamada-Johnston. But maybe more important is the choice of the zero-order Hamiltonian H_o --
because the G-matrix calculation is, after all, just the beginning of a perturbation expansion. H_o is a one-body
operator. H_o is fixed by choosing its eigenvalues and
eigenvectors. The eigenvalues of H_o determine various
energy denominators in the calculation, both for G_{bare} and
the renormalization corrections. The eigenvectors of H_o
affect the matrix elements that enter into the numerators of
the perturbation series. In particular, they affect the
Pauli operator Q; and if (as is usual) some of the zero-
order wave functions are chosen or approximated as harmonic
oscillator states, then the selection of an H_o obviously
affects the numerical answers. The choice of H_o is important because so few terms in the perturbation series are
calculated. It's a question of optimizing the convergence.
Various numerical approximations may affect the calculation,
too. Some of these approximations are closely related to,
and intertwined with, the choices made for H_o. In short:
we can't be supremely confident about the realistic interactions we have now, and that's a good reason for continued
interest in other kinds of shell-model interactions.

SHELL-MODEL BASIS-STATES

The details of our many-particle shell-model basis-states
would not be important for the present discussion, except
that their form does play a big role in determining the kinds
of problems we can do easily. (And therefore, it plays a big
role in determining the kinds of problems we do -- period.)
Consider a state ψ_5 formed entirely from $1d_{5/2}$ particles.
Suppose that it's quantized in the number of $d_{5/2}$-particles,
and in angular momentum J_5, isotopic spin T_5, and enough
other things to complete its specification:

$$\psi_5 \equiv \psi_5 \ (n_{5/2}, \ J_5 \ T_5 \alpha_5).$$

We couple this ψ_5 to a state ψ_1 formed entirely from $2s_{1/2}$
particles, to get resultants $\tilde{J} \tilde{T}$. Then we couple this two-
shell result to a state ψ_3 formed entirely from $1d_{3/2}$ particles, to get final resultants JT:

$$[(\psi_5 \times \psi_1)^{\tilde{J}\tilde{T}} \times \psi_3]^{JT}.$$

The entire wave function is made antisymmetric; and that's a
typical basis-state in our calculation.

This choice has great virtues, because -- with the help
of Bruce French's second-quantized treatment -- we can very
easily (5) calculate matrix elements between such states.
(We can essentially factor each matrix element into three
parts: one for the $d_{5/2}$ shell, one for the $s_{1/2}$ shell, and
one for the $d_{3/2}$ shell.) On the other hand, for s-d-shell
nuclei this basis has some disadvantages. In particular, it
has some disadvantages compared with an SU_3 representation,
or a basis derived from deformed Hartree-Fock considerations. In our representation we find that eigenvectors of
our model Hamiltonians have their intensity spread thinly
over many many basis-states. This means that our scheme is
not so good for truncation of the s-d space. This disadvantage is partly overcome by the fact that we can do un-
truncated calculations in rather large spaces. (5) A second,
related disadvantage is that it is not so easy to extract
from our eigenvectors a simplified description of the
nuclear state. This disadvantage can be partly overcome by
using simplified schemes (such as rotational schemes) after-
ward, to classify and discuss the results we get from detailed calculation.

RESULTS

In the rest of this talk I'll give broad and shallow
coverage to several projects. Together they touch on most
s-d-shell nuclei. The gist is that most of these nuclei are
at least "attackable" with conventional shell-model methods,
and that the Princeton realistic interactions (1-3) work remarkably well. I'll run through the shell twice -- first to
abstract the most prominent results. Since the general
picture is pleasing, I'll avoid distractions on this first
run and suppress most of the uncertainties and disappoint-
ments. Then in a second run through the shell, I'll describe some further aspects and details of each project.

A = 17-22

At the lower end of the shell, from mass-17 through
mass-22, we can handle the full s-d-shell space. We have
used the realistic interaction of Kuo and Brown (1) published in 1966, and that published by Kuo (2) in 1967. For
this region we can compare calculated spectra with observed
spectra. We can also compare calculated B(E2) strengths
with data; and we have a few results on spectroscopic
factors, too.

Figure 1 shows results for the two-nucleon case of
^{18}F (T = 0). The mass-18 spectra are of course Princeton's
results (1-2), but they're shown here to give you a quick
three-way comparison of both two-nucleon interactions and
the two-nucleon s-d data. These renormalized G-matrix
interactions were to some extent adjusted to -- or at least
influenced by -- the observed mass-18 spectra. A choice of
$\hbar\omega$ = 14 MeV was found to give better agreement than $\hbar\omega$ =
15.6 MeV; and Fig. 1 shows the 14-MeV results. For the
1966 G-matrix, it was found that when all three of the proposed renormalization corrections were added, the resulting
mass-18 spectrum didn't look so nice. For this reason --
and because other reasons could be invoked (1) -- only the
three-particle one-hole renormalization correction has been
included for the energy-level results marked "K-B 1966" in
Fig. 1. For the 1967 G-matrix calculation (which treated
more carefully the hard core of the Hamada-Johnston potential) good spectra were obtained when all three renormalization terms were added; and all three are included for the
energy-level results marked "Kuo 1967".

Figure 1 shows that for ^{18}F just the lowest three
states -- 1,3,5, -- are fit; and after that things get more
troublesome. Figure 2 shows the direct results of both
effective interactions in the T=1 two-particle case, ^{18}O.
Again, these are Princeton's results (1,2). Here the lowest

E. C. Halbert

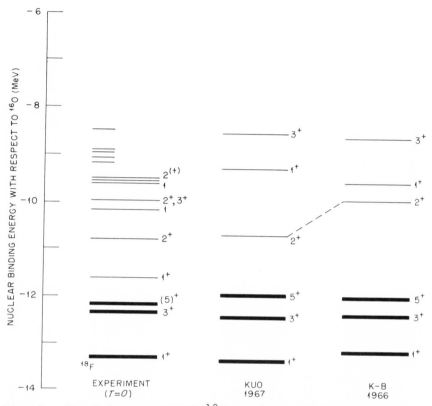

Fig. 1. The T=0 spectrum of ^{18}F as observed experimentally
(Ref. 6), and as calculated by Kuo (Ref. 2), and by Kuo and
Brown (Ref. 1). Observed levels known to have negative parity
have been omitted.

0,2,4 look nice; the triad 2,3,4 looks not too bad; but
there is only one theroetical 0+ in the excited region,
against two experimental 0+. But at least one of these observed excited 0+ states is thought to involve strongly
mixed s-d-shell and core-excited configurations; and I remind you that the Kuo and Kuo-Brown interactions are designed to reproduce only the <u>perturbing</u> effects of non-s-d
configurations (that is, perturbations on energy levels
associated with predominatly s-d configurations).

In calculating the mass-18 spectra shown in Figs. 1-2,
Kuo and Kuo-Brown added the ^{17}O single-particle energies to
their two-nucleon interactions to obtain their effective
Hamiltonians. Figures 3-8 show the shell-model spectra for
masses 19-22 calculated from the same two effective
Hamiltonians. In each of Figs. 3-8, the observed and calculated level schemes are lined up at the ground state of
minimum T. But aside from that, there are <u>no</u> adjusted
parameters in the model spectra shown.

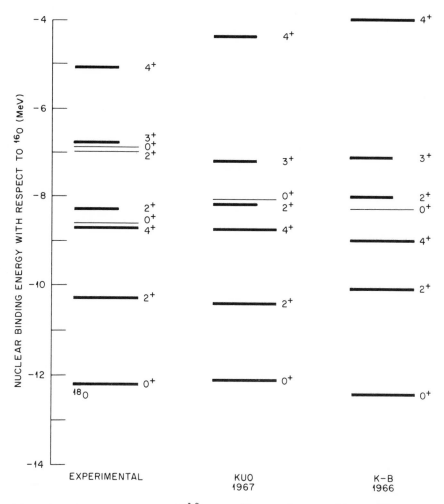

Fig. 2. The spectrum of ^{18}O as observed experimentally
(Ref. 6), and as calculated by Kuo (Ref. 2), and by Kuo and
Brown (Ref. 1). Observed levels known to have negative parity
have been omitted.

Figure 3 displays the mass-19 results. Heavy lines have
been drawn for the sequence 1/2, 5/2, 3/2, 9/2 in ^{19}F, and
the sequence 3/2, 5/2, 7/2, 9/2 in ^{19}O. These are the lowest sequences you'd expect on a Nilsson-rotational model.
But the levels here are not those of a pure rotational band:
you'd get this spacing only after band-mixing.
        Calculations for masses 20, 21, 22 show the same gen-
eral features as those for mass-19. These features can be
summarized briefly. The shell-model spectra are qualitatively the same for both the 1966 and 1967 interactions.
The shell model fits the lowest band for each nucleus --
a band that may be perturbed quite strongly by higher bands.

E. C. Halbert

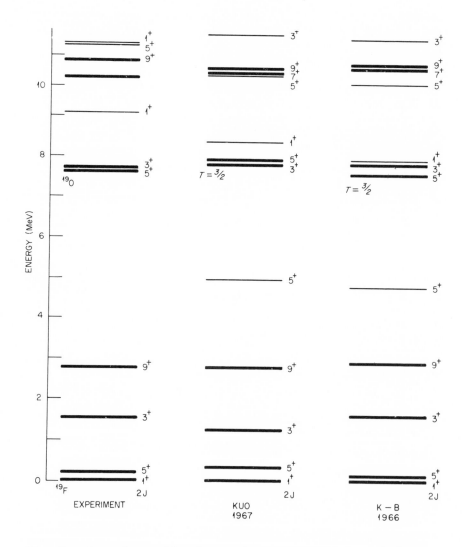

Fig. 3. Experimentally observed spectrum for A = 19 (Ref.
6), and shell-model spectra calculated (in the full s-d-
shell space) from the same realistic effective Hamiltonians
as used by Kuo (Ref. 2) and by Kuo and Brown (Ref. 1). Observed levels known to have negative parity have been
omitted. In each of Figs. 3-8, the model spectra have been
lined up with experimental data on the ground state of lowest T. The plotted separations between levels of different
T represent differences in <u>nuclear</u> energy. (The experimentally observed energy-separations between different isobars were adjusted, before plotting, by subtracting Coulomb-
energy differences estimated as explained in Ref. (7).)

However, the shell model doesn't do so well on the relative positions of different perturbed bands.

For example, in ^{19}F we fit 1/2, 5/2, 3/2, and 9/2 (see Fig. 3). And in ^{19}O we do pretty well on 3/2, 5/2, 7/2, and 9/2 -- although in the 1967 case, the order of the two lowest levels is inverted. The next band in ^{19}O would start out 1/2, 5/2, 3/2, 9/2; but the lowest member, 1/2+, is calculated about an MeV too low. It does happen that the 1/2+ - 5/2+ spacing for both shell models is the same as the experimentally observed spacing.

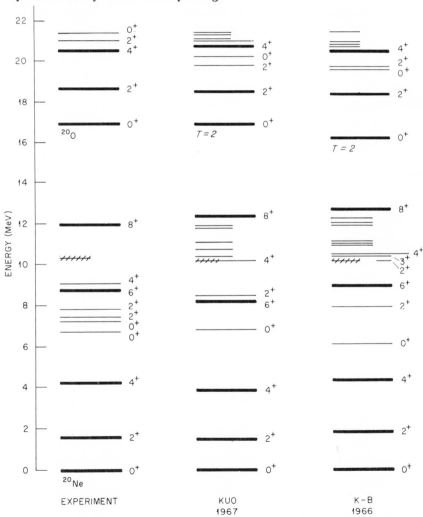

Fig. 4. Observed spectrum (Ref. 6) and shell-model spectra of T=0 levels in ^{20}Ne and T=2 levels in ^{20}O. See caption to Fig. 3. Here the cross-hatched level indicates the ground state of ^{20}F.

Figure 4 shows some results for mass-20. (The scale here is rather compressed.) For ^{20}Ne the shell model fits the lowest sequence, 0,2,4,6,8, fairly well. Then there is another theoretical triad 0,2,4; but the experimental data show not only a 0,2,4 triad, but also an additional 0,2 sequence. For ^{20}O the shell model matches the first 0,2,4 sequence, but it gets the next two states (2 and 0) too low. The cross-hatched level in Fig. 4 shows the lowest T=1 state. For this level, the calculations line up fairly well with data. The known ^{20}F spectrum would fall just about between the cross-hatched state and the 8$^+$ state for ^{20}Ne; so the ^{20}F results are shown separately, in Fig. 5 (on a scale that is very much expanded). The shell model shows a 2,3,4,5 sequence for ^{20}F. The data are quite uncertain in spin assignments, and most of the parities are unknown. The 2$^+$-3$^+$ spacing of the shell models match the observed 2$^+$-3$^+$ spacing.

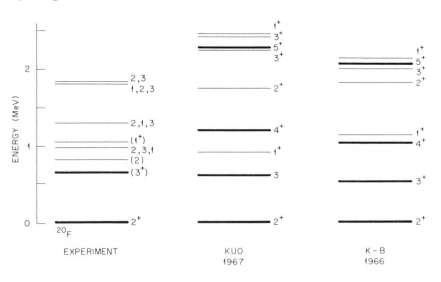

Fig. 5. Observed spectrum (Ref. 6) and shell-model spectra
for ^{20}F. See caption to Fig. 3.

The spectra for mass-21 are shown in Fig. 6. For ^{21}Na-^{21}Ne there is a good match between theory and experiment for the lowest level sequence, 3/2, 5/2, 7/2, 9/2, 11/2; and in ^{21}F the shell model exhibits the 1/2, 5/2, 3/2, 9/2 levels expected on the Nilsson-rotational model, though it doesn't quite match the 5/2, 1/2 order shown by the data. I think it's likely that two or three of the higher observed levels in ^{21}F have negative parity; so the agreement for ^{21}F may look good, some day. For ^{21}Na (T = 1/2), mixed-band calculations (6) indicate that the 5/2, 7/2, 9/2 levels,

which appear to be within a ground-state rotational band,
are very much perturbed from their positions in the unperturbed band; and the total effect is a severe compression of
the original spacing. Nevertheless, the sequence 3/2, 5/2,
7/2, 9/2 still looks like a band, and our no-parameter shell
models fit it quite well. For the next sequence, there is
obvious trouble: both shell models exhibit a too-low 1/2+.

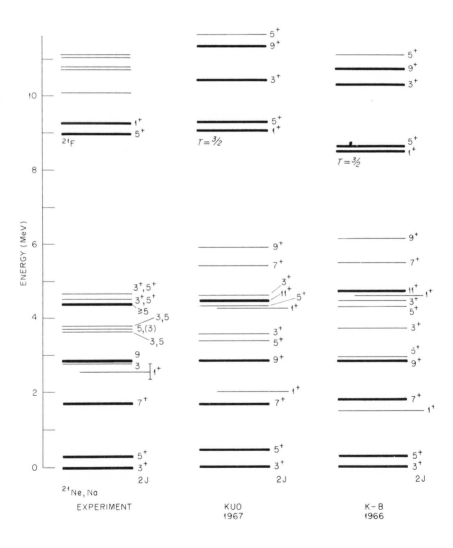

Fig. 6. Observed spectrum (Ref. 8) and shell-model spectra
for A = 21. See caption to Fig. 7.

Figure 7 shows T=0 spectra for the odd-odd nucleus^{22}Na. (The scale here is very much expanded, as it was for ^{20}F.) For ^{22}Na the lowest expected sequence is 3,4,5,6. The two observed states marked $\geq$ 2 are good candidates for the $5^+,6^+$ pair (11). Again, the shell model does not do so well in matching observed excitations of levels associated with higher bands. There are several higher bands expected to have importance in the energy region shown. In particular, we expect bands 1,2,3,4 and 1,3,5. Apparently these two bands get mixed together, and the 1^+ levels push each other apart. But the shell model gets both 1^+ levels too low, and not pushed far enough apart. Also, these shell models do not yield quite the right energy for the lowest T=1 state, shown cross-hatched in Fig. 7.

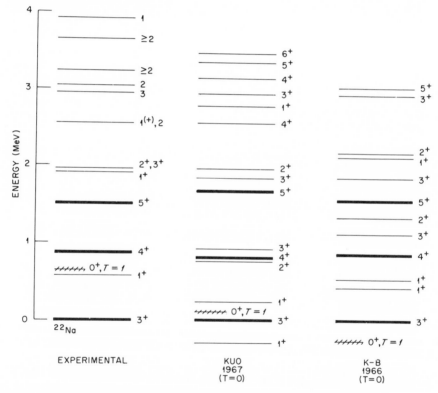

Fig. 7. Observed spectrum (Ref. 10) and shell-model spectra of T=0 levels in ^{22}Na. See caption to Fig. 3.

Figure 8 shows spectra for Ne (T=1). The shell model fits o,2,4,6. The next expected sequence would start off 2,3,4. The shell model gets the 2+ too low. However, the calculated 2+-3+ spacing does match the observed 2+-3+ spacing.

Short summaries of our shell-model projects throughout the s-d shell are collected in Table V. In this summary-table, I've entered the following short appraisal of the agreement between the observed 17-22 spectra, and spectra calculated from the Kuo and Kuo-Brown realistic Hamiltonians:

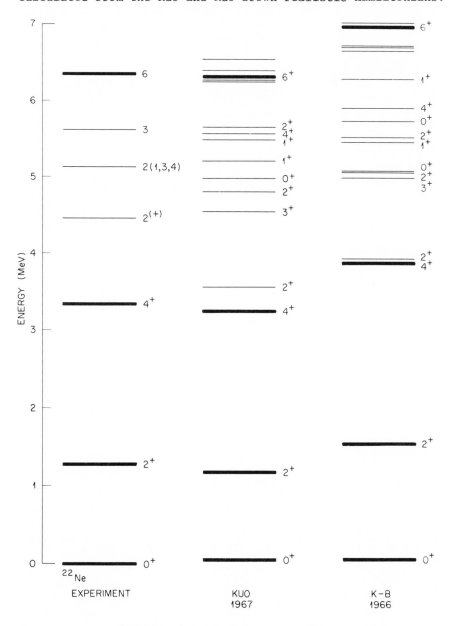

Fig. 8.   Observed spectrum (Ref. 12) and shell-model spectra for Ne^{22}. See caption to Fig. 3.

                        GOOD   for "Band-1" levels
            fair-to-poor   for other levels

That's meant to be a modest opinion. (Actually, I think
these spectra are astonishingly good. All I'd hoped for was
ball-park agreement.)
    We have used the eigenvectors from these calculations to
calculate transition rates for A = 17-22. Table I shows
some measured B(E2) values, and values computed from the
many-particle shell-model eigenvectors of the 1967 Kuo
Hamiltonian. (19) The shell-model B(E2)-values are calculated with a conventional effective-charge approximation.
For all the nuclei 17-22, we assume an added effective
charge of 0.5 e. In other words, we assume that the neutron
has total effective charge 0.5 e, and the proton 1.5 e.
This added charge of 0.5 e has been suggested by Wilkinson
(15), who has discussed its use in light s-d-shell nuclei to
simulate the effects of exciting the ^{16}O core. In our B(E2)
calculations, the nucleon radial wave functions are taken
to be harmonic oscillator functions for $\hbar\omega = 41 \ A^{-1/3}$ MeV
(a formula which gives $\hbar\omega$ = 13.6 for A=18, 14.5 MeV for
A=22).
    The upper part of Table I shows calculated and observed
B(E2) values for transitions from first excited states to
ground states for A = 18-22. The last three entries in
Table I show calculated B(E2) values for transitions connecting known members of the K=3 ground-state band in ^{22}Na.
Agreement between the calculated and measured values is
generally quite good.
    Among the calculated rates shown in Table I, only two
disagree with the measured values listed. The two disagreement are for ^{18}O and ^{21}Ne. For ^{18}O, a possible excuse
is that the calculated B(E2) depends entirely on the
effective-charge approximation. For ^{21}Ne, there's good
reason to suspect that the observed value listed here is in-
correct, and way too high. (I'll come back to this point
later.) For the present, then, I'll put down GOOD, in Table
V, as a one-word opinion of our A = 17-22 B(E2) results.
    So far we have calculated very few spectroscopic factors
for this 17-22 model. Table II includes these few results.
Most of the information in this table comes from a paper by
Siemssen, Lee, and Cline (16). The column marked "Ex" lists
the spectroscopic factors which these authors extracted, via
DWBA calculations, from their experimental data. The values
marked "Nilsson" and "SU(3)" (17) come from the same paper;
they are theoretical predictions calculated from two simple
models. Our contributions to Table II consists of shell-
model results from the Kuo interaction; these are listed in
the column marked "Full s-d". These full s-d results happen

TABLE I. B(E2↓) values (in units of e^2fm^4). In the upper section of the table, each transition is from the first excited to the ground state, except for ^{19}O (second excited to ground). The last three entries in the table, for ^{22}Na, are between the lowest states of the spins indicated. UL and LL stand for upper limit and lower limit, respectively. The entries under "Shell Model" are values calculated from eigenvectors associated with the spectra labeled "Kuo 1967" in Figs. 1-8.

	Spins	B(E2) from Experiment (Ref. 14)	B(E2) from Shell Model
^{18}O	$2^+ \to 0^+$	$6.5 \pm 20\%$	3.0
^{18}F	$3^+ \to 1^+$	$16.4 \pm 10\%$	14.8
^{19}F	$5/2 \to 1/2$	$20.8 \pm 20\%$	19.0
^{19}O	$1/2 \to 5/2$	$(.04 \to 1.1)_{LL}$	2.5
^{20}O	$2^+ \to 0^+$	$(38.7)_{UL}$	4.7
^{20}F	$3^+ \to 2^+$		27.8
^{20}Ne	$2^+ \to 0^+$	$57.3 \pm 10\%$	48.3
^{21}Ne	$5/2 \to 3/2$	$161.8 \pm 20\%$	81.0
^{21}F	$1/2 \to 5/2$	$57.1 \pm 5\%$	68.8
^{22}Ne	$2^+ \to 0^+$	$42.4 \pm 30\%$	55.4
^{22}Na	$1^+ \to 3^+$	$.03 \pm < 1\%$	.7
^{22}Na	$4^+ \to 3^+$	$108 \pm 17\%$	102
^{22}Na	$5^+ \to 3^+$	$25 \; {}^{+ 28\%}_{- 17\%}$	25.3
^{22}Na	$5^+ \to 4^+$	$76 \pm 33\%$	91.2

TABLE II. Experimental and theoretical spectroscopic factors for the $^{19}F(^3He,d)^{20}Ne$ reaction. Here C^2S implies the quantity $(C^2)\mathcal{S}$ defined in Ref. 18. The column marked "Ex" lists values extracted (via DWBA analysis) by Siemssen, Lee, and Cline (16) from their experimental data. The column marked "Full sd, Kuo" lists values calculated on the same $(d_{5/2}-s_{1/2}-d_{3/2})$ shell model that was used in producing the spectra marked "Kuo 1967" in our Figs. 3-8.

Excitation in ^{20}Ne (MeV)		Ex (Ref. 16)	Models		
			Full sd, Kuo	Nilsson (Ref. 16)	SU(3) (Refs. 16,17)
0	$C^2S(0^+)_1$	.31	.44	.41	.43
1.63	$C^2S(2^+)_1$	.63	.48	.32	.24
6.72	$C^2S(0^+)_2$	.47	.51	.22	.17
7.20	$C^2S(0^+)_3$	$\leq$ .027	.00	0	0
7.43	$C^2S(2^+)_2$	.16	.10	.15	.007
	$C^2S(0^+)_2/C^2S(0^+)_1$	1.5	1.2	.5	.4
	$C^2S(2^+)_2/C^2S(2^+)_1$	.24	.20	.47	.03

to turn out closer to the "Ex" results than do the predictions from the other two models. Notice the C^2S-values
for the 1.6-MeV and 6.7-MeV states of ^{20}Ne, and also the
ratios in the last two lines of the table. Since we have so
little information on spectroscopic factors, I'll put down
"good" in Table V but spell it with a small g.

A = 20-28

Above mass-22, dimensions mount rapidly, and we must
truncate. For nuclei of mass A=28, we've tried an extremely
simple model (19). We reduce the shell-model basis to wave
functions involving $d_{5/2}$ and $s_{1/2}$ particles only (outside a
closed 16-particle core). This model allows as many as four
particles to be excited from $d_{5/2}$ to $s_{1/2}$. So it's an improvement on a one-shell model allowing $d_{5/2}$-particles
only, outside the core. But even this one-shell model would
give model states for all the nuclei A = 17-28 with
$N \leq 14$ and $Z \leq 14$. Hence we felt there was some chance that
our two-shell model could make sense up to mass-28 for
$N \leq 14$ and $Z \leq 14$ -- and that's as far as we've used it.

An effective Hamiltonian for this two-shell model is
specified by 16 two-body matrix elements, together with the
$d_{5/2}$ and $s_{1/2}$ single-particle energies: 18 parameters alto-
gether. We might have tried computing these 18 parameters
by starting with the $d_{5/2}$-$s_{1/2}$ matrix elements of a realistic interaction, and renormalizing these matrix elements
to make up for our neglect of the $d_{3/2}$ shell. But instead -- since there were plenty of observed level energies
to fit -- we chose to make a least-squares search, and so
find an effective Hamiltonian directly from the nuclear-
structure data.

Of course, because of the expected importance of $d_{3/2}$
particles, it should not be surprising if a mass-independent
(1 + 2)-body effective Hamiltonian turns out to be inadequate to describe the entire range of nuclei 17-28. For example: if we were to calculate an effective interaction by
renormalizing a (two-body) three-shell interaction, and if
we included all renormalization terms to second order in
perturbation theory, we'd get three-body part associated
with the diagram

And probably second-order perturbation theory would be inadequate, anyway.

But -- throwing inhibitions to the wind -- we did search
for a mass-independent (1 + 2)-body Hamiltonian. We found
that there was indeed difficulty in fitting the entire
range 17-28 with a (1 + 2)-body effective Hamiltonian.
In particular, the observed ^{18}F spectrum was fit poorly.
However, the optimized interaction from searches on 17-28
was very much dominated by the levels for nuclei above
mass-19; and therefore it was decided to concentrate on the
region from 20 to 28.

We find that the optimized 18-parameter Hamiltonian obtained from a fit to observed 20-28 levels has the same
general features whether we fit on the binding energies of
all levels, or alternatively, on the binding energies of
ground states and the excitations of higher levels. Furthermore, these general features are quite stable against
changes in the selection of levels included in the fit. For
example, we obtained very similar interactions from separate searches on three nested sets of data -- the largest
set comprising 90 levels; the next set, 72 levels; and the
smallest set, 54 levels. (The 72-level set was obtained
quite arbitrarily, by omitting every fifth level in our list
of 90. And the 54-level set was obtained by omitting every
fourth level from our list of 72.) This stability of the
solution encourages us to believe that our two-shell search-
results do indeed make sense.

I'll show you some of the theoretical spectra resulting
from a search on the binding energies of 80 levels. The
final RMS deviation from these 80 fitted levels was .43 MeV
(not too marvelous, for an adjusted fit -- but certainly a
solution worth serious consideration).

Figure 9 shows level schemes for the odd-odd nucleus
^{22}Na, and for the even-odd nucleus ^{25}Mg. Here all spectra
are plotted as binding energies. (The experimental and calculated ground states have not been lined up with each
other.) The heavy lines in this figure indicate levels included in the search. The fits shown in Fig. 9 are of about
the same quality as those obtained for masses 21-22 from the
Kuo interaction in our three-shell model. But in these two-
shell 20-28 fits, we don't see the "goodness" so heavily
concentrated in ground-state bands. Incidentally, the low
theoretical 2^+ in ^{22}Na, which looks so disturbing in Fig. 9,
has a counterpart in the three-shell Kuo spectrum (though a
bit higher, just below the first 4^+). And all the two-shell
^{22}Na theoretical levels above the 5^+ bear a strong resem-
blance to the three-shell levels calculated from the Kuo
interaction. On the right of Fig. 9, we see that the calculated mass-25 spectrum does have the right ordering for the

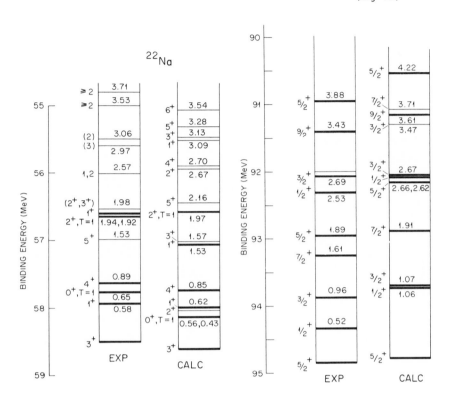

Fig. 9.   Energy levels of ^{22}Na and ^{25}Mg-^{25}Al -- as observed
experimentally (Refs. 10, 20), and as calculated on a
(1d$_{5/2}$-2s$_{1/2}$) shell model.   The shell-model Hamiltonian is
one that has been adjusted to yield a least-squares fit to
observed levels of A = 20-28.   The vertical scale represents
binding energy with respect to ^{16}O.   Observed levels known
to have negative parity have been omitted from the figure.

first seven levels; however, the spacing is poor.

Figure 10 shows results (from the same 80-level search)
for two even-even nuclei.   Again, the calculation reproduces the main features of the data.   The eight even-parity
levels observed in the first 7.4 MeV of the ^{24}Mg spectrum
are reproduced one-to-one, though with a few inversions.   A
similar one-to-one correspondence is obtained for ^{28}Si, except for the high observed 1+.

For the odd-odd nucleus ^{26}Al, the fit to data is much
poorer than those shown in Figs. 9-10.   But for all the
other nuclei having N $\leq$ 14 and Z $\leq$ 14, the fits are about
as good as those shown in Figs. 9-10.   So, as a short opinion
on spectra from this 20-28 calculation, I'll write FAIR-poor
in our summary-table V.

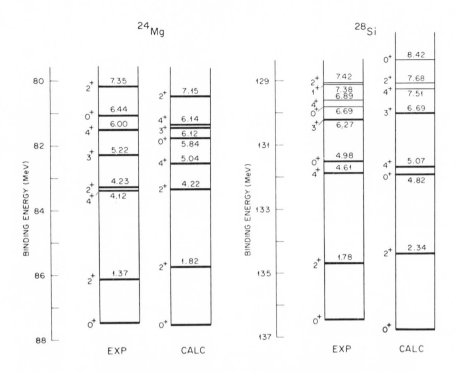

Fig. 10. Experimentally observed levels of ^{24}Mg and ^{28}Si (Ref. 20), and levels calculated on a $(1d_{5/2}-2s_{1/2})$ shell model. See caption to Fig. 9.

We've calculated some spectroscopic factors from this two-shell model; some examples are listed in Table III. Experimental and theoretical excitations are shown together in column 3. The spectroscopic factors marked "ex" come from DWBA analysis of (d,^{3}He) data taken at Oak Ridge (21). Again, the results presented here are typical of all the results calculated so far. I assess the agreement between theory and experiment here as generally GOOD.

$$A = 30-33$$

The next project I'll discuss is for masses 30 through 33. Here we've used a three-shell model, but allowed no more than two holes in the $d_{5/2}$ shell; that is, we restrict the number of $d_{5/2}$ particles to be ≥ 10. Initial results with a realistic interaction in this truncated space seemed to show some unwanted features in the wave functions. Besides, the three-shell realistic interactions as calculated by the Kuo-Brown or Kuo methods are (as I mentioned earlier) more appropriate for the <u>full</u>

TABLE III. Experimental and theoretical spectroscopic factors. Here $C^2S(\ell)$ implies the quantity $(C^2)\mathcal{S}$ defined in Ref. 18. The values marked "ex" were extracted (via DWBA analysis) by B. H. Wildenthal and E. Newman (19) from their experimental data. The theoretical values were calculated on the same $(d_{5/2}-s_{1/2})$ shell model used in producing the spectra marked "CALC" in Figs. 9-10.

Reaction	Initial J	Final J	Final Excitation $E_{ex}-E_{th}$ (MeV)	$C^2S(0)$ ex[a]	$C^2S(0)$ th	$C^2S(2)$ ex[a]	$C^2S(2)$ th
^{23}Na(d,^{3}He)^{22}Ne	$3/2^+$	0^+	0.0	—	—	.08 ± 20%	.00
		2^+	1.28-1.58	≤ .02	.04	1.15	1.15
		2^+	1.47-4.20	.10	.09	.39	.003
		4^+	3.35-3.86	—	—	.41 ± 20%	.23
^{27}Al(d,^{3}He)^{26}Mg	$5/2^+$	0^+	0.0	—	—	.30	.29
		0^+	3.58-3.74	—	—	≤ .01	.0008
		2^+	1.81-2.34	≤ .01	.001	1.05	.75
		2^+	2.90-3.08	≤ .01	.003	.23	.29
		3^+	3.94-4.77	≤ .005	.05	.03	.008
^{28}Si(d,^{3}He)^{27}Al	0^+	$5/2^+$	0.0	—	—	3.76	3.85
		$5/2^+$	2.73-2.14	—	—	.61	.52
		$1/2^+$	0.81-0.83	.49	.85	—	—
		$1/2^+$	3.67-3.64	≤ .02	.001	—	—

[a] The techniques for extracting spectroscopic factors from the experimental data contribute an uncertainty of about 25% to the numbers listed. In cases where the statistics of the data themselves contribute significantly to the overall uncertainty, this extra percentage uncertainty is listed.

three-shell space. So here again we chose to find an
effective Hamiltonian by making a least-squares fit to
level data. But for the vector-space choses, we need a
three-shell Hamiltonian -- 63 two-body matrix elements and
three single-particle energies. Sixty-six independent
parameters are too many to search for. Instead, we con-
strained the effective interaction to be a particular modified for (22) of Moszkowski's surface delta interaction.
There were seven parameters in all: four parameters
affecting the two-body interaction, and three single-
particle energies.

The search was carried out only over the energy levels
of masses 30 and 31. Very nice fits were obtained.

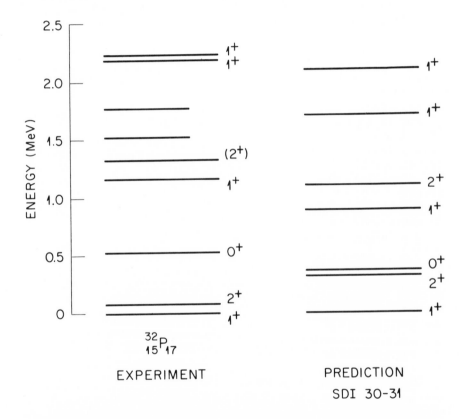

Fig. 11. Experimentally observed spectrum of [20]P (Ref. 20),
and shell-model prediction. The shell-model levels were
calculated in a truncated $1d_{5/2}$-$2s_{1/2}$-$1d_{3/2}$ vector-space,
from an effective surface-delta Hamiltonian parameterized to
fit observed levels of A = 30 and 31. Observed levels known
to have negative parity have been omitted from the figure.

Furthermore, when the optimized interaction was applied (without further adjustment) to masses 32 and 33, the calculated spectra still looked good. Instead of showing you fitted spectra, I'll show results for nuclei not included in the search.

Figure 11 shows spectra for ^{32}P. This figure illustrates two ways in which the calculated three-shell spectra for 30-33 differ from those we found for 17-22. First: here we find no particular difficulty for odd-odd nuclei. And second: if we consider the levels as assignable to rotational sequences (according to their spins), then for 30-33 we don't find that the agreement between calculation and experiment drops off sharply after band-1. For example, suppose we were to assume that all the observed ^{32}P levels of Fig. 11 belong to bands in which the lowest few members are relatively unperturbed. According to this picture, the ^{32}P spectrum would involve first a band starting as 1,2,3; then a band starting as 2,3,4; then 0,1,2; then perhaps a second 1,2,3 band and a third 1,2,3 band. Yet the ordering of states predicted from our shell model -- 1,2,0,1,2,1,1 (all within 2.3 MeV) -- matches the experimentally observed order.

Figure 12 shows the observed and predicted spectra for ^{32}S. There are six observed T=0 levels marked with positive parity; and the predicted shell-model spectrum matches these six, except for inversion of the $1^+, 2^+$ pair between 4 and 5 MeV. (Possibly four different "rotational bands" are involved.)

I am pleased enough to mark these 30-33 spectra GOOD, in the summary of Table V.

For this region 30-33, some single-nucleon spectroscopic factors have been calculated with our model. Table IV includes some of these results, in comparison with S-factors extracted via DWBA from experimental data. We have made a few more comparisons between experiment and theory, but the results presented here are typical. Again I'm pleased, and mark the results GOOD in the summary of Table V.

$$A = 35-37$$

In the mass region 34-39 we can again use the full space of all s-d-shell functions; and so we turn again to realistic interactions. Today I want to limit the discussion to masses 35 through 37. I'll show you spectra calculated with effective interactions generated from Kuo's codes (3) for $\hbar\omega = 12.5$ MeV. We have used an interaction "K" calculated in 1968 according to the techniques described in Ref. (2), and an interaction "K-B" calculated in 1966 according to the techniques of Ref. (1). To avoid the introduction of adjustable parameters in our shell-model Hamiltonians,

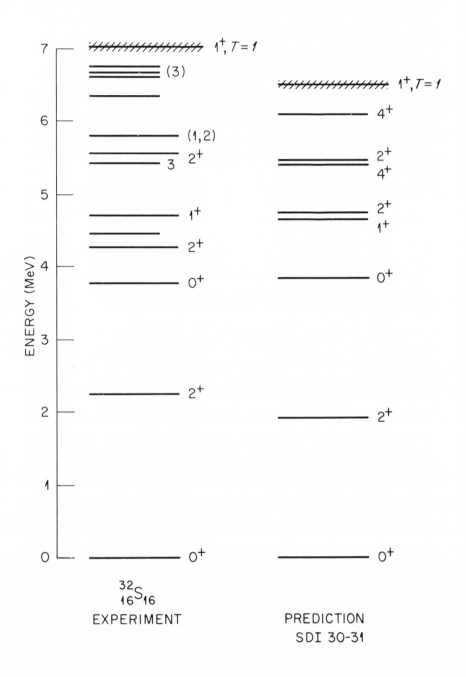

Fig. 12. Observed spectrum (Ref. 20) and predicted spectra
          for S^{32}. See caption to Fig. 11.

TABLE IV. Experimental and theoretical spectroscopic factors for stripping on ^{30}Si. Here the quantity S is the same as the $\mathcal{S}$ defined in Ref. 18. The experimental values for the (^{3}He,d) reaction come from Ref. 23, and those for the (d,p) reaction from Ref. 24. The theoretical values were calculated on the same shell model used in producing the "SDI" spectra shown in our Figs. 11-12.

Reaction	Final J	Final Excitation E_{ex},E_{th} (MeV)	S_{ex}	S_{th}
^{30}Si(^{3}He,d)^{31}P	$1/2^{+}$	0.0	.78	.62
	$3/2^{+}$	1.27, 1.08	.67	.50
	$5/2^{+}$	2.23, 2.31	.06	.04
	$1/2^{+}$	3.13, 3.49	.02	.06
^{30}Si(d,p)^{31}Si	$3/2^{+}$	0.0	.86	.69
	$1/2^{+}$	0.75, .74	.25	.19
	$5/2^{+}$	1.69, 1.74	.02	.02
	$3/2^{+}$	2.32, 2.32	.06	.01
	$5/2^{+}$	2.79, 3.02	.04	.01

we've used the ^{17}O single-particle energies with both of these two-body interactions.

Figure 13 shows spectra for mass-35, from experimental data and from the 1968 interaction, K. The shell model matches the observed levels 3/2, 1/2, 5/2, 7/2, but seems to get the second $3/2^{+}$ too low. In both the observed and calculated spectra there are gaps, about one MeV wide, between 3 and 4 MeV and between 4 and 5 MeV. Figure 14 shows spectra for mass-36 from experimental data, and from the interaction K, and from the 1966 interaction K-B (both calculated at $\hbar\omega$ = 12.5 MeV). The energy-splitting between isobars is too much when calculated from interaction K, but too little from interaction K-B. For ^{36}Ar, both models give the observed 0,2,4 sequence, and then miss some probable levels. For the odd-odd nucleus ^{36}Cl, both interactions give a 2,3 sequence; and the interaction K even shows some promise of roughly fitting the uncertain third, fourth, fifth and sixth excited levels. Figure 15 shows spectra for A=37, again from the same two interactions for $\hbar\omega$ = 12.5 MeV. The position of the lowest $1/2^{+}$ level is sensitive to which interaction is used. The agreement with experiment is

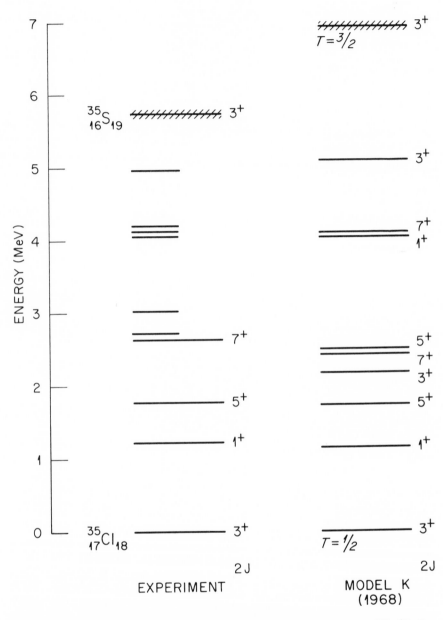

Fig. 13. Experimentally observed spectrum for A = 35 (Ref. 20), and shell-model spectrum calculated (in the full s-d-shell space) from a realistic effective Hamiltonian, "K". This model Hamiltonian, K, includes the O^{17} single-particle energies, together with a renormalized two-body G-matrix calculated at $\hbar\omega = 12.5$ MeV according to the techniques of Kuo (Ref. 2). Here, and also in Figs. 14-15, the plotted separations between levels of different T represent differ-

better with the 1968 interaction, K. However, it is disturbing to find two calculated high-spin states (5/2+, 7/2+)
near 2 MeV. For ^{37}Cl, both interactions give a 3/2, 1/2,
5/2 sequence. The spacing from interaction K comes closer
to matching the observed spacing.

In our summary of Table V, I'll mark the spectra for 35-
37 as FAIR-GOOD. For a "no-parameter" calculation in this
region, I think that's justified.

This entry completes Table V, which summarizes briefly
the results described above for mass regions 17-22, 20-28,
30-33, and 35-37.

FURTHER RESULTS AND COMMENTS

Now I'll return to give more information about these
four regions -- mostly about 17-22, since that's where we've
done the most work.

Least-Square Searches for A = 17-22

For 17-22, I want to tell you about some comparisons
we've made with models in which the effective interactions
were obtained from least-squares fits to observed energy
levels.

As I mentioned earlier, an effective (1 + 2)-body
Hamiltonian for the 2s-1d shell involves three single-
particle energies and 63 two-body matrix elements -- too
many to vary independently, in a least-squares search.
During all our three-shell searches for 17-22, we do allow
the three single-particle energies to vary independently,
but we assume a restricted form for the two-body interaction. We've tried the following restricted forms:

a. The modified surface delta interaction (SDI).

This is the form used for searching on the levels of
A = 30 and 31, you remember. There are four two-body
strengths to adjust, and three single particle energies --
7 parameters in all.

b. A (non-local) central potential specified by its Talmi
    integrals $I_{n\ell T}$.
    These Talmi integrals are matrix elements between
states of <u>relative</u> motion of the two interacting particles.
For example, I_{101} denotes the interaction-energy matrix ele-

---

ences in <u>nuclear</u> energy. (The experimentally observed
energy-separations between different isobars were adjusted,
before plotting, by subtracting Coulomb-energy differences
estimated as explained in Ref. 7.) Observed levels known
to have negative parity have been omitted from the figure.

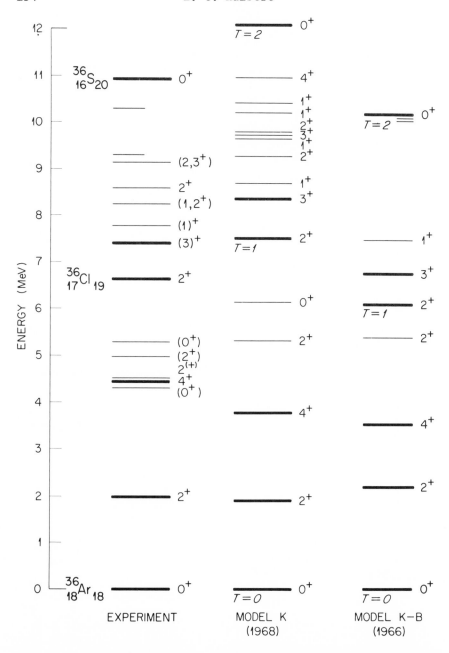

Fig. 14. Observed spectrum (Ref. 20) and shell-model spectra of T=0 levels in Ar^{36}, T=1 levels of Cl^{36}, and the ground state of S^{36}. See caption to Fig. 13. The effective Hamiltonian for "Model K-B" includes the O^{17} single-particle energies, together with a renormalized two-body G-matrix calculated at $\hbar\omega$ = 12.5 MeV according to the techniques of Kuo and Brown (Ref. 1). (Here and in Fig. 15, "K-B 1966" implies $\hbar\omega$= 12.5 MeV -- though in Figs. 3-8 it implied hω=14 MeV.)

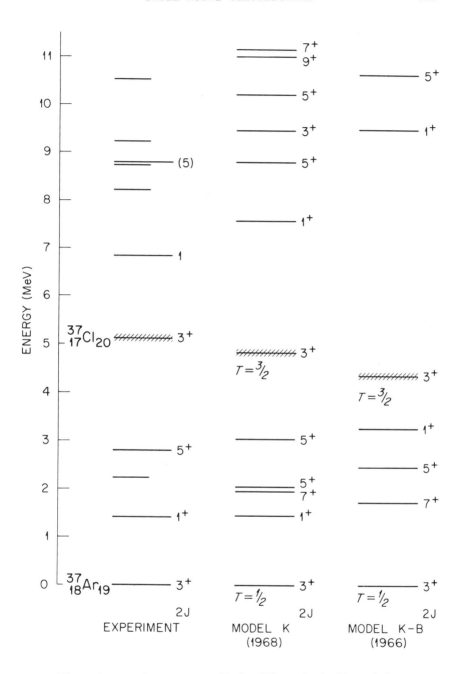

Fig. 15. Observed spectrum (Ref. 20) and shell-model spectra for A = 35. See captions to Figs. 14 and 15. Here the cross-hatched levels, and all levels above these, are Cl^{37}(T = 3/2) levels.

TABLE V. Summary of models used, and brief opinions on the quality of agreement between calculated and experimentally observed results. See text for details.

Mass Region	Space of basis wave functions	Effective Hamiltonian	Spectra	B(E2) Values	Spectroscopic Factors
17–22	Full $d_{5/2}$-$s_{1/2}$-$d_{3/2}$	Realistic[a]	GOOD for "Band-1" levels FAIR-poor for other levels	GOOD[b]	good
20–28	$d_{5/2}$-$s_{1/2}$	Least-squares	FAIR-poor		GOOD
30–33	$d_{5/2}$-$s_{1/2}$-$d_{3/2}$ ($n_{5/2} \gtrsim 10$)	Least-squares (SDI)	GOOD		GOOD
35–37	Full $d_{5/2}$-$s_{1/2}$-$d_{3/2}$	Realistic	FAIR-GOOD		

[a] A report of results obtained with least-squares interactions is given below (in the text).

[b] As discussed below (in the text), the B(E2) agreement for ^{21}Ne is poor.

ment between two nucleons in a relative 1s state, with total isotopic spin 1. For s-d-shell nucleons there are 14 independent parameters in this two-body interaction (25); but we fixed three of these parameters (those involving higher angular momentum) at zero. Thus we used 3 single-particle variables and 11 two-body variables -- 14 parameters in all.

c. Various modifications of the Kuo ($\hbar\omega$ = 14 MeV) interaction.

First we kept the Kuo two-body matrix elements fixed, and optimized the fit by adjusting only the three single-particle energies. (This particular variation was tried for the Kuo-Brown (1) interaction, too.)

Then we searched by varying not just the three single-particle energies, but also all those two-body matrix elements which explicitly involve either the $d_{5/2}$ shell or the $s_{1/2}$ shell or both. The idea here was that the $d_{3/2}$ shell might be considered as a perturbation (though it's an awfully important one); and so it seemed reasonable to satisfy ourselves with Kuo's values as estimates of the perturbative elements, while adjusting the main contributions to fit level data. This search had 18 free parameters.

In another search, similar to the one just described, we varied only nine of the $d_{5/2}$ and/or $s_{1/2}$ matrix elements. This search had 12 free parameters.

Finally, we ran a 4-parameter search in which the adjustable parameters were the three single-particle energies, plus an overall scaling factor affecting only that subset of Kuo matrix elements in which each member explicitly involves both the $d_{5/2}$ and $d_{3/2}$ shells but not the $s_{1/2}$ shell. This variation was tried because it's been suggested that the Kuo interaction overemphasizes the interaction between $d_{5/2}$ and $d_{3/2}$ nucleons.

In these 17-22 searches we minimized the RMS deviation to 41 pieces of data. These data include 12 ground-state binding energies, 18 excitations within the ground-state rotational bands, and 11 excitations in higher bands. Thus the searches were somewhat biased toward fitting levels belonging to ground-state bands.

Each of these least-squares searches ended up by fitting the observed levels with an RMS deviation somewhat smaller than that for the "no-parameter" Kuo result (and Kuo-Brown result). The RMS deviations from these several searches decreased as the number of free parameters increased. But none of these least-squares fits struck us as looking far better in all respects than the no-parameter fits. We don't

have much reason to believe that we've found solutions
really preferable to the Kuo solution. But, at least, we've
found a variety of interactions worth consideration and comparison. That comparison is not easy for me to summarize
briefly. However, I have picked out a few points to describe.

Since the fits to energy-level data are not perfect,
there is interest in comparing the calculated spectra. In
many cases levels not included in the fit -- i.e. not included in the least-squares criterion -- turn out to be
sensitive to which effective Hamiltonian we use. And the
same thing often happens to searched-on levels which are
not fit well by the Kuo Hamiltonian. In fitting a given
nucleus, one of our converged 17-22 solutions may outshine
all its competitors. But then for a neighboring nucleus,
another solution will get the honors. A few features common to all the solutions are noticeable: for example, in
^{22}Na none of our 17-22 fits get the first two 1^{+} levels high
enough.

How about the wave functions? Sometimes there are
striking differences, even for levels which are fit well by
all the interactions. One extreme case is for the ground
state of ^{18}F, J=1, T=0. For this level, I'll write down the
intensities of the largest three components as computed from
three different effective Hamiltonians:

Configuration	Percentage Intensity		
	Kuo	SDI	Central
$(s_{1/2})^2$	18	10	50
$d_{5/2}d_{3/2}$	45	11	14
$(d_{5/2})^2$	35	77	35

These wave-function differences can be traced back to particular differences in the two-body matrix elements themselves (but I won't go into that now.)

How about the B(E2)-values calculated from different
interactions? Within the ground-state bands, all interactions give essentially the same results, with very rare
exceptions. For transitions within higher bands, and for
interband transitions, disagreements are considerably more
frequent; but in none of these cases is there an experimental number to favor one interaction over another.

B(E2) Values for Ne

Now I'll show you a problem about the B(E2)'s in Ne[21]. On a previous slide (Table I), I showed our shell-model value for the first-to-ground B(E2), compared with an experimentally determined B(E2) as listed in the compilation of Skorka et al. (14). That experimental value was a Russian Coulomb-excitation number, twice as big as our theoretical number. In Table VI you see some recent experimental determinations, from Freiburg (26), for several E2 transitions in Ne[21]. These new determinations are much <u>smaller</u> than our shell-model values. The Freiburg numbers are based on lifetime measurements (26,27). Except for the 7/2 → 3/2 transition, all the decays listed in Table VI are dominated by M1 contributions; thus the Freiburg numbers are sensitive to errors in the M1-E2 mixing ratios used in the extraction of BE(2)'s from data. However, it seems unlikely that all such errors, for different transitions, are in the same direction. So the Freiburg results cast considerable doubt on our shell model for Ne[21].

TABLE VI. B(E2↓) values for transitions in Ne[21]. All transitions listed are between levels diagrammed as heavy lines in Fig. 6. The entries under "Ex" are B(E2) values deduced by Rolff, Pronko, and Maier (26) on the basis of lifetime measurements (26,25). (The level observed at 4.4 MeV was assumed to have spin 11/2+.) The entries under "Shell Model" are values calculated from eigenvectors associated with the spectrum labeled "Kuo 1967" in Fig. 7. An added effective charge of 0.53 was used in the shell-model B(E2) calculation.

| | B(E2) in e^2fm^4 | |
$J_i \rightarrow J_f$	Exp	Shell Model
5/2 → 3/2	17	81
7/2 → 3/2	16	34
7/2 → 5/2	24	57
9/2 → 5/2	22	45
9/2 → 7/2	21	31
11/2 → 7/2	43	52
11/2 → 9/2	13	26

Perhaps this trouble is related to particularly strong departures of the ^{21}Ne states 5/2, 7/2, 9/2, 11/2 from properties associated with a pure rotational band. As I mentioned earlier, calculations on a Nilsson-rotational model (9) indicate that the energies of these levels are strongly perturbed from those expected for a pure band based on the $3/2^+$ ground state. However, our shell-model does reproduce the observed (3/2, 5/2, 7/2...) level-energies, rather than the unperturbed-band energies. We hope that further theoretical (and perhaps experimental) investigations of ^{21}Ne, and of the similar nucleus ^{23}Na, will shed more light on this problem.

Further Results and Comments for A ≥ 20

As I mentioned earlier: for our two-shell searches on level data of A = 20-28, the optimized solution is, happily, fairly independent of the data chosen to represent these nine masses. However, the optimized solution is much more sensitive to the mass region searched on. We have concluded this after comparing results from $d_{5/2}$-$s_{1/2}$ searches in several different mass regions -- the Argonne results (28) for 17-20, and our own two-shell results for 17-22, 20-25, and 20-28. These two-shell searches are attempts to find an effective interaction which implicitly takes into account the presence of $d_{3/2}$ particles as well as $p_{1/2}$ holes, $f_{7/2}$ particles, etc. -- at least insofar as these particles and holes affect low-lying even-parity spectra. It seems likely that an adequate effective interaction must include three-body (and perhaps more-body) terms. But when we search for an optimized two-body interaction, we don't get the two-body part of this "adequate", many-body effective interaction. Rather, we get a two-body interaction that's trying to incorporate, as best it can, the effects of such many-body terms on the nuclear levels being fit.

We may be able to extend our three-shell calculations at least one or two masses beyond A = 22. We are investigating the possibility of using a truncated three-shell basis, and then incorporating some effects of the omitted s-d states via detailed second-order perturbation theory. This perturbative treatment could be applied also -- and probably more successfully -- in the mass region 30-33.

Finally, I mention that in our three-shell calculations at the upper end of the shell, we should be using renormalized hole-hole interactions rather than renormalized particle-particle interactions. These two kinds of interactions, when calculated according to the techniques of Ref. (2), will not be quite equivalent. (They would be equivalent, were it not for the fact that the renormalization procedures (2) neglect some of the contributions arising from second-order perturbation theory.) I have asked Tom Kuo to calculate some hole-hole interactions for us.

SUMMARY

A brief summary of models used, and opinions on the quality of agreement with experimental data, is given in Table V.

ACKNOWLEDGEMENTS

As stated earlier, the work reported here has been done principally by P. W. M. Glaudemans, J. B. McGrory, B. H. Wildenthal, and me. All the shell-model results were calculated with the Oak Ridge-Rochester shell-model computer-codes (5). The least-squares searcing programs were written by P. W. M. Glaudemans and B. H. Wildenthal. T. T. S. Kuo sent us many realistic-interaction results (1,2) before publication; he also calculated the realistic interaction K-B at 12.5 MeV, and wrote the codes from which the interaction K was calculated. S. P. Pandya participated in the work of searching in the 17-22 region with the Talmi-integral parameterization.

REFERENCES

1. T. T. S. Kuo and G. E. Brown, Nucl. Phys. 85, 40 (1966).
2. T. T. S. Kuo, Nucl. Phys. A103, 71 (1967).
3. T. T. S. Kuo, private communication
4. T. Hamada and I. D. Johnston, Nucl. Phys. 34, 382 (1962).
5. J. B. French, E. C. Halbert, J. B. McGrory, and S. S. M. Wong, to be published.
6. A collection of references for level data in the mass region 17-20 is available in the theoretical paper of A. Arima, S. Cohen, R. D. Lawson, and M. H. Macfarlane, Nucl. Phys. A108, 94 (1968).
7. P. W. M. Glaudemans, G. Wiechers, and P. J. Brussaard, Nucl. Phys. 56, 529 (1964).
8. A. J. Howard, J. P. Allen, D. A. Bromley, J. W. Olness, and E. K. Warburton, Phys. Rev. 157, 1022 (1967); P. Harvat, Nucl. Phys. 52, 410 (1964).
9. See, for example, M. Lambert, G. Duzamet, H. Beaumevieille, A. Tellez, and M. Yaker, in Proceedings International Conference on Nuclear Structure, Tokyo, Sept., 1967, p. 111.
10. E. K. Warburton, A. R. Poletti, and J. W. Olness, to be published in Phys. Rev. 168,   (1968).
11. E. K. Warburton, private communication.
12. S. Buhl, D. Pelte, and B. Povh, Nucl. Phys. A91, 319 (1967).

13.   E. C. Halbert, J. B. McGrory, and B. H. Wildenthal, to
      be published in Phys. Rev. Letters 20, 1112 (1968).
14.   S. J. Skorka, J. Hertel, and T. W. Retz-Schmidt,
      Nuclear Data 2, 347 (1967).
15.   D. H. Wilkinson, Comments in Nuclear and Particle
      Physics 1, 139 (1967).
16.   R. Siemssen, L. L. Lee, and D. Cline, Phys. Rev. 140B,
      1258 (1965).
17.   The SU(3) predictions were calculated by M. Harvey.
18.   M. H. Macfarlane and J. B. French, Rev. Mod. Phys. 32,
      567 (1960). See especially Appendix 1, pp. 686-7.
19.   B. H. Wildenthal, J. B. McGrory, E. C. Halbert, and
      P. W. M. Glaudemans, to be published in Physics Letters
      (1968).
20.   P. M. Endt and C. Van der Leun, Nucl. Phys. A105, 1
      (1967).
21.   B. H. Wildenthal and E. Newman, Phys. Rev. 167, 1027
      (1968); and to be published.
22.   P. W. M. Glaudemans, P. J. Brussaard, and B. H.
      Wildenthal, Nucl. Phys. A102, 593 (1967).
23.   M. Betigeri et al., Z. Naturf. 21a, 980 (1966).
24.   B. H. Wildenthal and P. W. M. Glaudemans, Nucl. Phys.
      A108, 49 (1969).
25.   S. Cohen, R. D. Lawson, and S. P. Pandya, to be
      published in Nucl. Phys.; S. Cohen, E. C. Halbert, and
      S. P. Pandya, to be published in Nucl. Phys.
26.   C. Rolff, J. G. Pronko, H. J. Maier, to be published.
      in Nucl. Phys.
27.   A. Bamberger, K. P. Lieb, B. Povh, and D. Schwalm,
      Nucl. Phys. A111, 12 (1968).
28.   A. Arima, S. Cohen, R. D. Lawson, and M. H. Macfarlane,
      Nucl. Phys. A108, 94 (1968).

DISCUSSION

KOLTUN: Just a matter of principle, I wonder if anyone can
comment on this: When you are varying parameters looking
for an interaction you still have in the back of your mind
that there is some way of deriving the interaction, hopefully,
from "realistic" interactions with core polarization, and so
on?

HALBERT: Yes; that means we're always hoping that there's
some kind of rational connection between our wave functions,
and wave functions which would be closer to the truth.

KOLTUN: Well, the following occurs to me: One usually tries
to say that if one takes too large a mass region, one is
going to get into trouble because things change; therefore,
you try to compare neighboring nuclei, when you're searching

for the best two-body matrix elements. Does it make more
sense if you're using a realistic plus polarization picture
but still looking for parameters, for example, to fit
separately even-even nuclei, odd nuclei, and odd-odd nuclei;
that is, instead of treating near neighbors, treating the
4n, the 4n plus 2 and the 4n plus one and three nuclei? That
is, you're searching for parameters. Why should the parameters be good for neighbors? They might be better if you
compared Mg^{24} and Si^{28}, and it might be better if you compare
the odd nuclei among themselves because what you expect on
theoretical grounds is that the so-called unrenormalized part
doesn't change so much. What does change is the core polarization, but that's going to be quite different for even nuclei
and odd nuclei on any model. Does anyone have a comment on
that?

HALBERT: Well, of course, if you take as your approximation
the way that Kuo-Brown and Kuo originally calculated their
renormalizations, then you would use the same renormalized
interaction for even-even, even-odd, and odd-odd nuclei.
Their renormalizations to the interaction operator were just
the two-body contributions from second-order perturbation
theory. For our applications--at least some of them--I
think this kind of approximation is inadequate. But if you
have this approximation in the back of your mind, then you
would indeed use the same effective interaction for all the
nuclei.
      Your suggestion may well help. We do have more problems
in fitting odd-odd nuclei. It would certainly be nice to feel
justified in leaving them out of a search. But probably we
wouldn't have enough data on the odd-odd nuclei to fit them
separately, as a group. That's a problem: when you're
searching, if you try to make separate fits to different
groups of nuclei, and if you subdivide too finely, then you
don't have enough data to search on. We can chop up the
mass region from 17 to 28 because there is so much data. What
we've done is to chop it up into sets of neighboring nuclei,
and you're suggesting a different way. I think we might try
your way. Still, there's another problem: certainly the
effective interaction is a many-body interaction. For our
17-28 model, I think that the three-body contributions are
not negligible. And so there may remain problems in fitting
from 17 up to 28 with the same (1 + 2)-body interaction, even
if we do allow separate interactions for even-even, even-odd,
and odd-odd nuclei.

PHILLIPS: Does the fact that you use the same effective
charge up to mass 22 and got reasonable B(E2)'s mean that
you wouldn't particularly do better on the parameter search
by choosing other than that whole mass region?

HALBERT: The measured B(E2)'s are rarely better than about
20%.   I think that we just don't have enough accuracy, either
in our theory or in the experimental data, to see whether we
need to vary the effective charge over the mass region 17 to
22.

In calculating B(E2)'s we did vary, a little bit, a parameter that is connected with the effective charge.   When we
did the calculations of spectra, we used an effective interaction for the same $\hbar\omega$ throughout 17-22.   But in our B(E2)
calculations, one of the parameters which comes in explicitly
is the ω from the harmonic oscillator wave functions, and
here we used the rule $\hbar\omega = 41\ A^{-1/3}$.   The calculated B(E2)
has contributions proportional to e^2/ω^2, where e is the
effective charge.   So it's really e/ω that comes into our
B(E2) calculations, and we did change the denominator, ω.

BARANGER: This is a very speculative question.   You mentioned
several times that there were some three-body effective forces
that might come in.   Now suppose someone came and told you:
"I've got this three-body force and it's right, I guarantee
it's good."

HALBERT: I wouldn't believe him.   I would think he was a
charlatan.

BARANGER: I mean, how much trouble would it be to put it
into that calculation?

HALBERT: I don't know.   At Oak Ridge, we've talked for
years about calculating and handling three-body interactions.
Now there's a man (Paul Goldhammer) sitting behind you who's
done it; so for him it's perfectly straight-forward.   For us,
it is no trouble in principle to calculate the many-body
matrix element of a three-body operator.   But when we do the
problem, we need the Hamiltonian operator expressed in a way
that is not the ordinary way.   The Hamiltonian is ordinarily
expanded in terms of operators which have two creation
operators coupled to (J,T), followed by two destruction
operators coupled to (J,T); and the whole thing is coupled
to zero.   But in our procedure we need a slightly different
representation for the Hamiltonian operator, in order to
calculate its matrix elements efficiently.   There is a part
of our computer program that takes the ordinary Hamiltonian
operator, and recouples it in a shell-ordered way--so that
all the creation and destruction operators for shell-one
(say, the $d_{5/2}$ shell) are coupled together, followed by all
the operators for shell-two, followed by all those for
shell-three; and the whole thing is coupled together to zero.
If somebody could give us a three-body interaction with
terms already shell-ordered in this way, that would be good.

The troublesome thing is to take somebody else's operator--
which is probably going to be three creation operators
followed by three destruction operators--and recouple it in
a shell-ordered way. I don't know how much work that would
be.

BARANGER: That's the big problem, I take it?

HALBERT: It's all Racah algebra. It doesn't seem like a
big problem. The only thing is, every time something seems
like a small problem, it turns out to be a lot of coding, and
a lot of work. And that's the reason we haven't done it;
but perhaps if we and Goldhammer could get together, then
that would be good. He knows how to do calculations with
three-body forces.

GOLDHAMMER: I just thought I'd comment. It depends on how
you write the program. If you write the program with single
particle CFP's or with one which handles the logic of creation and destruction operators, then for example in our program it's no harder basically to work the three-body forces
or four-body forces, or whatever, than it is with two-body
forces. It takes longer on the machine. It depends on how
you do it, but basically there's no complication.

HALBERT: There's another complication in our case, though,
that I should have mentioned. What we do is pre-calculate
and save "single-shell matrix elements." These are generali-
zations of c.f.p.'s. They are double-barred matrix elements
of various tensor operators within a single j-shell--for
example, a tensor operator formed by coupling together one
creation operator and two destruction operators. We save
these numbers on magnetic tape. But we don't have on tape,
now, all the single-shell matrix elements that would be
needed to handle three-body interactions; and there would be
a lot of these needed. It's not as hard as calculating
c.f.p.'s, for there is no group theory involved. But we
would have to calculate and tape all these numbers.
      It would be a year's project or so, to gear up for
handling three-body interactions. If Michel Baranger told
us it would be worth it, though, we might do it!

RIPKA: I'd like to comment on the question asked by Dr.
Phillips concerning the possibility of the effective charge
being different as you go through the s-d shell. Microscopic
calculations of this closed shell polarization effect have
been made in Hartree-Fock theory and they do not show that
the effective charge changes as you go through the s-d shell.
And this, by the way, is predicted from the earliest
Mottleson model which tells you how much to change the

oscillator axes according to the population of the orbits.
I would also like to make another comment concerning keeping
h constant as you go through the shell. It is well known
that matrix elements go down as you increase the number of
particles roughly as a 1/A effect...

HALBERT: Are you talking about the interaction matrix
elements?

RIPKA: Yes. Well, if you keep both the spin orbit interaction and the two-body matrix elements constant as you
progress through the s-d shell, you are in effect making
the spin-orbit interaction weaker in the second half of the
shell because experimentally the spin-orbit interaction does
not change or if anything it increases a little bit, but
the two-body matrix elements decrease substantially and this
may affect, for example calculations of magnetic effects
which are very sensitive to the $d_{5/2} - d_{3/2}$ splitting.

HALBERT: What do you mean? I think I don't understand what
you mean by the spin-orbit interaction. Do you mean the
splitting?

RIPKA: Yes, I'm sorry. Every time I said spin orbit interaction I meant really the splitting between the $d_{5/2}$ and the
$d_{3/2}$ states.

HALBERT: Well, we have done calculations with realistic
interactions, which involve $\hbar\omega$, in two mass regions:
A = 17-22 and A = 35-40. We have used different values of
$\hbar\omega$ in the two regions. For the 17-22 region we use the
splittings as observed in O^{17}. At the upper end of the
shell, we would like to have Kuo calculate the splittings.
He did calculate these for us about a year and a half ago
(with the Kuo-Brown method); and as I remember it, the
calculated splittings between single-particle energies didn't
change a great deal from what was calculated at the lower
end of the shell.

IV. A. THEORY AND EXPERIMENT IN 2s-1d SHELL NUCLEI

G. Ripka

Princeton and Rutgers Universities. (On leave from
the Centre d'Etudes Nucleaires de Saclay, France.)

This is a very opportune time to hold a conference on
2s-1d shell nuclei. Indeed both Hartree-Fock and SU3 calculations have been carried out in considerable detail with
a systematic comparison between theory and experiment
throughout the 2s-1d shell.[2,3,22] Extensive diagonaliza-
tions[16,20] of limited 2s-1d shell configuration mixing are
available and in progress. On the other hand experimental
values of electromagnetic transitions, single particle
strengths obtained from pickup and stripping reactions and
even the spectra all seem to show that whereas in the first
half of the 2s-1d shell strong deformations warrant strong
coupling, deformations in Si^{28} are smaller than those which
theory predicts. I wish therefore to review some of the
experimental data which appear to be in fair agreement with
theory in the first half of the 2s-1d shell but which appear to disagree in the Si^{28} region. I do not wish to
insist again on the numerous data which show that nuclei
close to Ne^{20} and Mg^{24} can be understood in terms of strongly
deformed intrinsic state which generates rotational bands
and strong-coupling.

ARE THE ROTATIONS OF LIGHT DEFORMED NUCLEI ADIABATIC?

It is well to realize an important difference between
the rotational spectra of light deformed nuclei and that of
the heavy deformed nuclei. In light deformed nuclei the
rotations are not as clearly adiabatic as in heavy deformed
nuclei. That is to say that the description of a state belonging to a rotational band by the strong coupling wave
function (1):

$$| \psi^J_{M(K)} > = \sqrt{\frac{2J+1}{16\pi^2}} \{ D^{*J}_{MK} (\psi) | \phi_K > + $$

$$(-)^{J-K} D^{*J}_{M-K} (\psi) | \phi_{-K} > \}$$

(1)

may not be very accurate . Indeed the validity of this
strong coupling wavefunction depends on overlaps between
intrinsic states $|\phi_K>$ and the rotated intrinsic state
$e^{-i\beta Jy}|\phi_K>$:

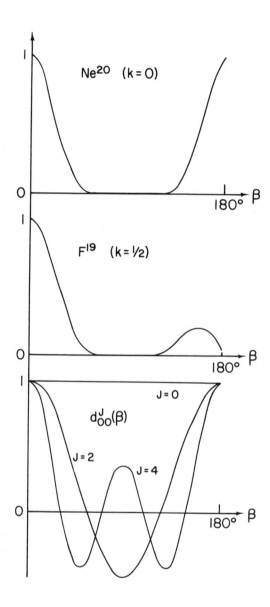

Fig. 1. Overlaps $\langle \phi_K | e^{-i\beta J_y} | \phi_K \rangle$ between the rotated Hartree-Fock state $|\phi_K\rangle$ and itself as a function of the angle β. The top two curves are for Ne^{20} and F^{19}. The bottom curve shows the variation of $D_{MO}^J(\alpha, \beta, \gamma) = e^{i\alpha M} d_{00}^J(\beta)$ for $K = 0$.

$$<\phi_K|e^{-i\beta Jy}|\phi_K> \text{ and } <\phi_K|e^{-i\beta Jy}H|\phi_K> \tag{2}$$

being peaked around $\beta \sim 0$ and $\beta \sim \pi$ compared to the corresponding variation of the $D^J_{MK}(\alpha,\beta,\gamma)$ wavefunction. Figure 1 shows that this is not so. Another way of stating this criterion for $K = 0$ rotational bands is to say that the rotations are adiabatic so long as

$$J(J+1) << <\phi_o | \vec{J}^2 | \phi_o>. \tag{3}$$

In light nuclei $<\vec{J}^2>$ varies between 15 to 25 (in units of $\hbar^2$) whereas in heavy deformed nuclei it is closer to 100. Thus strong coupling wavefunctions must be used with some caution and they should be checked with projected wavefunctions. Typically decoupling coefficients of $K = 1/2$ bands are not predicted correctly[3] in the strong coupling model. In spite of this strong coupling wavefuctions are quite useful and they may often be accurate enough to test the intrinsic wavefunction.

MAGNETIC MOMENTS

This is illustrated in Table 1 which shows magnetic moments obtained from Hartree-Fock wavefunctions both projected[22] and used in the strong coupling approximation[3,9] together with the magnetic moments obtained with SU3 wavefunctions[2]. For F^{19}, Ne^{21} and Na^{23} the three theoretical values agree quite well with the experimental values. The disagreement in the case of Mg^{25} is puzzling. For nuclei around S^{32} Hartree-Fock calculations show that the spin-orbit splitting between the $d_{5/2}$ and the $d_{3/2}$ states makes S^{32} near spherical[3] and this invalidates both the strong coupling model and the SU3 wavefunctions. The use of a weakly deformed but projected Hartree-Fock state is also questionable in this region.

The Hartree-Fock state of Ar^{36} is more deformed than that of S^{32} but the spin-orbit splitting makes it considerably different from the SU3 wavefunction thus explaining the discrepancy between the values of the magnetic moment which is sensitive to configuration mixing between the $d_{5/2}$ and $d_{3/2}$ states.

QUADRUPOLE DEFORMATIONS

The Hartree-Fock wavefunctions discussed so far are single-major-shell calculations which assume that 2s-1d shell orbits are expanded on states belonging to the 2s-1d

TABLE 1

Magnetic moments of odd A nuclei. The first three columns
indicate the nucleus and the K, J quantum numbers assigned
to the nuclear state. The fourth column gives magnetic
moments μ calculated by Gunye and Warke[22] who projected the
Hartree-Fock wave function. The fifth column gives values
calculated by Zamick and Ripka[9,3] in the strong coupling
model using Hartree-Fock wave functions. The sixth column
gives magnetic moments calculated by Elliott and Wilsdon[2]
using SU3 wave functions. The Hartree-Fock wave-functions
used in Ref. 3 and 22 are very similar.

Nucleus	K	J	μ^{22} Proj.	$\mu^{3,9}$ S.C.	μ^2 SU3	μ Exp.
F^{19}	1/2	1/2	2.89	2.82	2.79	2.63
F^{19}	1/2	5/2	3.78	3.86		3.5+0.5
Ne^{21}	3/2	3/2	-0.57	-0.58	-0.88	-0.66
Na^{23}	3/2	3/2	2.11	2.44	2.16	2.22
Mg^{25}	5/2	5/2	-0.58	-1.01	-0.49	-0.85
Al^{27}	5/2	5/2	3.61	3.78	3.07	3.64
Si^{29}	1/2	1/2	-0.38	-0.47		-0.56
S^{33}	3/2	3/2	0.54	0.05	2.15	0.64
Cl^{35}	3/2	3/2	0.73	0.63	-0.27	0.82

shell only:

$$|\lambda> = \sum_j c_j^\lambda \ | \ jm_\lambda> \quad j = d_{5/2}, 2s_{1/2} \text{ and } d_{3/2}. \tag{4}$$

and which use central forces and experimental spin-orbit
splitting. Quadrupole deformations however are very sensitive to polarization of the O^{16} closed shell by the 2s-1d
shell nucleons. Thus in evaluating quadrupole deformations
it is necessary to extend the expansion of the orbits so as
to allow the p-shell orbits to admix 2p-1f states and to
allow 2s-1d shell orbits to admix 1g-2d-3s states (so as to
allow the 2s-1d shell orbits to increase their quadrupole

moment because of an appreciable mutual polarization effect of the closed p-shell and the 2s-1d shell orbits). A measure of the quadrupole deformation is given by the ratio

$$
D = \frac{\langle\phi|\ \sum_{i=1}^{Z}\ (2Z_i^2 - X_i^2 - Y_i^2)\ |\phi\rangle}{\langle\phi|\ \sum_{i=1}^{Z}\ (X_i^2 + Y_i^2 + Z_i^2\ )\ |\phi\rangle}
$$

of the quadrupole to the monopole moments. The monopole moments are known experimentally from elastic electron scattering data.[8] The quadrupole moments of even-even nuclei may be deduced in the strong coupling model either from the B(E2) obtained from life-time measurements of the 2[+] state[6] or from inelastic scattering.[14,15] In the strong coupling model the B(E2) is given in terms of the intrinsic quadrupole moment Q_0 by the expression:

$$
B(E2) = \frac{5}{16\pi}\ Q_0^2
$$

$$
Q_0 = \langle\phi|\ \sum_{i=1}^{Z}\ (2Z_i^2 - X_i^2 - Y_i^2)\ |\phi\rangle
$$

(5)

Table 2 shows the experimental deformations compared to those obtained from a major-shell-mixing Hartree-Fock calculation[3] which takes full account of the mutual polarization of the closed p-shell and of the 2s-1d shell orbits. The quadrupole deformation of the Hartree-Fock state may be compared to that of the Mottelson model[23]. This model assumes the orbits to be those of a deformed oscillator the axes ω_X, ω_Y and ω_Z of which are in the same ratio as that of the density distribution of matter. The ratios of the axes are then given in terms of the quantities N_X, N_Y and N_Z

where
$$
N_X = \sum_{\lambda=1}^{A}\ (n_X^{(\lambda)} + \tfrac{1}{2})
$$

by the relation

$$
N_X\omega_X = N_Y\omega_Y = N_Z\omega_Z \ .
$$

(6)

In Ne[20] and Mg[24] the calculated quadrupole deformation is

TABLE 2

Quadrupole deformations defined by Eq. (4). The column three
gives the quadrupole deformation obtained from a major shell
mixing calculation. H.F. calculation with axial symmetry[3].
The fourth column gives the deformation assuming the intrinsic
wave function to be that of a deformed oscillator with axial
symmetry and whose axes are given by the relation $N_x \omega_x = N_y \omega_y$
$= N_z \omega_z$. The fifth column gives the quadrupole deformation obtained from the lifetime of the lowest 2+ state[6]. The last
column gives the quadrupole deformation obtained from a DWBA
(JULIE) analysis of inelastic (p,p') scattering.[15] The value
in parentheses in the last column is the deformation obtained
from inelastic (d,d') scattering.[10]

Nucleus	Shape	$D_{H.F.}$	$D_{osc.}$	$|D|_\tau^6$	$|D|_{p,p'}^{15}$
Ne^{20}	prolate	0.59	0.66	0.86	
Mg^{24}	prolate	0.63	0.64	0.67	0.54
Si^{28}	prolate	0.75	0.63		
				0.43	0.61
	oblate	−0.49	−0.54		(0.46)
S^{32}	prolate	0.35	0.36		
				0.4	0.4
	oblate	−0.13	−0.40		
A^{36}	oblate	−0.24	−0.32		

somewhat smaller than the experimental one. The prolate
shape of Si^{28} has a deformation larger than the experimental
one. Note that the (p,p') inelastic scattering gives a
considerably larger deformation of Si^{28} than the lifetime
measurement. Inelastic deuteron scattering[10] on Si^{28} however
gives a deformation equal to 0.47 which is smaller than the
one obtained from (p,p') scattering and closer to the lifetime measurement. It would be useful to have a confirmation
of the exceptionally large deformation of Ne^{20}.

The quadrupole deformation may also be compared to experiment by calculating static quadrupole moments of odd-A
nuclei. Table 3 gives the quadrupole moments of Odd-A nuclei
calculated in strong coupling using the quadrupole deformation
of a major-shell mixing Hartree-Fock calculation[3] and the
experimental mean square radius. The agreement with experi-

TABLE 3

Quadrupole moments of odd-A nuclei calculated in the strong-
coupling using the quadrupole deformation of a major-shell-
mixing Hartree-Fock calculation.[3] The last column gives the
experimental values. The quadrupole moments are measured in
fm^2 = 0.01 barns = 10^{-26} cm^2.

Nucleus	K	J	Q	Q_{exp}
Ne^{21}	3/2	3/2	9.6	9
Na^{23}	3/2	3/2	12.0	11
Mg^{25}	5/2	5/2	23.2	22
Al^{27}	5/2	5/2	-20.0	
				15
(obl.)	1/2	5/2	16.0	
S^{33} obl.	3/2	3/2	- 4.3	
				- 5.5
pro.	3/2	3/2	11.8	
Cl^{35}	3/2	3/2	- 9.8	- 7.9

ment is good for odd-A nuclei around Ne^{20} and Mg^{24}. The
quadrupole moment of Al^{27} can only be accounted for with the
oblate Si^{28} Hartree-Fock core and assuming further that the
$5/2^+$ ground state of Al^{27} is a J = 5/2 member of a K = 1/2
band.[11] A K = 5/2 band would give a quadrupole moment of
the wrong sign. The reason why the Hartree-Fock prolate
shape does not give the correct quadrupole moment is that the
prolate Hartree-Fock orbit of Si^{28} does not have a K = 5/2
occupied orbit. This is best seen on a Nilsson diagram[1].
Hartree-Fock and Nilsson orbits differ essentially by the
presence of an energy gap separating filled and empty orbits.
But the order of the orbits is quite similar in both cases.
Figure 2 shows the diagram of Nilsson orbits. The Hartree-
Fock states correspond to strong deformation. Thus the
oblate Si^{28} solution consists of filled K = 1/2, 3/2 and 5/2
orbits. The prolate solution consists of filled K = 1/2, 3/2
and 1/2' orbits. The ground state spin and the quadrupole
moment of Al^{27} would be must better understood if Al^{27} was a
K = 5/2 hole in a prolate Si^{28} core. It may be seen on the
Nilsson diagram that for smaller prolate deformation the
K = 1/2 and K = 5/2 orbits cross so that a more weakly de-

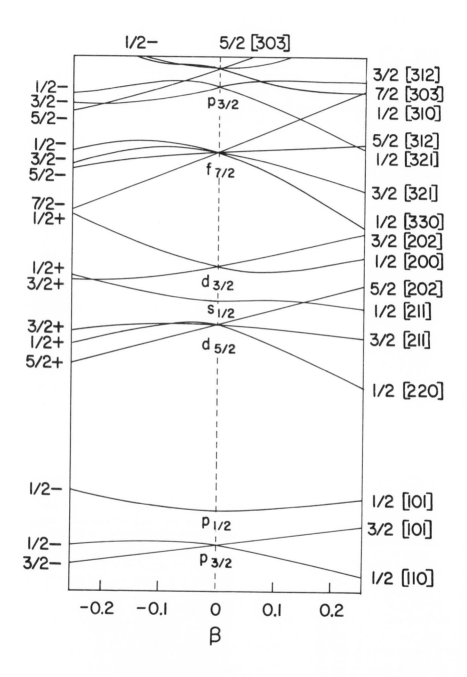

Fig. 2. The Nilsson Diagram[1].

deformed prolate state of Si^{28} would contain a K = 5/2 band.
This deformation may be so weak as to invalidate the strong
coupling hypothesis. For a very weak deformation weak coupling would be more adequate. Al^{27} would then consist of a
$d_{5/2}$ hole coupling to the 0^+ ground state and 2^+ first
excited state of Si^{28}. The B(E2) transitions between the
ground state of Al^{27} and the $1/2^+(0.842)$, $3/2^+(1.013)$,
$7/2^+(2.212)$, $5/2^+(2.731)$ and $9/2^+(3.000)$ excited states of
the Al^{27} may in fact be understood in terms of the weak
coupling model[19]. It is remarkable that when the parameters
of the weak coupling model are derived from these B(E2) transitions they may be used to obtain the correct value of the
quadrupole moment of the Al27 ground state . The failure of
Hartree-Fock and SU3 calculations to produce a low K = 5/2
band so as to make it a filled orbit of the prolate equilibrium shape of Si^{28} is not without a relation to a similar
problem encountered in Mg^{25}. In Mg^{24} the K = 1/2 and K = 3/2
are filled on the prolate side. In Mg^{25} an odd neutron may
be placed in the empty K = 1/2' or K = 5/2 bands. Both
K = 1/2 and K - 5/2 rotational bands have been observed in
the Mg^{25} spectrum but both Hartree-Fock and SU3 fail to lower
the K = 5/2 band below the K = 1/2 band. On Figure 3 it may
be seen that the K = 1/2' and the K = 5/2 orbits cannot be
mixed by a quadrupole-quadrupole force because although they
differ by δK = 2 a transition between these orbits involves
a spin-flip. If any mixing between these K = 1/2 and K = 5/2
orbits exists it is probably caused by non-central forces.

STRIPPING AND PICK-UP REACTIONS

Stripping and pick-up reactions give single particle
strengths which also depend on the coupling. The amplitudes
of transfer reaction relate states of different nuclei so
that they may be used to detect a change of shape, if any,
of the intrinsic state as particles are added or subtracted
from a nucleus. Both Hartree-Fock and SU3 theories predict
such changes in shape. Table 4 gives a list of the lowest
equilibrium shapes of even-even nuclei, their binding energy
relative to the 0^{16} binding energy and the (λ,μ) quantum
numbers of the SU3 state which has maximum overlap with the
Hartree-Fock state. One may first observe that in both Mg^{24}
and in Si^{28} there are two equilibrium shapes near degenerate
in energy. In Mg^{24} the two equilibrium shapes may be related
by essentially transferring four particles from the (011) to
the (020) orbits[3], and in Si^{28} the near degenerate oblate and
prolate shapes may be related by exchanging the twelve filled
2s-1d shell orbits with the remaining twelve empty ones. We
have seen that the electromagnetic properties of Al^{27} are
better understood in terms of a hole in a prolate Si^{28} core.
Magnetic properties of Si^{29} are better understood in terms

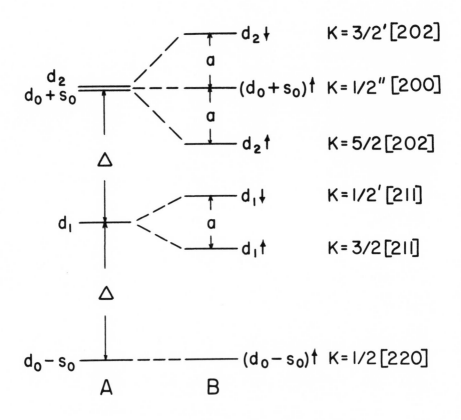

Fig. 3. Nilsson orbits in the case of large prolate deformations. The notation d_1 is used to represent the $\ell = 2$ $m = 1$
state of the 2s-1d shell. The symbol $d_0 \mp s_1$ is used for the
combinations $\sqrt{2/3}\, d_0 \pm \sqrt{1/3}\, s_0$ of the d_0 and s_0 states. A
field with a prolate Y_{20} deformation and zero spin-orbit
interaction will produce the spectrum A on the left with
equal spacings Δ proportional to the strength of the Y_{20}
deformation of the field. A spin-orbit interaction $\vec{\ell} \cdot \vec{s}$ acting as a perturbation will split the levels of given m but
having different K = m ± 1/2.

of a neutron outside an oblate Si^{28} core in strong coupling[9].
The spin-orbit splitting also favors the oblate Si^{28} shape
although only by a small amount. It has also been argued[10]
that the low-lying 7/2⁻ state at 3.62 MeV in Si^{29} is due to
the lowering of the K = 7/2⁻ Nilsson level due to an oblate
deformation. In order to see whether there is a change in

TABLE 4

Energies in MeV of source of the lowest equilibrium states
obtained in a single major shell Hartree-Fock calculation.
The second column gives the shape of the intrinsic state.
The last column gives the (λ,μ) quantum numbers of the SU3
state which has maximum overlap with the Hartree-Fock state.
The spherical shape of Si^{28} consists of a closed $d_{5/2}$ shell
and in the spherical shape of S^{32} consists of a closed $d_{5/2}$
and $s_{1/2}$ shells.

Nucleus	Shape	E(MeV)	(λ,μ)
Ne^{20}	prolate	− 35.8	(8,0)
	oblate	− 31.4	(0,4)
	ellipsoidal	− 76.7	(8,4)
Mg^{24}		− 75.1	(0,8)
		− 72.5	(4,0)
	oblate	−123.0	(0,12)
	prolate	−122.0	(12,0)
Si^{28}	ellipsoidal	−119.1	(4,8)
	ellipsoidal	−118.5	(8,4)
	spherical	−114.2	
	ellipsoidal	−171.8	(4,8)
S^{32}		−170.6	(8,0)
	spherical	−168.1	
	oblate	−220.5	(0,8)
A^{36}	prolate	−218.2	(4,0)

deformation, from prolate to oblate as one goes from Si^{27} to
Si^{29} simultaneous (d,p) and (d,t) reactions were performed
on a Si^{28} target by Mermaz, Holland, Whitten and Bromley[10],[12]
using 21 MeV deuterons of the Yale MP tandem. Neither reaction leading to the ground state of the residual nucleus
showed any unusually low cross section thus making it unlikely that a change of shape occurs as one goes from Si^{27}

TABLE 5

Spectroscopic factors S_j of the $Si^{28}(d,t)^{29}$ reaction.[10,12]
See text for explanation of the last column.

Si^{29} Energy Level	Spin	S_j	$|C_j|$
Ground State	$1/2^+$	0.42	0.65
1.28 MeV	$3/2^+$	0.57	1.05
2.03 MeV	$5/2^+$	0.12	0.61
2.43 MeV	$3/2^+$	weakly excited anomalous	
3.07 MeV	$5/2^+$	0.05	0.38
3.62 MeV	$7/2^-$	0.43	1.3
4.08 MeV	$7/2^+$	weakly excited anomalous	

to Si^{29}. Note also that the $Al^{27}(p,He^3)Mg^{25}$ and the
$Al^{27}(p,t)Al^{25}$ reactions have been measured[18] and they give a
high yield to the ground states of the residual nuclei; this
makes it unlikely that Al^{27} should have a very different
deformation than Mg^{25} which is prolate. The pickup reaction
$Si^{28}(d,He^3)Al^{27}$ was also studied with 34.4 MeV deuterons of
the Oak Ridge Isochronous Cyclotron by Wildenthal and Newman[13]
and by Gove, Purser, Schwartz, Alford and Cline[25] using 20
MeV deuterons of the MP tandem at the University of Rochester.
Tables 5 and 6 give the spectroscopic factors S_j extracted
from these stripping and pickup reactions on Si^{28}.

In strong coupling the spectroscopic factor S_j obtained
in a pick-up reaction is related to the coefficient C_j^λ of
the orbit (see equation 4) from which the neutron or proton
is picked up by the relation (24):

$$S_j = 2C_j^{\lambda 2} \tag{7}$$

The spectroscopic factor cannot therefore exceed the
value of 2 in strong coupling. This is because there are
only two magnetic substates (namely K and -K) from which the
proton or the neutron may be picked up. Similarly the
spectroscopic factor S_j of a stripping reaction is related
in strong coupling to the coefficient C_j of the orbit into
which the neutron is captured by the relation:

$$S_j = \frac{2}{2J + 1} C_j^{\lambda 2} \tag{8}$$

TABLE 6

Spectroscopic factors of the $Si^{28}(d,He^3)Al^{27}$ and of the
$Si^{28}(d,t)Si^{27}$ reaction. $S_j{}^a$, $S_j{}^b$, and $S_j{}^c$ are the values
extracted from Ref. 13, 25, and 10 respectively. The values
of C_j are derived from the mean values of the S_j in a manner
explained in the text. The last column gives the calculated
S_j as explained in the text.

Al^{27} Level	Spin	$S_j{}^a$	$S_j{}^b$	$S_j{}^c$	$|C_j|$	$S_{j\ s.m.}$
Ground state	$5/2^+$	3.8	3.1	4.0	1.35	3.9
0.842	$1/2^+$	0.5	0.79	0.8	0.6	0.8
1.013	$3/2^+$	0.56	0.75		0.57	
2.212	$7/2^+$	$\leq .4$				
2.731	$5/2^+$	0.61	0.75		0.6	0.5
2.980	$3/2^+$	$\leq .4$	$< .24$			
3.000	$9/2^+$	$\leq .6$				

and it cannot therefore exceed the value $2/(2j+1)$. The
Tables 6 and 7 give the values of $|C_j|$ deduced from the
spectroscopic factors S_j by the equations (7) and (8). Any
value of C_j which exceeds unity suggests that the wave-
function is closer to j-j coupling than to strong coupling
and that the deformation is therefore weaker. Pickup leading
to the ground state of Al^{27} strongly suggests this. In fact
the experimental spectroscopic factors of Al^{27} are in reasonable agreement with those of a shell model calculation[13]
which takes into account the full configuration mixing in
the $d_{5/2}$ and $2s_{1/2}$ subshells. The exclusion of the $d_{3/2}$
subshell makes the wave functions obtained for Si^{28} and Al^{27}
closer to j-j coupling.

Table 7 shows the spectroscopic factors of the
$S^{32}(d,p)S^{33}$ reaction measured by Mermaz and Whitten using
18 MeV deuterons of the Yale MP tandem[17]. The large values
of $|C_j|$ which the spectroscopic factors imply shows, if need
be, that strong coupling is inadequate for S^{32}. The experimental spectroscopic factors agree quite well with those
obtained from a shell model calculation   which includes all
configurations with a closed $d_{5/2}$ subshell.

TABLE 7

Spectroscopic factors S_j of the $S^{32}(d,p)S^{33}$ reaction.[17]
See the text for an explanation of the last two columns.

S^{33} Energy Level	Spin	S_j	$|C_j|$	$S_{j\ s.m.}$ [16]
Ground State	$3/2^+$	0.69	1.4	0.82
0.842 MeV	$1/2^+$	0.27	0.52	0.24
1.968 MeV	$5/2^+$	very weak-no stripping pattern		
2.313 MeV	$3/2^+$	0.05	0.31	0.013
2.937 MeV	$7/2^-$	0.63	1.6	
3.221 MeV	$3/2^-$	0.33	0.81	
4.213 MeV	$3/2^-$	0.06	0.35	

MOMENTS OF INERTIA OF THE ROTATIONAL BANDS

It is also worth comparing the spectra of the rotational
bands generated by the Hartree-Fock intrinsic states with the
experimental spectra. The spectra obtained[3] by projecting
angular momentum from the Hartree-Fock states of C^{12}, Ne^{20},
Si^{28} and A^{36} are shown on Figure 4. The rotational bands
obtained by projecting the Hartree-Fock states do not depend
on any particular theory of the moment of inertia. For C^{12}
and Ne^{20} the agreement is quite satisfying. In fact a complete diagonalization of all the 2s-1d shell configurations
of Ne^{20} gives a rotational band[21] very similar to that obtained by projecting the Hartree-Fock state as shown on
Figure 5. In Si^{28} the calculated rotational band is compressed so that the moment of inertia of the Hartree-Fock
state is too large by a factor of two. This is a serious
discrepancy suggesting again that the Hartree-Fock state of
Si^{28} is too strongly deformed.

In summarizing the experimental data it should be recalled that properties of nuclei close to Ne^{20} and Mg^{24} are
fairly well accounted for by assuming a strongly deformed
intrinsic state. Hartree-Fock theory implies in this region
similar 2s-1d shell configuration mixing as SU3 wave functions
and it also accounts for the closed shell polarization effects
quite successfully. But experimental data do not show any
abrupt change in the shape of the intrinsic states as one
proceeds through the 2s-1d shell. Furthermore the data on
Al^{27} seem contradictory unless one assumes Al^{27} to be a

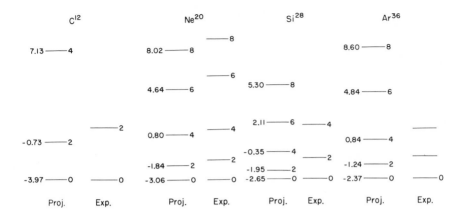

Fig. 4. Projected Hartree-Fock spectra[3] of C^{12}, Ne^{20}, Si^{28} and A^{36}. The oblate solution of Si^{28} was used. The prolate solution generates a rotational band quite similar to that of the oblate solution. The projected spectra are drawn to the left of the experimental spectra for each nucleus. The number on the right of each level is the spin of the level. The number on the left of each projected level is the difference (in MeV) between the energy of the projected level and the Hartree-Fock energy of the intrinsic state.

proton hole in a prolate but weakly deformed Si^{28} core. If the deformation is weak prolate and oblate shapes are no longer orthogonal and they are therefore not entirely distinguishable. Beyond Si^{28}, in the region of S^{32} oblate deformations are not observed and the data suggest weak coupling. The situation for nuclei close to A^{36} is not clear for lack of experimental data. Hartree-Fock calculations suggest that A^{36} is more deformed than S^{32} and that this deformation is oblate.

THEORETICAL CALCULATIONS

How much of this is accounted for by theory? I wish to discuss only microscopic descriptions. Calculations made so far belong to two types. 1. Those calculations which include the whole 2s-1d shell but which restrict the wave functions to be independent particle wave functions. 2. Those calculations which restrict the configuration space to given subshells of the 2s-1d shell but which allow complete configuration mixing within this subspace.

1. Calculations of the first type comprise the Hartree-Fock calculations in a certain sense the SU3 wave functions. As mentioned previously these calculations give good agreement with experiment in the Ne^{20} and Mg^{24} region where strong

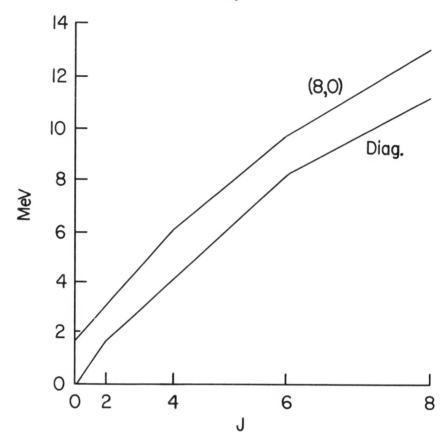

Fig. 5. Complete diagonalization of Ne^{20} (A. Arima[21]). The
lower curve shows the variation of the lowest states of each
J in Ne^{20} plotted against J on a $J(J + 1)$ scale. All the
2s-1d shell configurations were diagonalized using a Yukawa
residual interaction. The upper curve gives the spectrum
obtained from the (8,0) SU3 configuration alone. The (8,0)
configuration of Ne^{20} is very similar to the Hartree-Fock
intrinsic state. Note that the complete diagonalization
[curve labeled "Diag."] lowers all the states by about 1.7
MeV but that it does not change appreciably the moment of
inertia.

coupling is suggested by experiment. Both Hartree-Fock and
SU3 wave functions fail to obtain a weak deformation for
Si^{28}. It is often thought that the spin-orbit splitting
will lower the $d_{5/2}$ so as to make Si^{27} more spherical.
Hartree-Fock calculations which use central forces definitely
show this to be wrong . The spin-orbit splitting is too
weak in Si^{28} to appreciably reduce the deformation produced
by the quadrupole-quadrupole force. The theory as yet has

not been able to produce a small deformation for Si^{28}. The
main difference between the Hartree-Fock and SU3 wave functions comes from effects of the spin-orbit splitting. Up to
Si^{28} this difference is small and noticeable only in magnetic
phenomena. But it becomes important in S^{32} and A^{36}. In S^{32}
Hartree-Fock theory shows that no permanent deformation may
be expected[3] and we can understand why weak coupling is
favored in this region.

2. Calculations of type 2 comprise those of Wildenthal,
McGrory, Halbert and Glaudemans[20]. They diagonalize all the
configurations with particles in the $d_{5/2}$ and $2s_{1/2}$ subshells.
An effective interaction is derived "a la Talmi" from experimental spectra. It is interesting that they obtain a correct moment of inertia for Si^{28} as well as satisfactory single
particle strengths for the $Si^{28}(d,He^3)Al^{27}$ reaction,[13] (see
Table 6) showing that their wave functions have smaller deformations than Hartree-Fock wave functions. This is because
the $d_{3/2}$ state has been excluded from the configuration space
thus forcing their wave functions closer to j-j coupling.
These calculations give a quantitative support to the specula-
tion that nuclei around Si^{28} are weakly deformed. However,
the weak deformation is not proved by the calculation since
the effects of including the $d_{3/2}$ state (strongly admixed in
Hartree-Fock wave functions) are not calculated even in
perturbation theory.

Calculations of type 2 comprise also those of Glaudemans,
Wieckers and Brussaard[16] which take into account the complete
configuration mixing in the $2s_{1/2}$ and $d_{3/2}$ subshells and
which assume a closed $d_{5/2}$ subshell. A large number of
nuclei belonging to the second half of the 2s-1d shell are
calculated this way and the wave functions are tabulated.
We have seen (Table 7) that they account quite well for the
single particle strengths of the $S^{32}(d,p)S^{33}$ reaction.

Finally, one should mention that complete diagonaliza-
tions involving all 2s-1d shell configurations are in progress[21]. As yet they have been limited to nuclei close to
Ne^{20} which are strongly deformed. From these calculations
we may expect to learn which states definitely do not belong
to 2s-1d shell configurations and whether there are any
noticeable effects of non-central residual interactions between the 2s-1d shell nucleons.

ACKNOWLEDGEMENTS

I wish to thank Professor G. T. Garvey and Dr. M. C.
Mermaz for help in clarifying experimental data and in
making recent data available.

REFERENCES

1. A. Bohr and B. Mottelson, Kgl. Danske Videnskab. Selskab.
    Mat. Fys. Medd. 27 (16) 1953 (3rd ed., 1964).
    S. G. Nilsson, Kgl. Danske Videnskab. Selskab Mat. Fys.
    Medd. 29 (16) 1955.
2. J. P. Elliott and C. E. Wilsdon, Proc. Roy. Soc. (London)
    A302 509 (1968) (further references are found there).
3. G. Ripka, Advances in Nuclear Physics, Vol. 1, edited by
    M. Baranger and E. Vogt, Plenum Press 1968.
4. I. Kelson, Phys. Rev. 132, 2189 (1963).
5. H. J. Lipkin, Ann. Phys. (N. Y.) 9 272 (1960).
6. P. H. Stelson and L. Grodsins, Nuclear Data, Sec. A,
    Vol. 1 21 (1965).
8. R. Hofstadter, Electron Scattering and Nuclear Structure,
    W. A. Benjamin, 1963.
9. L. Zamick and G. Ripka, Phys. Lett. 23, 347 (1966).
10. M. C. Mermaz, G. E. Holland, C. A. Whitten, Jr., D. A.
    Bromley, Proceedings of the International Conference on
    Nuclear Structure, Tokyo, 1967, Supp. Jour. of Phys. Soc.
    Japan, Vol. 24, 1968.
11. G. Ripka, International Nuclear Physics Conference,
    Gatlinburg, 1966, Ed. Becker and Stelson, Academic Press
    1967. (page 833).
12. M. C. Mermaz and C. A. Whitten, Jr., private communica-
    tion, to be published.
13. B. H. Wildenthal and E. Newman, Phys. Rev. 167 1027 (1968).
14. G. M. Crawley and G. T. Garvey, Phys. Lett. 19 228 (1965).
15. G. M. Crawley and G. T. Garvey, Phys. Rev. 160 981 (1967).
16. P. W. M. Glaudemans, G. Wiechers and P. J. Brussaard,
    Nucl. Phys. 56 548 (1964).
17. M. C. Mermaz, C. W. Whitten, to be published.
18. J. C. Hardy, D. J. Skyrme, (S7) 701, Proceedings of the
    Conference on Isobaric Spin in Nuclear Physics, Talla-
    hassee, March 1966, Academic Press.
19. G. M. Crawley and G. T. Harvey, Phys. Rev. 167 1070
    (1968).
20. B. H. Wildenthal, P. W. M. Glaudemans, E. C. Halbert and
    J. B. McGrary, Bull. Am. Phys. Soc. 12 48 (1967). Another
    preprint by these authors available.
21. A. Arima, The Structure of 2s-1d Shell Nuclei, to be
    published.
22. M. R. Gunye and C. S. Warke, Phys. Rev. 156 1087 (1967).
23. B. Mottelson, The Many-Body Problem, Ecole d'Ete de
    Physique Theorique des Houches, John Wiley, Inc., 1958.
24. G. R. Satchler, Ann. Phys. (N. Y.) 3 275 (1958).
25. H. E. Gove, K. H. Purser, J. J. Schwartz, W. P. Alford,
    D. Cline, Annual 1967 Report of the Nuclear Structure
    Laboratory of the University of Rochester (UR-NSRL-PR1),
    unpublished.

DISCUSSION

KOLTUN: The procedure for extracting the spectroscopic factor
in the case of Hartree-Fock: you say that you don't believe
that the theory is adiabatic but you use an analysis which is
based on adiabatic approximations. Isn't that true? Well the
question could be phrased a different way. Would you get
very different spectroscopic factors if you used projected
Hartree-Fock from the C_j's that you quote?

RIPKA: I think one should always occasionally check whether
the projected wave functions give the same result as in the
adiabatic approximation. In the case of magnetic moments and
in the case of quadrupole moments the agreement between the
two is often very good. I have not seen any extensive calculations of single particle strengths except in the case of
neon which I believe is published in the work of Harvey. I
think the kind of disagreement we were discussing in the
aluminum region is probably beyond disagreement due to the
non-adiabaticity. But I admit that one should worry about
this.

GEDCKE: I would like to offer a word of caution about using
spectroscopic factors from the stripping reactions on Si^{28}.
Several groups at the University of Alberta spent some time
analyzing the (d,d) elastic scattering, (d,n) and (d,p)
reactions on Si^{28} in the energy range of 4 to 6 MeV. The
most depressing result that came out of this work is that all
three reactions show very violent fluctuations in the yield
curve as a function of energy. If anything is apparent from
the study, it is quite clear that one should be rather
skeptical about using straightforward DWBA analysis for this
nucleus. Consequently, the resulting spectroscopic factors
may not have too much significance.

RIPKA: Are you a theorist or an experimentalist?

GEDCKE: An experimentalist.

RIPKA: Well I'm very glad to hear an experimentalist doubt-
ing the values of spectroscopic factors. Now, I think one
can use the spectroscopic factors in a manner which is
systematic. If it works well in say the neon and the mag-
nesium region and the same analysis fails in silicon, then
perhaps it does mean something. If I had only one number
for one transition, I think that I would certainly be exposed
to your critism of the DWBA analysis. It seems to work
surprisingly well in some other nuclei where we understand
the coupling better.

GEDCKE: Some of the most sensitive parameters in the DWBA
calculations come from the (d,d) elastic scattering and if
one isn't very careful about choosing the energy at which
the reaction is done he finds that the elastic scattering
parameters vary quite a bit for Si^{28}, depending on where
these cross section fluctuations exist. Some of the spectroscopic factors that have come up in the past, I believe, have
been done only at one energy without too much care about the
yield curves. Now if you look at cases such as the stripping
reactions on Ca^{40}, the problem is not nearly so severe. The
yield curves look very smooth and you can believe a simple
direct reaction is all that is going on, and consequently the
spectroscopic factors in that sort of a case have a bit more
meaning.

RIPKA: Yes, that's very interesting. There is, nonetheless,
in the data I have given here one confirmation which dis-
qualifies the strong coupling [assumption]. This is in the
(d,t) experiment made at Yale with 21 MeV deuterons and the
Oak Ridge (t,He^3) experiment made at higher deuteron energy.
As far as the transition to the ground state is concerned
the two are comparable enough.

GEDCKE: I think there will be some more information
published shortly--I think at the Washington meeting-- on
this reaction.

RIPKA: Yes, very good.

PURSER: I think I should clarify that we actually did our
experiment at 20 MeV and we took an excitation function
between 16 and 20 MeV.

LEGG: I will say also that I don't think your variation in
spectroscopic factors is a function necessarily of fluctuations in the curves. We published some work some time ago
on Cr^{52} showing that even though our excitation curves in
(d,d) and (p,p) were rather smooth, the distorted waves did
not do a good job of fitting around 5 MeV although they
seemed to do a good job of fitting when we went up to 10 and
12 MeV bombarding energy. In other words, even a yield curve
is not sufficient but any DW analysis at 5 MeV is probably
suspect.

PHILLIPS: There's a class of information which neither you
nor Dr. Halbert this morning compared with your theories,
and these are beta decay matrix elements which are often
very accurately known and more accurately than some of the
things we have been talking about. And, these can sometimes
show large discrepancies with some of these calculations.

I'm thinking in particular of one I calculated using the
Glaudemanns, Brussaard et al. wave functions of the mass 30
system. This was the beta decay of the ground state of S^{30}
to the first excited 1+ [0+?] of P^{30}, and it is, if I did the
calculation correctly, in gross disagreement with the predictions of the Glaudemanns wave functions.

RIPKA: Yes, well that's very interesting. Now, you see, I
think you're talking about the Glaudemanns, Brussaard, Wiechers
wave functions. These wave functions eliminate the $d_{5/2}$
state. I think whenever one computes a quantity one should
first ask the question: what will first order perturbation
theory do with the operator I'm considering? And, you will
find then, of course, that this operator being the M1 operator
will not link the $s_{1/2}$ and the $d_{3/2}$ states but on the contrary
will produce particle-hole excitations between the $d_{5/2}$ and
$d_{3/2}$ states. And in S^{33} it seems to be a very important process which will give you the experimental deviation from the
Schmidt line. Now, I just wonder whether you wouldn't get a
much better agreement by throwing out most of the Glaudemanns
configurations except the leading ones and adding those
particle-hole excitations which are produced by the magnetic
moment operator itself. It seems to me this would be the
first thing to try in that case.

PHILLIPS: I'm just pointing out that beta decay matrix
elements are often very accurately known whereas the spectroscopic factors are dependent on parameters that sometimes are
not well known.

RIPKA: Yes, I agree entirely with you that this is probably
a more significant test of a wave function than the spectroscopic factor.

IV. a. SU(3) SYMMETRY AND REALISTIC INTERACTIONS[*]

J. Flores

(Read by M. de Llano)

Instituto de Fisica, Universidad de Mexico

We have developed[1]) a computer program to construct the
wave functions for a system of particles in the 2s-1d shell,
and the matrix elements with respect to them of an arbitrary
two-body interaction. The wave functions are classified in
the SU(3) scheme, that is they correspond to a definite orbital symmetry [h] and a given irreducible representation
(λ, μ) of the SU(3) group; total orbital angular momentum,
total spin and isospin are also good quantum numbers of the
states so constructed.

In the calculations reported here we have used as the
two-body interaction the effective interaction derived by Kuo
and Brown[2]), including core polarization.

In Fig. 1a we show the results of the calculation Ne^{20}
using the complete four particle basis, and in Figs. 1b and 1c
we analyze the effect in the spectrum of the basis truncation;
in Fig. 1b we restrict the model space by the orbital symmetry
of the wave functions and in Fig. 1c by taking into account
kets such that the SU(3) indices (λ, μ) correspond to represen-
tations higher than $(\lambda_0, \mu_0) = (3,1)$ only. In both cases, as
can be seen from the figures the spectrum is not affected by
the truncation. The experimental spectrum is shown in Fig.
1d, and we can see that the ground state is very well reproduced. However, at about 6 MeV of excitation energy there
appear two experimental $J = 2^+$ levels, of which only one is
obtained in our calculation; this could be a manifestation
of core excitation, which we have not included.

The fact that the truncation of the basis has almost no
effect on the spectrum of Ne^{20} seems to indicate that the
degree of violation of both orbital and SU(3) symmetry by the
realistic interaction is low in this case. This is shown in
Fig. 2, for the ground state of Ne^{20}; in this figure we plot
the wave function representing it by the square of the overlap it has with each possible SU(3) ket of 4 particles in the
2s-1d shell. We can see that the intensity of the leading
SU(3) state is of the order of 81% and that the contribution
from lower weight SU(3) states is very low.

We analyze now the case of O^{20} (T = 2). In Fig. 3 we
show the energy levels, comparing in Fig. (3a) and Fig. (3d)

[*]Work supported by Comision Nacional de Energia Nuclear,
Mexico.

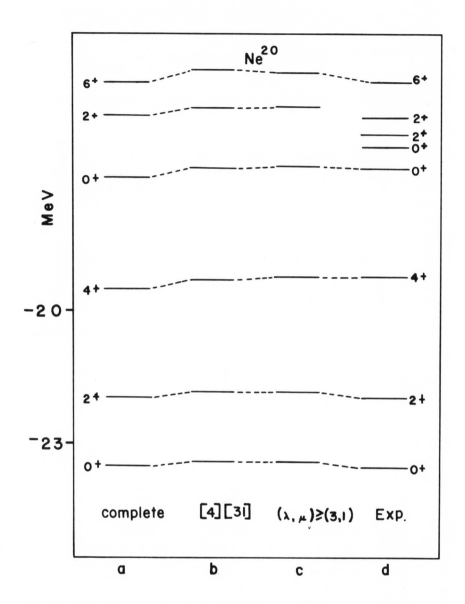

Fig. 1. Energy levels of Ne^{20}.

the results of the complete shell-model calculation with experimental energies. The spectrum is now not well reproduced,
since the second 0^+ as well as second 2^+ levels are predicted
too low. Furthermore, as can be seen from Figs. (3b) and (3c)
the truncation of the basis has drastic effects on the energy
levels in this case; we consider, therefore, that the truncation according to the SU(3) scheme is not justified in this
case.

We have also obtained results for O^{19} and F^{19}. Again
the spectrum of F^{19} is very well reproduced and the truncation along the SU(3) scheme is possible. On the other hand,
the case of O^{19} is similar to the O^{20} nucleus; first of all,
our results do not reproduce correctly the experimental spectrum and secondly, no truncation is possible without altering
the results seriously.

It seems, therefore, that the restriction to a few SU(3)
states is correct only for low values of total isospin and
that in these cases the experimental energies are very well
reproduced by the Kuo-Brown interaction.

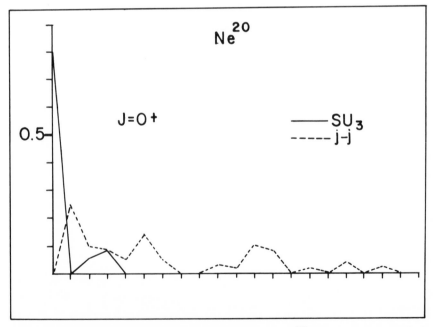

Fig. 2. Ground state wave function of Ne^{20} represented by
the square of the overlap of the physical wave function with
the SU(3) states (solid lines) and j-j coupling states (dotted
lines). These states are ordered by increasing energy of a
           Q^2 force and spin-orbit coupling, respectively.

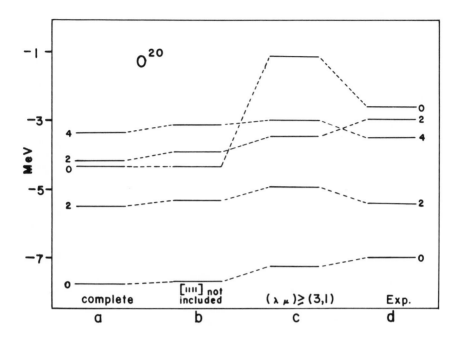

Fig. 3.   Energy levels of O^{20}.

REFERENCES

1.   J. Flores and R. Perez. Phys. Letters <u>26B</u> 55 (1967).

2.   T. T. S. Kuo and G. E. Brown, Nucl. Phys. <u>85</u> 87 (1966).

IV. B. Gamma-Ray Spectroscopy in Light Nuclei:
Na^{22}, an Example

J.W. Olness

Brookhaven National Laboratory

I. INTRODUCTION

The success achieved by the collective model in the description of nuclei in the s-d shell—which began approximately 13 years ago with the observation (1) of the rotational character of the A=25 mirror nuclei Al^{25} and Mg^{25}—has certainly had a happy influence on theoretical and experimental progress towards our understanding of the nuclear structure. This is not to say that the collective model has represented the only point of interest as is evidenced by the concurrent interest and progress reported at this conference in obtaining a satisfactory shell-model description of these nuclei. But the Nilsson (2) model has provided the experimentalist with a convenient scheme for the sorting of the experimentally observed levels in terms of rotational bands based on the intrinsic (single-particle) states, and its predictions have further served as a useful guide in studies of the higher-lying levels and the γ-ray transitions linking them. The array of experimental evidence thus obtained, together with the systematics evident from the collective model interpretation of these nuclei, has also led to significant refinements and progress in the descriptions provided by the shell-model and more recently by the SU_3 version of this latter model.

At the time the present work on Na^{22} was begun, (3) some 3 years ago, there was already a considerable body of experimental evidence on nuclei of A=20, 23, 25...etc., pointing to a collective character for these nuclear systems, and leading one to expect therefore a collective character also for the A=22 system of which the odd-odd nucleus Na^{22} is the $T_z=0$ member. Because of difficulties attached to the experimental investigation of its structure, not much was known about the character of the Na^{22} levels beyond the first two excited states, although the excitation energies were well established from particle-transfer studies. (4) Some information on the T=1 levels was available from previous studies (4) of Ne^{22} ($T_z=+1$), but information on the T=0 levels must necessarily come from the Na^{22} studies.

The immediate problem therefore was that of obtaining an experimental description of the Na^{22} level structure, with sufficient completeness and certainty that the resultant experimental description could serve as a basis for a comparison with various model predictions.

Fortunately, there are available a variety of recently developed techniques which are applicable to the particular problem. While some have been possible only within the past-half decade, they have nevertheless been so widely used as to become standard at many laboratories—in particular those represented by the speakers at this conference and also at the two host institutions. Therefore it should not be necessary to describe the particular experimental measurements in detail, since such descriptions have already been presented at this conference and the methods are given in detail in the literature.

Rather I would like to illustrate by example the advantages to be gained by a broad application of some techniques of γ-ray spectroscopy to the study of a particular nucleus: Na^{22}. Most of the examples are drawn (as a matter of convenience) from work done at Brookhaven during the past three years in various collaborations with E.K. Warburton, A.R. Poletti, and P. Paul. For completeness I have included as one example work of A. Gallmann et al. (5) on Mg^{22} positron decay to states of Na^{22}. And also, the work of other groups on correlation studies (6) and lifetime measurements (7,8) which are incorporated in the final summary of the Na^{22} level scheme should be noted.

Levels of Na^{22} of excitation energy less than 5.78 MeV are bound against particle emission and may decay only by electromagnetic transitions to lower-lying states. We have therefore used reactions such as $F^{19}(\alpha,n)Na^{22}$ and $Ne^{20}(He^3,p)Na^{22}$ to form Na^{22} in its various excited states, and have specifically undertaken the following measurements in the investigation of these states:
1. High resolution Ge(Li) measurements of γ-spectra.
2. Beta decay (to states of Na^{22}).
3. Angular correlation studies:
   a. Simple γ-ray distributions,
   b. Particle-γ correlations,
   c. γ-γ correlations.
4. Linear polarization of gamma rays.
5. Doppler shift attenuation measurement of lifetimes.
6. Magnetic moment measurements (g-factor).

All involve the study of electromagnetic transitions linking various states of Na^{22}, and in the case of β-decay, linking states of Na^{22} with another member of the T=1 triad which includes Ne^{22} and Mg^{22}. While it was not our initial intention to apply all of these techniques, it was nevertheless convenient in obtaining a description

of the level scheme to be able to switch from one technique
to another, using as a criterion that the particular method
selected should provide (as simply as possible) a unique
determination of the quantities of interest—spins,
parities, mixing ratios, etc.

Of course, this list omits the particle-transfer
studies which provide additional independent information
on the excitation energies E_{ex}, and for the stronger transitions unique determinations of spin-parity assignments
J^{π} for the final state. Unfortunately, these studies are
frequently restricted by our limited knowledge of the
pertinent reaction mechanism, and hence orbital angular
momentum assignments are sometimes suspect—particularly
for those states formed only weakly. Thus it is clearly
desirable to check the latter results by techniques in
which the interpretations do not depend upon the reaction
mechanism.

II. EXPERIMENTAL INVESTIGATIONS

The pertinent low-lying levels of Na^{22} are shown
schematically in Fig. 1. The indicated branching ratios,
excitation energies, and spin-parity assignments are taken
from an intermediate report (3) of the work I will
summarize here, and incorporates also such previously
available information as summarized therein. The
$Ne^{20}(He^3,p)Na^{22}$ (Q = + 5.783 MeV) reaction was selected
for use in the particle-gamma triple-correlation studies,
while the endoergic reaction $F^{19}(\alpha,n)Na^{22}$ (Q = - 1.951
MeV) was found to be more suitable for those studies
where the outgoing particle was not observed. The
$Na^{23}(He^3,\alpha)Na^{22}$ reaction was investigated briefly, but
because of numerous strongly competing reactions such as
(He^3,n) and (He^3,p) the resultant complex spectra were
more difficult to interpret, and this reaction was not used.

These measurements were carried out using doubly-
ionized beams of He^3 and He^4 of intensities ranging from
20-100 nA and targets (in the form of Ne^{20} gas or CaF_2
films) of the order of 50-1000 µg/cm^2 thickness. Within
this range of target thickness and beam intensity
(easily achieved with the BNL 4-MeV accelerator) the
reaction yields were quite sufficient for the various
coincidence and singles experiments. The efficiency of
data accumulation was considerably enhanced by the use
of a 16384-channel 2-parameter analyzer which allowed the
assignation of up to 1024 channels for a given spectrum
(subject of course to the restriction $N_x \cdot N_y = 16384$).
Thus several coincidence relationships could be studied
in a single run. The resolving times of the coincidence
circuit (2 $\tau \sim$ 100 nsec) generally provided an upper
limit on the useful reaction yield which could be used

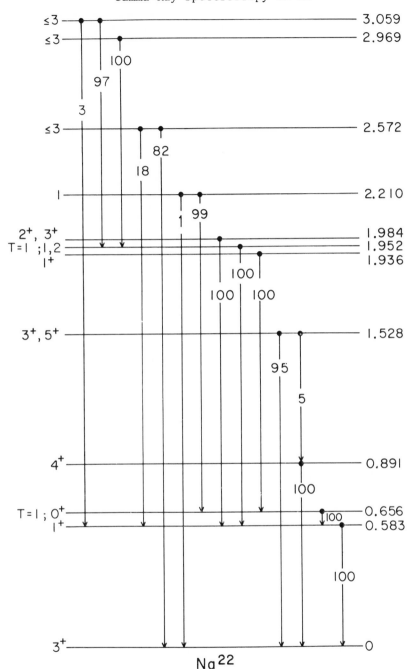

Fig. 1. Level diagram for Na^{22} showing major decay modes for levels of E_{ex} < 3.1 MeV. The spin-parity and isotopic-spin assignments are from an intermediate report (Ref. 3) based primarily on the p-γ correlation measurements.

in the coincidence studies, while the Ge(Li) measurements
were by choice restricted to count rates of $\leq$ 2000 cts/sec
in order that the intrinsically good resolution of the
detector ($\triangle E$ < 4 keV) be not spoiled by pulse pile-up
problems.

A. Ge(Li) Studies of Gamma Ray Spectra: Beta Decay

One of the most useful pieces of experimental information was obtained from high-resolution Ge(Li) studies
of the γ rays from the above reactions. Because of the
excellent resolutions obtainable with the Ge(Li) detectors,
the singles spectra provided accurate determinations of
transition energies and subsequently excitation energies,
typically with errors of < 1 keV. This is illustrated in
Fig. 2 which shows portions of spectra obtained in the
$F^{19}(\alpha,n\gamma)Na^{22}$ studies at a He^4 bombarding energy of 7.0
MeV, using an 8-cc Ge(Li) detector with a resolution (FWHM)
of 4.0 keV. Transitions from the triplet of levels in
Na^{22} at $E_{ex} \sim 1.9$ MeV are clearly well-resolved, and
illustrate the principal decay modes of these levels.
From the absence of peaks corresponding to alternate decay
routes, upper limits on branching ratios were obtained.
The initial and final state excitation energies are
indicated, as well as the measured transition energies
based on internal calibration lines. Measurements at two
angles have helped to sort out the Na^{22} lines from those
originating from the competing $F^{19}(\alpha,\alpha'\gamma)F^{19}$ reaction,
and have also provided information on the Doppler shifts
of these transitions, as will be discussed later. From
data such as these values of E_γ and subsequently E_{ex} were
determined (3) for all of the 11 excited states of
E_{ex} < 3.1 MeV, with errors in the latter values of < 1
keV.

Two-parameter coincidence measurements, using a 3x3-in.
NaI(Tℓ) detector and the Ge(Li) detector, were also
carried out to search for weak cascade transitions. In
this case 32 channels were allotted for the NaI(Tℓ)
detector to cover the primary de-excitation γ rays from
the low-lying Na^{22} levels, and 512 channels were allotted
to the pertinent region of higher-energy γ rays viewed in
the Ge(Li) detector. From the resultant matrix of
512x32-channels of coincidence data values for, or upper
limits on, the intensity of weak cascade transitions not
easily observable in the direct Ge(Li) singles spectrum
were obtained. Similar measurements were later undertaken
(9) to study states up to $E_{ex} \sim 5$ MeV.

In conclusion, it should be noted that while the close
spacing of the doublet levels at 0.583 and 0.657 MeV and
of the triplet levels at $\sim$1.9 MeV represented a severe
stumbling block to previous investigations of the Na^{22}

decay scheme, which used NaI(Tℓ) detectors (resolution 40-100 keV), the interpretation based on data such as that of Fig. 2 is quite unambiguous, due to the excellent resolution of the Ge(Li) detector.

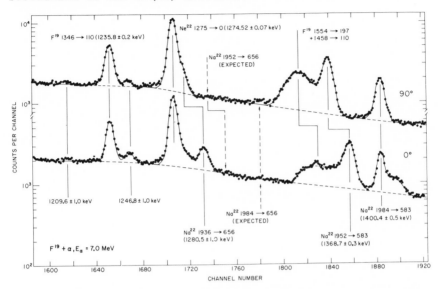

Fig. 2. Portions of Ge(Li) spectra showing γ rays from the F^{19}(α,nγ)Na^{22} reaction measured at E$_\alpha$ = 7.0 MeV. The indicated transition energies were obtained from the 90° spectra; the 0° spectrum illustrates the influence of the nuclear lifetimes on the Doppler-shifted line shapes.

B.   Beta Decay to States of Na^{22}

Partial results of a study by Gallmann et al. (5) of the positron decay of Mg^{22} to excited states of Na^{22} are shown in Fig. 3. Mg^{22} (half-life = 4 sec) was formed by the Ne^{20}(He^3,n)Mg^{22} reaction, and the delayed γ spectrum showing the deexcitation γ rays from states of Na^{22} populated in the positron decay of Mg^{22} were measured with an 8-cc Ge(Li) detector. Evident in Fig. 3 is a peak at 1279.8 ± 0.2 keV due to deexcitation of the Na^{22} 1.936-MeV level, which from the previous Ge(Li) studies of the F^{19}(α,nγ)Na^{22} reaction is known to proceed via the 1.936 → 0.657 cascade with a branch of 100%. From the intensity of the 1280-keV γ ray relative to the 74-keV and 583-keV γ rays deexciting, respectively, the 657- and 583-keV states, branching ratios for the positron decay of Mg^{22} to the indicated final states of Na^{22} were obtained as follows: 1.936 (5.1 ± 0.4)%; 0.657 (59 ± 6)%; 0.583 (36 ± 6)%. Upper limits of < 0.35% were set on positron

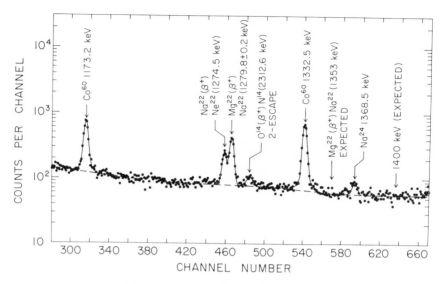

Fig. 3.   Spectrum of γ-rays obtained with an 8 cc Ge(Li)
detector of resolution 3.4 keV (FWHM), showing the 1279.8
keV γ ray resulting from deexcitation of the Na^{22} 1936 keV
level populated in the Mg^{22}(β$^+$)Na^{22} decay.

branches to all other states of Na^{22} of E$_x$ < 3.6 MeV.
Using the measured lifetime of Mg^{22}, the branch to the
1.936-MeV Na^{22} level corresponds to a log ft of 3.55 ±
0.04. Therefore the transition is <u>allowed</u>, and the spin-
parity of the 1.936-MeV level is J$^\pi$=1$^+$, since J$^\pi$=0$^+$ is
ruled out by its observed γ-decay to the J$^\pi$=0$^+$ 0.657-MeV
level.

These measurements (5), which result in a unique J$^\pi$=1$^+$
assignment for the Na^{22} 1.936 MeV level, together with the
information on the positron transitions linking Mg^{22} and
Na^{22}, were carried out through a joint effort between
laboratories at Strasbourg, France, and BNL. The results
illustrate the relative ease with which some beta-decay
studies can be performed with Ge(Li) detectors, and the
sort of information that is forthcoming. The principle
advantage obtained with the Ge(Li) detector again results
from its excellent resolution, which permits the observation of the very weak γ-ray lines which could otherwise
be lost in the complex background spectrum.

C. Angular Correlation/Polarization Studies

The analysis of the various correlation data (as well
as the linear-polarization measurements) were carried out
using the methods initiated by Warburton and Rose (10) and
developed by Litherland and Ferguson. (11) This method
utilizes the fact that the theoretical correlations may be

specified in terms of the population parameters $P(m)$ which define the alignment of the initial γ-emitting level where m, the projection on the z-axis (beam axis) of the intrinsic spin of this initial state, ranges from values $-J \leq m \leq +J$. The normalization is such that $\sum_m P(m)=1$. For the case of an unpolarized beam and polarization insensitive detectors, we have the restriction that $P(-m) \equiv P(m)$, and the correlations may be specified in terms of the ratios $P(m)/P(m=0)$, which are J-1 in number. These ratios are then included as additional parameters to be determined from the theoretical fits to the experimental data, together with the unknown spins J of the initial and final states linked by the γ-ray transitions and the mixing ratios x $[(L+1)/L]$ specifying the mixing of multipoles of order L+1 and L (i.e., quadrupole/dipole etc.).

In principle the γ-γ correlation studies represent the more powerful technique, since one may readily measure the independent correlations corresponding to the seven different "Octant Geometries" of Litherland and Ferguson (11). One therefore obtains as "knowns" seven sets of the correlation coefficients a_2 and a_4 which is generally more than sufficient to allow a unique determination of the unknown quantum numbers describing the alignment of the initial state, the spins of the states linked by the γ-transitions, together with the mixing ratios of these transitions. (Here the a_ν are the coefficients determined from an even-order Legendre polynomial fit to the experimental data, normalized so that $a_0 = 1$.)

In contrast, a given particle-γ correlation (measured in a colinear geometry) provides only one set of coefficients (a_2 and a_4) which will in general not be sufficient to determine all of these unknown quantities, unless additional restrictive information is included, such as that which would be provided by the measurement (if possible) of the particle-γ correlation for another γ ray proceeding from this same initial nuclear level.

Two principal advantages accrue to the particle-γ coincidence measurements: (1) The excellent resolution of presently available solid-state particle detectors results in a sharp identifiable peak for the various particle groups leading to the initial γ-emitting levels, which permits a convenient sorting of the particle-γ coincidence spectra. (2) Measurements utilizing a colinear geometry (i.e., particles detected on the beam axis) restrict the magnetic substates which may be populated to $m \leq I_1+s_1+s_2$, where I_1,s_1,s_2 are respectively the intrinsic spins of the target nucleus, projectile, and outgoing (detected) particle. For the Ne^{20}(He^3,p)Na^{22} reaction, we thus have the restriction $m \leq (0+1/2+1/2)=1$; i.e., $P(m) = 0$ for $m > 1$. Therefore one has only one unknown in the p-γ correlation studies: the ratio

$P(1)/P(0)$, which greatly simplifies the analysis.   The particle-γ correlations were measured using the $Ne^{20}(He^3,p\gamma)Na^{22}$ reaction, while the $F^{19}(\alpha,n\gamma)Na^{22}$ reaction was used for the γ-γ triple-correlation measurements as well as the γ-ray angular distribution and linear polarization measurements.

The general theory of these measurements is given in considerable detail in Litherland and Ferguson (11) and also Poletti and Warburton. (12) A presentation of the method has also been given by F.W. Prosser, Jr., at a previous conference (13). The computer implemented methods for the reduction of data, as well as the details of our measurements on Na^{22}, have also been given in the literature (3,9,14,15). At present therefore we choose to illustrate the general approach by examining the results obtained specifically in the investigation of the 1.528-MeV fourth-excited state of Na^{22}, which has employed all of these techniques.

1. Angular Distribution Measurements

Figure 4 shows the angular distributions measured (3) in the $F^{19}(\alpha,n\gamma)Na^{22}$ reaction at a bombarding energy of E_α=5.48 MeV. Data were acquired with an 8-cc Ge(Li) detector at a source-detector distance of ~10 cm, for a net running time per point of ~1 hour. The solid curves show least-squares fits to the data of the form $W(\theta) = A_o(1+a_2P_2(\theta)+a_4P_4(\theta))$. The distributions are identified in Fig. 3 by giving the initial and final states in Na^{22} between which the transitions occur. In these cases we are not prepared to describe the mechanism producing the initial state (either directly in the (α,n) reaction or by cascade transitions from higher lying levels) and since there is not sufficient information in the individual distributions to ascertain the alignment, no detailed analysis is possible. However, from the complexity of the angular distributions, one has rigorously for the 2.211-, 1.952-, and 1.936-MeV levels the restriction $J \geqslant 1$. For the 1.984-, 1.528-, and 0.891-MeV levels one has the restriction $J \geqslant 2$, with the further information that the transitions deexciting these states have components of at least quadrupole character; i.e., $L \geqslant 2$. (We note that the measurement of angular distributions for two or more γ-rays deexciting the same level may, in some cases, be sufficient to determine not only the population parameters but also the character of the deexcitation transitions. An example is given in Ref. 16 for the 2.57-MeV level.)

2. Proton-Gamma Correlation Measurements

A series of 4 proton-γ correlation measurements in the

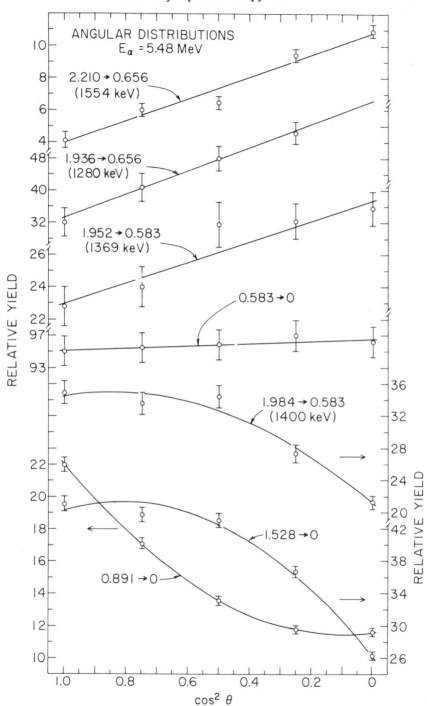

Fig. 4. Angular distributions of γ-rays from F^{19}(α,nγ)Na^{22}
measured at E$_\alpha$ = 5.48 MeV.

$Ne^{20}(He^3,p\gamma)Na^{22}$ reaction were carried out (3,9) for He^3
bombarding energies in the range 5-7 MeV, with the energy
and range of 2-parameter analysis being selected for the
particular region of excitation energies in Na^{22} ranging
up to $E_{ex} \sim 5$ MeV. Figure 5 shows a portion of the two-
parameter data measured at $E_{He^3} = 5.65$ MeV, illustrating
the proton spectra measured in coincidence with γ-rays
of energy > 550 keV. The various particle groups are
identified according to the Na^{22} excitation energies (in
keV). Clearly the net resolution obtained with this
particle detector (~40 keV) and target (thickness ~50 keV)
is insufficient to resolve the triplet of states at ~1.9-

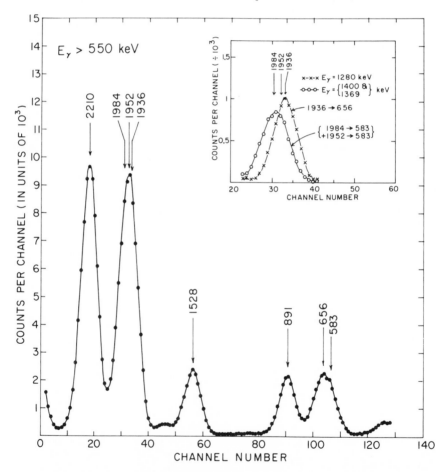

Fig. 5. Partial results of a two-parameter analysis of p-
coincidence spectra from $Ne^{20}(He^3,p\gamma)Na^{22}$ at $E(He^3) = 5.65$
MeV. The main plot shows the proton spectra coincident with
γ rays of energy $E_\gamma > 0.5$ MeV, while the insert illustrates
a partial decomposition of the ~1.9-MeV triplet peak.

MeV excitation energy. In this case however the resolution
of the 3x3-in. NaI(Tℓ) detector is sufficient·to resolve
the 1280-keV transition (1.936-MeV state) from those of
1400 and 1369 keV from the other members of the 1.9-MeV
triplet, as indicated by the partial decomposition of
the proton groups indicated in the insert.

Figure 6 shows the γ spectra measured in coincidence
with the proton groups leading to the 1.528-MeV and 2.210-
MeV levels. From these data, after corrections for
possible p-γ correlation effects, one computes branching
ratios for the 1.528 $\rightarrow$ 0 and 1.528 $\rightarrow$ 0.891 transitions
of 95.5 $\pm$ 1.2 and 4.5 $\pm$ 1.2% respectively. Similar data
for the 2.21-MeV level indicate the principal deexcitation
is to the 0.657-MeV second-excited state, (99 $\pm$ 1)%, and
a possible weak branch, (1 $\pm$ 1)%, to the ground state.
Two-parameter data similar to that shown in Figs. 5 and 6
were acquired at this bombarding energy for five angles
of observation: θ_γ=0º, 30º, 45º, 60º, and 90º. A least-
squares fit to the resultant data on the relative intensity
of the 1.528 $\rightarrow$ 0 transition, yields the results: W(θ) =
A$_0$[1+0.55 P$_2$(cosθ) - 0.23 P$_4$(cosθ)] . Figure 7 shows the
results of a χ^2-analysis of these correlation data in an
attempt to determine the J of the initial state and the
(L+1)/L mixing of the ground state transition. Here χ^2,
representing the goodness-of-fit,is plotted as a function
of x, the mixing of the lowest two allowed multipoles in
the 1.528 $\rightarrow$ 0 transition for the various assumed values J
indicated for the spin of the initial state. The abscissa
is actually given in terms of arctan x, corresponding to
the range - $\infty \leq$ x $\leq$ + ∞ . These results were obtained
through a computer program which fits the correlation data
for discrete values of x in the above range; the population
parameters P(0) and P(1) are treated as variables in this
fitting procedure. From probability tables we see that
the probability (for a correct solution) that χ^2 > 8.0 is
only 0.1%. Thus we reject possible assignments J=2 or 4,
since for all values of x we find χ^2 is greater than this
limit. For J=5, the results are consistent with x $\sim$ 0,
the expected value for a 5 $\rightarrow$ 3 transition. For J=3, the
most probable solution for the mixing ratio is x=
-(1.36 $\pm$ 0.18), although the region allowed by the
0.1% limit includes x=0; i.e., pure dipole emission.

These correlation results have thus placed a rigorous
restriction on the spin of the 1.528-MeV state: J=3 or 5,
and for either possibility have defined the amplitude of
the quadrupole component in the 1.528 $\rightarrow$ 0 transition.
One would also like to know the relative quadrupole
strengths for the members of the 1.528 $\rightarrow$ 0.891 $\rightarrow$ 0
cascade, since these states are thought to be (in inverse
order) the 3$^+$, 4$^+$, 5$^+$, members of the K=0 rotational band.

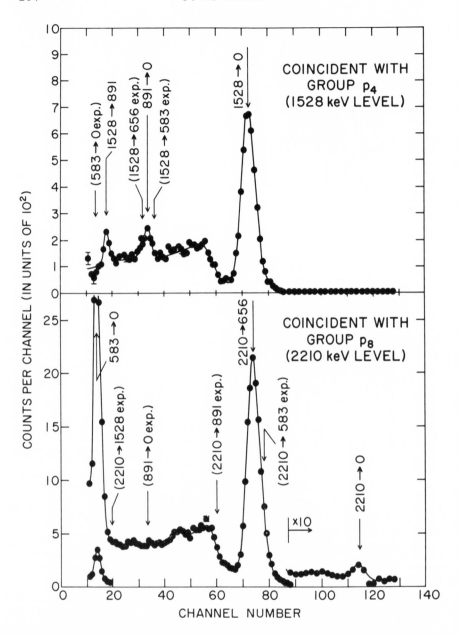

Fig. 6. Spectra of γ-rays from $Ne^{20}(He^3,p\gamma)Na^{22}$ measured in coincidence with proton groups P_4 and P_8 populating respectively the 1.528- and 2.211-MeV levels of Na^{22}. These data are part of the two-parameter spectrum illustrated also in Fig. 5.

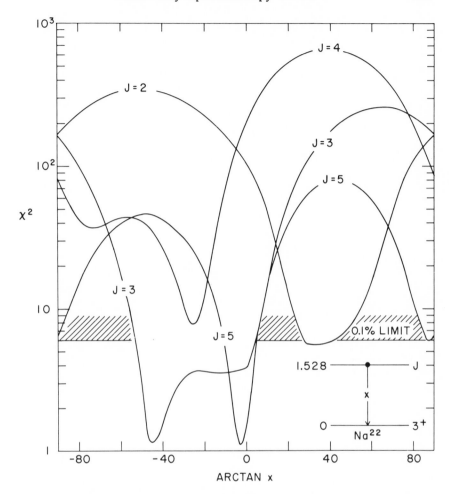

Fig. 7. Results of an analysis of p-γ correlations for the
Na^{22} 1.528-MeV level illustrating the goodness-of-fit for
various assumed values for J, the spin of the initial level.
Here χ^2 is plotted as a function of the (L+1)/L mixing in
the deexcitation transition. Clearly only J=3 or 5 are
allowed from these results.

As is evident from Fig. 5 however, the cascade intensities
are too weak for a definitive analysis of their angular
distributions: the desired information was gotten more
easily from an analysis of γ-γ triple correlations.
        Fortunately, not all of the correlation data were
so difficult to interpret. For example, there can be no
mixing in the decay of the 2.211-MeV level to the 0$^+$ 0.657-
MeV level (see Fig. 6). Fits to the measured correlation
data for assumed spins J=1, 2, 3 yielded values of χ^2
of 1.4, 160, and 214, thus determining uniquely J=1 for the
2.211 MeV level.

Since the p-γ coincidence data show all of the major
transitions resulting from decay of the initial level, these
data were particularly useful for determining the branching
ratios of the principal decay modes. These results,
combined with the Ge(Li) singles and also γ-γ coincidence
measurements, provide the decay scheme shown in Fig. 1,
which illustrates the origin of the transitions discussed
in the next subsections.

3. Measurements of γ-γ Triple Correlations

The $F^{19}(\alpha,n\gamma)Na^{22}$ reaction was used (15) at an α
bombarding energy of 4.9 MeV to study the correlation of
the 1.528 → 0.891 → 0 cascade γ rays. Two 3x3-in. NaI(Tl)
detectors were used, in a two-parameter analysis, to
record the coincidence counting rates, with one detector
fixed in the horizontal plane at $\theta_1=90°$, $\emptyset_1=0°$, while the
second moving detector traced out the three edges of the
Octant Geometry of Litherland and Ferguson (11); i.e.
($\emptyset_2=180°$, $0° \leq \theta_2 \leq 90°$), ($0° \leq \emptyset_2 \leq 90°$, $\theta_2=90°$), and
($\emptyset_2=90°$, $90° \leq \theta_2 \leq 0°$). Since the data were recorded in
a 2-parameter analysis, one obtains the correlation results
for 5 independent geometries from a single traversal of the
octant. Figure 8 shows the measured correlation data,
where the geometries are labelled according to Litherland
and Ferguson. The solid curves show a fit to the data for
the indicated level spins and multipole mixing ratios. In
these fits the 1.528-MeV level has been assigned $J^\pi=5^+$, on
the basis of the linear polarization results to be discussed
later. Since all of the level spins are known, it was
necessary to determine only the mixing ratios x_1 and x_2
for the two members of the cascade. This was done by
constructing a contour map of χ^2 (representing the
goodness-of-fit) versus each of the two parameters x_1 and
x_2. The minima provide the unique solutions indicated in
the figure for both. We thus see that the 5^+ → 4^+ → 3^+
cascade proceeds by predominantly E2 transitions in
competition with the (pure E2) 5^+ → 3^+ ground-state
crossover.

Similar measurements were carried out to study the
cascades from the 2.97- and 3.06-MeV levels of Na^{22}. Both
levels decay via transitions to the 1.95-MeV level. The
p-γ correlation studies were unable to determine the spins
of these three levels, but when combined with the γ-γ
correlation results determine uniquely the assignments
$J=3$ (2.97-MeV level), and $J=2$ (3.06-MeV level), and
$J=2$ (1.95-MeV level).

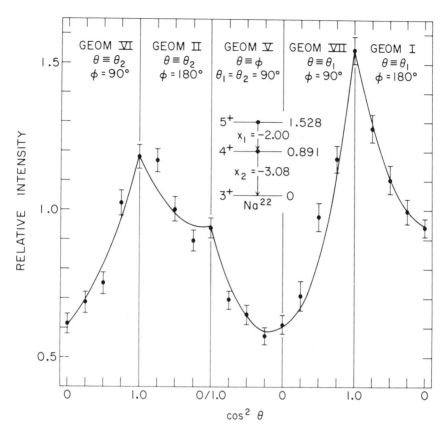

Fig. 8. Results of the γ-γ triple correlation measurement for the Na^{22} 1.528 → 0.891 → 0 cascade. The experimental points are shown for the five indicated geometries as explained in the text and in Refs. (11,15). The solid curve is the fit to these data for the spin values and mixing ratios indicated in the insert.

4. Linear Polarization of γ-Rays

The observation of significant anisotropies in the γ rays from the F^{19}(α,nγ)Na^{22} reaction (see Figs. 2 and 3) shows clearly that the (α,n) reaction mechanism has produced a significant alignment of the initial γ-emitting level: the magnetic substate populations are <u>not</u> equal. This is perhaps to have been expected since the states were formed in an endoergic reaction at bombarding energies only moderately above threshold, in which case one expects $\ell_n=0$ neutron emission to predominate in the (α,n) cross section. But for $\ell_n=0$ only the m=0, ± 1 substates of Na^{22} are populated. Since this is the same constraint as that imposed by the collinear geometry used in the Ne^{20}(He^{3},pγ)Na^{22} correlation measurements it is not

surprising that the γ-ray distributions measured in the
two experiments were found to be very similar. In any
event, since the initial states are aligned, one can
measure the γ-ray linear polarization to obtain additional
information on states of Na^{22} and the character of the γ-ray
transitions linking them.

The polarimeter consisted (14) of three NaI(Tℓ)
detectors which were fixed rigidly in an aluminum casting
and placed at an angle θ relative to the incident α beam.
Coincidence techniques were used to define each scattering
event, and thus determine the relative probability for
Compton scattering of the incident γ rays from the central
scattering detector into either one of the two detectors
located (a) in the reaction plane or (b) perpendicular to
the reaction plane. The degree of polarization is then
given by $P(\theta) = S(\theta)/Q$ and $S(\theta) = (N_a - N_b)/(N_a + N_b)$ where
N_a and N_b are simply the counts recorded in the two
analyzing detectors. While Q can, in principle, be
computed from the geometry of the experiment and the
theoretical Compton-scattering cross section, it was
easier to treat it as a parameter whose value was determined by measurements on γ transitions of known multi-
polarity (14).

The results of a polarization measurement on the Na^{22}
1.528 → 0 transition are shown in Fig. 9. The experimentally determined value of $P(\theta=90°)$ is shown in the
lower plot. The curves show the expected polarizations
computed for assumed spins $J^\pi=3^+$ and $J^\pi=5^+$ for the initial
state, where the alignment has been fixed by the angular
distribution measurement indicated in the upper plot. It
is thus clear that $J^\pi=3^+$ is inconsistent with these data.
Possibilities $J^\pi=3^-$ or 5^- are similarly ruled out, and
thus one has determined uniquely both the spin and
parity for the 1.528-MeV level as $J^\pi=5^+$.

The polarization apparatus was designed so that θ_γ
could be varied over the range 0°-90°, since the polarization is not always maximum at 90°. A useful approach
to the selection of an appropriate angle has been given
previously (14). Figure 10 shows the results of a
measurement for the 0.891 MeV level, in which case the
polarization effect is maximum at θ ~ 45°. The alignment
has been specified by the 0.891 → 0 distribution measurement; these results subsequently lead to an even parity
assignment for the 0.891-MeV level.

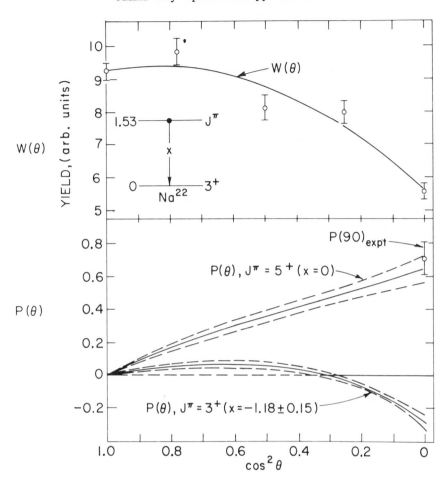

Fig. 9. Results of a linear-polarization measurement for the 1.528 → 0 γ rays from F^{19}(α,nγ)Na^{22}. The alignment is specified by the γ ray angular distribution measurements shown in the upper plot. The measured polarization P(θ=90°) leads to a Jπ=5$^+$ assignment for the 1.528-MeV level, since the possibility for a 3$^+$ assignment (as well as 3$^-$,5$^-$) is clearly ruled out.

5. Summary of Correlation/Polarization Measurements

We have considered as an example only one of the levels of Na^{22}: the 1.528-MeV level. Each of the four different experimental investigations provided (rather easily) a rigorous restriction on the quantum numbers describing the state. The important thing is that the information taken jointly results in a unique assignment of spin-parity for this level, and also determines the multipole character of the deexcitation γ rays.

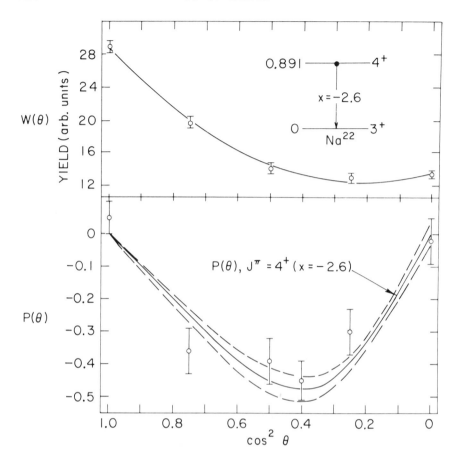

Fig. 10. Results of a determination of the linear polarization P(θ) as a function of θ for the 0.891 → 0 γ rays from
$F^{19}(\alpha,n\gamma)Na^{22}$. The experimental polarization data are well-
fitted for the assignments given in the insert, where again
the alignment is specified by the indicated distribution
measurements. These results lead to an even-parity assignment for the 0.891-MeV level.

　　Fortunately, not all of the levels required such
intensive study. Proton-γ correlation measurements were
carried out for all of the 14 levels of Na^{22} of $E_{ex} < 4$
MeV, while additional measurements were undertaken for
levels of $4 < E_{ex} < 5.1$ MeV. γ-γ triple-correlations were
carried out for the 1.528-, 2.97-, and 3.06-MeV levels,
while polarization measurements were performed only on
γ rays from the 0.891-, 1.528-, 1.937-, and 2.211-MeV
levels. Conclusions on spin-parity assignments are
summarized in Fig. 11. It is important to note that in
obtaining these conclusions, we have used the results of
the lifetime measurements (to be discussed in the following
section) together with applicable sum-rule limits (17,18)

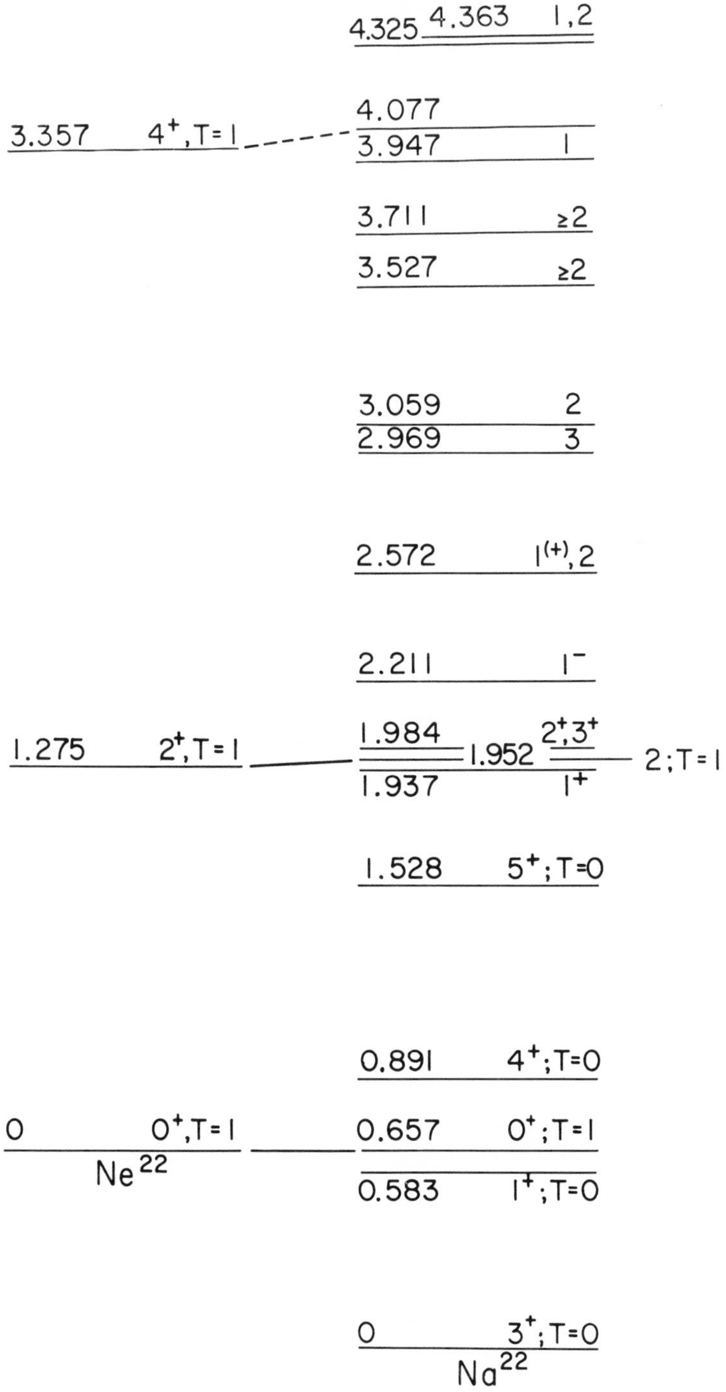

		4.325	4.363	1,2
3.357	4$^+$,T=1	4.077		
		3.947		1
		3.711		≥2
		3.527		≥2
		3.059		2
		2.969		3
		2.572		1$^{(+)}$,2
		2.211		1$^-$
1.275	2$^+$,T=1	1.984	1.952	2$^+$,3$^+$
		1.937		1$^+$
		1.528		5$^+$;T=0
		0.891		4$^+$;T=0
0	0$^+$,T=1	0.657		0$^+$;T=1
	Ne^{22}	0.583		1$^+$;T=0
		0		3$^+$;T=0
			Na^{22}	

2;T=1 (for the 1.952 level)

Fig. 11.   Summary of spin-parity and isotopic-spin assignment
for Na^{22}.   The T=1 spectrum of Ne^{22} is also shown.

to rule out possible assignments involving inordinately
large octupole or quadrupole components in the deexcitation transitions.

D. Measurements of Nuclear Lifetimes by the DSAM

Experiments such as we have just described can in
themselves provide unique determinations of J^π for the
nuclear levels, and also the branching ratios and multipole
mixing ratios (x) of the transitions connecting them. A
measurement of the lifetime of the (particle-bound) state,
through the relationship $\Gamma \cdot \tau \cong \hbar$, then allows one to
compute the <u>absolute</u> partial widths $\Gamma_{\gamma\lambda}(L)$ for the γ-decay
by competing multipoles to specific final states designated
λ. It is this latter quantity in which we are primarily
interested, since these partial widths are directly
proportional to the square of the matrix elements M(L) for
the particular multipole operator connecting the initial-
final states. As such, the experimental results permit
a further stringent testing of the applicable nuclear
model, which must not only predict the magnitude of these
matrix elements but also the relative phases of competing
multipoles.

The principal methods which would seem appropriate to
the study of lifetimes for the states which can be formed
through the types of nuclear reactions considered here
are listed in Table I, together with estimates of the
range of applicability for each. As can be seen from

Table I. Methods and estimated ranges
for measuring lifetimes of
states formed in nuclear
reactions.

Method	Range in τ (in psec)
Electronic	$\tau \gtrsim 50$
Recoil Distance	$5 \lesssim \tau \lesssim 5000$
DSAM	$0.005 \lesssim \tau \lesssim 10$

Table I there is a sufficiently good overlap that by a
proper selection of techniques one can study a very broad
range of lifetimes. With the exception of the first
excited state, for which a mean lifetime of 350 ± 3 nsec
was previously determined (4) by electronic techniques,
the excited states of Na^{22} were found to decay by dipole-
quadrupole emission with lifetimes in the range open to
measurement by the Doppler-shift attenuation method (DSAM),
which is the method we have used. We note, however,
that for some of the longer lived of these states the
Recoil Distance Method (18,19) would also be appropriate.

1. Theory of the DSAM

If the initial velocity of an excited recoil nucleus
formed in a nuclear reaction (at time t=0) is v_i, then
the γ-rays emitted at an angle θ relative to the recoil
direction may have a maximum energy, as defined by the
kinematics of the reaction, of

$$E_K = E_0 (1 + \frac{v_i}{c} \cos\theta)$$

where E_0 is the transition energy corresponding to emission
from nuclei at rest. For simplicity, we assume that the
initial recoil velocity is along the beam axis (z-axis)
and that the recoil is slowing down in a stopping medium
such that its velocity is now a function of time. For
those cases where the lifetime of the nuclear level is of
the order of the slowing down time in the stopping medium,
one then obtains a distribution of γ-ray energies, with
the energy corresponding to emission at time t being
simply

$$E = E_0 (1 + \frac{v(t)}{c} \cos\theta)$$

where θ is now measured relative to the beam axis. Since
there is sufficient experimental (as well as theoretical)
data to provide a satisfactory representation of the
slowing down process, one can subsequently describe v as
a function of t, and thus obtain the frequency distribution of recoil velocities $dN(v)/dv$ in terms of the
nuclear lifetime and the parameters describing the
slowing down process. Further, since the Doppler-shifted
energy is linear in v(t), the γ-ray spectrum may be
obtained directly from $dN(v)/dv$ by folding in the appropriate detector response function to yield the energy
distribution $dN(E)/dE$. Figure 12 shows how the Doppler-
shifted line shape varies as a function of the mean
nuclear lifetime τ . These results are from a computer
calculation appropriate for γ-ray emission from Na^{22}
nuclei slowing down in a nickel backing. (Here α is the
"characteristic stopping time" (3) for ions slowing down
in the stopping medium.) The presence of two distinct
components in these line shapes is obvious: a "stopped"
component at E_0 corresponding to γ-ray emission from
nuclei at rest [v(t) = 0] and a "fast" component
corresponding to emission from nuclei with velocities
$0 < v(t) \le v_i$, with energies in the range E_0 to E_K. For
very short lifetimes ($\tau \ll \alpha$) the intensity is all in the
fast peak at E_K, with a width σ = FWHM determined by the
detector resolution. As the assumed lifetime becomes
longer, the relative intensity of the stopped component
grows, until for $\tau \gg \alpha$ the intensity is all in the
stopped peak at E_0. The presence of these two components

in the line shape is due to the difference in the two
stopping processes which slow down the Na^{22} ions: i.e.,
in the electronic and nuclear stopping processes.

   Two somewhat different approaches (3,20,21) have been
taken in describing the slowing down process. We have used
(3,20) a semi-empirical approach based on the observation
that the specific energy loss for various combinations of
ions and stopping materials may be adequately represented
as

$$dE/dx = K_n(v/v_o)^{-1} + K_e(v/v_o) + K_3(v/v_o)^3$$

where K_n, K_e, and K_3 are parameters to be determined from
fits to experimental data, and where $v_o = c/137$. The
third term (with K_3 negative) reproduces the well-known
decrease in dE/dx for large ion velocities, as would be
obtained by interchanging the role of target and projectile
(22); for the range of ion velocities encountered in
reactions such as $F^{19}(\alpha,n\gamma)Na^{22}$, corresponding to $v_i/v_o \lesssim 2$,
the effect is negligible and we may set $K_3 = 0$. Then dE/dx
is given by the first two terms only: The second of these
is linear in v and describes the well-known electronic
stopping, which produces a continuous reduction in velocity
with no large direction changes. The first term, which is
steeply rising as $v \rightarrow 0$, describes the nuclear stopping
which is important only for small velocities where it may
produce a large and discontinuous change in both the
velocity and direction of the recoiling ion. However,
since the values for K_n are extracted from projected range
data, the discontinuous nature of the process should be
approximately accounted for in the values thus obtained (3).

   Specific expressions for Doppler shifted line shape
dN(E)/dE have been given (3,20) in terms of the ratio
Kn/Ke and the "characteristic stopping time" defined as
$\alpha = M v_o/K_e\rho$, where M is the moving ion mass and ρ is the
density of the stopping medium. The important thing to
note here is that the equations predict that the line shape
shall have the two components as illustrated in Fig. 12.
The fast component represents essentially the line shape
that would be obtained if there were no nuclear stopping
($K_n = 0$). The effect of the <u>discontinuous</u> nuclear stopping
mechanism is to remove a fraction of the low-velocity
ions from the tail of this distribution by suddenly
stopping them: these ions subsequently decay to produce the
stopped peak at E_o. Expressions for the relative intensity
of these two components as a function of the nuclear lifetime have also been given (20).

   Also shown in Fig. 12 are the values of the attenuation
factors $F(\tau)$ for each shape where

$$F(\tau) = (\bar{E} - E_o)/\Delta E_K$$

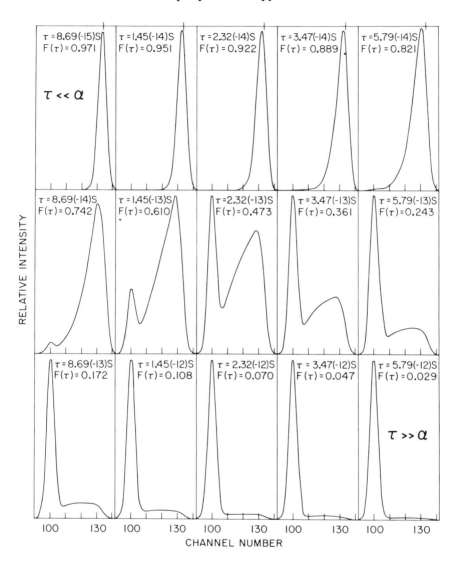

Fig. 12. Doppler line shapes as a function of assumed mean lifetime. These data are appropriate for γ rays emitted at θ=0° from Na^{22} nuclei slowing down in a nickel backing, with α=0.39 psec and K_n/K_e=0.16. Specifically, the shapes correspond to those expected from the $F^{19}(\alpha,n\gamma)Na^{22}$ reaction for a detector resolution of 3.0 keV (FWHM), dispersion of 0.5 keV/channel with E_γ=2.25 MeV, and v_i/c=0.75%.

where $\bar{E}$ is the average energy (defined by the centroid of
the distribution) and $\Delta E_K = E_K - E_0$ is the maximum energy
shift allowed by the kinematics, i.e., the full "vacuum
shift." Prior to the advent of Ge(Li) detectors, lifetime
determinations by the DSAM utilized measurements of $F(\tau)$,
since the available detectors were incapable of resolving
the structure evident in Fig. 12, and one could at best
determine the centroid of the Doppler-shifted distribution.

It is evident from Fig. 12 that for a particular transition from a level with $\tau \sim \alpha$, a single measurement at
$\theta=0^0$ is sufficient to allow a determination of the lifetime
provided in particular that the following obvious criteria
are satisfied: (a) the resolution of the γ-ray detector
is adequate to determine the line shape; (b) the kinematic
requirements are satisfied; i.e., the reaction produces a
homogeneous beam of Na^{22} ions traveling along the beam
axis. Procedures for dealing with somewhat less than the
idealized case have been given (3,20). In the present
experiment conditions (a) and (b) were readily satisfied
using a Ge(Li) detector to study γ-rays from the
$F^{19}(\alpha,n\gamma)Na^{22}$ reaction. By selecting α-bombarding energies
as close as possible to the threshold for production of a
given state, the reaction kinematics insured that the
excited Na^{22} nuclei recoil within a fairly narrow cone
along the z-axis, with an initial velocity large enough
(of the order $v_i/c \sim 1\%$) to obtain significant Doppler
shifts—of the order of 10 keV for a 1 MeV γ-ray.

2. Experimental Measurements

The data shown in Fig. 2 for the 1.984 ⟶ 0.583
transition illustrate the sort of results one can obtain
with a detector resolution of ~4.0 keV. The presence of
two components in the 0^0 spectrum is evident: a "stopped"
peak at $E_0=1400$ keV, and the fast component which extends
towards high energies. For comparison, we see in the 90^0
data that the "stopped" peak has not moved, but that the
line shape is now broadened (symmetrically, as it must be)
by the underlying fast component. The shape of the peak
spectrum (after removal of the dotted-line background) is
seen to correspond to that illustrated in Fig. 13 for
$F(\tau) \sim 0.2$, indicating a lifetime in the range $\tau \sim 1$ psec.
From a computer fit to these data, using values of α and
Kn/Ke appropriate to Na^{22} ions stopping in CaF_2, a value
of $\tau = (1.6 \pm 0.34)$ psec was obtained. The corresponding
attenuation factor is $F(\tau) = 0.214 \pm 0.012$.

It is evident from Fig. 12 that as τ approaches either
of the extremes, the information contained in the line
shape is correspondingly more difficult to extract. Since
the important parameter here is really the ratio τ/α, one
can shift the useful range by going to different stopping

materials. In Table II we have listed the various stopping
materials used in the Na^{22} studies, together with their
stopping parameters. Changing the stopping material from

Table II. Stopping parameters for Na^{22} ions stopping
in different materials.

Stopping media	Ni	CaF_2	SrF_2	Li^6	Li_2^60	"Li^6"	SF_6 gas
α (psec)	0.39	0.69	0.75	2.14	0.59	1.37	253
K_n/K_e	0.16	0.14	0.13	0.08	0.09	0.09	0.09

Ni to Li^6 results in changing the characteristic stopping
time α by a factor of ~5, with a corresponding change in
the range of lifetimes which can be studied by this method.

The targets used in the lifetime measurements were
prepared in the form of thin (~50-100 $\mu g/cm^2$) layers of
CaF_2 or SrF_2 on nickel and Li^6 backings, and thick
~$1 mg/cm^2$ targets of CaF_2, SrF_2, and also gaseous SF_6. For
the latter cases the "effective target" was again a thin
layer on the front surface of the material since all
measurements were carried out at bombarding energies close
to threshold for formation of the states of interest. Thus
in all cases one obtained a thin-target yield of Na^{22} ions
recoiling into the desired backing material. Small
corrections for the finite "effective target" thickness
were applied when necessary. For the Li^6 backing, which
was unstable against formation of a thin oxide-hydroxide
layer, the "effective" stopping power of the backing
material was found by experiment to be intermediate between
pure Li^6 and Li^6 oxide.

Figure 13 shows the line shapes measured at $\theta_\gamma = 0^\circ$ for
the Na^{22} 1.528 → 0 transition with 3 different stopping
materials. The solid curves are theoretical fits to the
data using the stopping parameters of Table II. The
solutions for τ from CaF_2 and SrF_2 results are in good
agreement and point to a value of $\alpha = 1.37 \pm 0.3$ psec for
the "Li^6" backing. This value was subsequently used in
evaluating the results of line-shape measurements on other
Na^{22} transitions. Also shown in Fig. 13 are the values of
R, defined as the ratio of the "stopped" and "fast"
components of the line shape.

Table III shows the results obtained from the measurements at BNL together with results from other laboratories.
Most of the BNL values were measured using the line-shape
analysis as described above, and are so designated in
Table III. The determination of the lifetime of the
0.583-MeV level was done by electronic techniques (23);
the values indicated for the 0.657- and 1.937-MeV levels

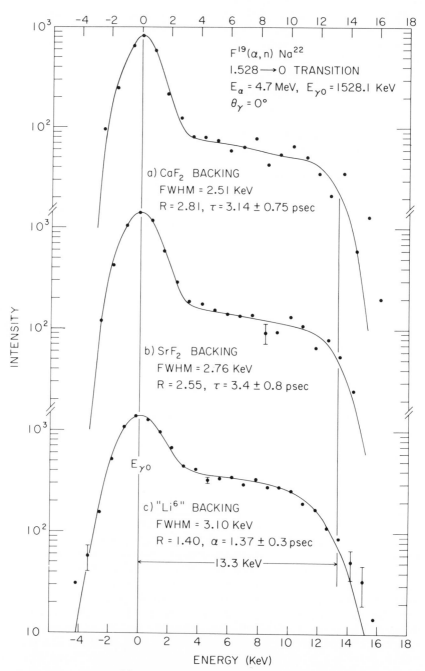

Fig. 13. The Na^{22} 1.528 → 0 Doppler-shifted line shape as measured in the F^{19}(α,nγ)Na^{22} reaction for various stopping materials. The points show the experimental data, after subtraction of the background: the fits to the experimental data determine the indicated lifetimes.

are those predicted (5) from the Mg^{22} positron decay
leading to this state. The value τ =20 psec determined
for the 2.211-MeV level, using a Li^6 backing, represents
approximately the longest lifetime that can be measured in
this way.

Table III.   Mean lifetimes of Na^{22} levels of E_{ex} < 3.1
             MeV. Those BNL results obtained from the
             line-shape analyses are designated by an
             asterisk. Unless otherwise specified, the
             remaining results are from conventional
             centroid-shift analyses.

Level in Na^{22}		Mean life τ (psec)	
E_{ex} (keV)	J$^\pi$	BNL	Other (averaged) (Ref)
583	1$^+$	---	$(351 \pm 3) \times 10^3$ (a)
657	0$^+$ (T=1)	---	66 ± 12 (b)
891	4$^+$	$13.4 \pm 3.0^*$	11.6 ± 1.8 (c,d,e)
1528	5$^+$	$3.5 \pm 0.7^*$	3.4 ± 1.8 (c,d,e)
1937	1$^+$	0.026 ± 0.022	0.024 ± 0.003 (b)
1952	2$^+$ (T=1)	< 0.09	---
1984	2$^+$,3$^+$	$1.74 \pm 0.34^*$	---
2211	1$^-$	20^{+25}_{-8}	12 ± 2 (c)
2572	2$^-$	$6.2 \pm 1.2^*$	4.5 ± 1.0 (c)
2969	3$^{(-)}$	0.060 ± 0.013	
3059	2	0.04 ± 0.01	

a   Measured by electronic techniques (Ref. 23).
b   Calculated from Mg^{22} positron decay to these states
    (Ref. 5).
c   Ref. 7.
d   Ref. 6.
e   Ref. 8.

The results shown for the 3-MeV doublet states in Na^{22}
are from a conventional centroid-shift determination,
since (see Fig. 12) it became evident that the lifetime was
too short to obtain a meaningful line-shape analysis; i.e.,
the lifetime effects (for θ_γ=0^0) comprise only a very
small low-energy tail extending over an energy region less
than the resolution spread of the detector. In this event,
however, the centroid-shift works fairly well, as shown in
Fig. 14. These data were measured at θ_γ=0^0 using a 2.5-cc
Ge(Li) detector with a 2.5-keV resolution. Also shown are
the rest energies E_0 for each of these transitions, as
based on energy determinations at θ_γ=90^0. From the
differences in the measured centroids in the solid and gas
targets, one computes the attenuation factors and mean

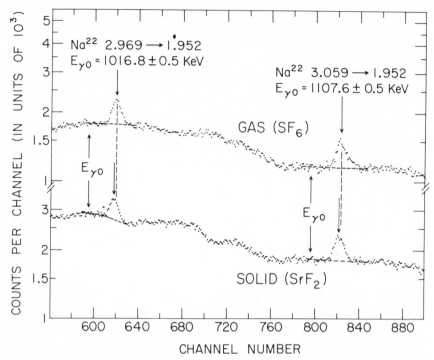

Fig. 14. Ge(Li) spectra measured in the $F^{19}(\alpha,n\gamma)Na^{22}$ reaction at $\theta=0°$ illustrating the difference in the Doppler shifts observed for gas and solid stopping materials. From the gas-solid centroid displacements for the 2.969 → 1.952 and 3.059 → 1.952 transitions, values were obtained for F(τ) and subsequently for the mean life τ of each initial level.

lifetimes as indicated: For the 2.969-MeV level, F(τ)=0.926 ± 0.012, τ =0.060 ± 0.013 psec; and for the 3.059-MeV level, F(τ)=0.950 ± 0.009, τ =0.04 ± 0.01 psec. The values of α and K_n/K_e are given in Table II. In this case the Doppler-shift observed in SF_6 gas is only negligibly different from the full "vacuum shift"; i.e., no discernible stopping effect is expected. We note that for lifetimes in the nano-second range one can, however, expect significant changes in the line shape as the gas pressure is varied, since α is inversely proportional to the density of the stopping material. This suggests a way of extending the DSAM measurements into the range of the Recoil Distance method, or alternately, of studying the relative importance of the electronic and nuclear stopping processes.

E. Magnetic Moment Measurements

It has been pointed out previously (23) that the magnetic moments determined for the ground state and first-excited state of Na^{22} are in good accord with both shell-model and rotational-model descriptions of this nucleus. One may expect the predictions to diverge for higher-lying states, and therefore, measurements on these latter states, which would provide an additional significant basis for model comparisons, are also of interest.

Measurements utilizing the Rabi technique have yielded a value (24) for the gyromagnetic ratio of the Na^{22} 3^+ ground state of $g=0.582 \pm 0.001$. Two techniques have been successfully applied to the measurement of excited state magnetic moments, both of which involve observation of the perturbation of the γ-ray correlation pattern due to precession of the aligned nuclear state in a magnetic field. The first technique, applicable to the somewhat longer-lived states, employs time-delay measurements to observe the _differential_ perturbation of the directional correlation induced by the application of an external field. The magnetic moment of the first excited state of Na^{22} was measured in this manner (23,25) by magnetically perturbing the $0.657(0^+)$ → $0.583(1^+)$ → $0(3^+)$ directional correlation. The 0^+ state was continuously prepared (in solution) through the $F^{19}(\alpha,n)Na^{22}$ reaction, and the Larmor spin-precession induced by an external magnetic field of 6111 Gauss was observed as a modulation of the time spectrum of delayed γ-γ coincidences. The observed precession frequency, $\omega = (0.565 \pm 0.025) \times 10^7$ rad/sec, corresponds (23) to a g-factor for the 0.583-MeV state of 0.535 ± 0.010. Because of the long lifetime of the 0.583-MeV state these measurements were able to follow the precession over several periods. We note that in this case the alignment of the intermediate state was essentially specified by the observation of the first member of the 0^+ → 1^+ → 3^+ cascade. The application of the general technique to the measurement of g-factors for states directly aligned in nuclear reactions has been previously described (26).

The second technique, which utilizes a comparison of _integral_ correlation shifts produced by ferromagnetic hyperfine fields, is required for study of the higher-lying Na^{22} states, which have lifetimes in the psec range. Measurements using this latter approach have been performed where the nuclear reactions recoil the residual nuclei into Fe backings (27,28). Since strongly aligned nuclear states can be produced by the reaction mechanism (without detection of the outgoing particles or γ rays) the

measurement in this case reduces to a comparison of γ-ray
singles spectra observed near the maximum slope of the
correlation pattern for both directions of the Fe hyperfine
field. A ratio of g-factors for two different excited
states of the residual nucleus can then be obtained provided
an integral shift is observed for each: this ratio is given
by $g_1/g_2 = \Delta\theta_1 \tau_2/\Delta\theta_2 \tau_1$. Clearly if one knows the value
of the average hyperfine field, then values for g may be
obtained directly. The angular distribution measurements
(Fig. 3) have shown that the $F^{19}(\alpha,n)Na^{22}$ reaction
mechanism can produce a significant alignment of the
initial level, and also impart enough forward momentum to
the Na^{22} nucleus to implant it in the iron backing.
Although the expected precession, for an average field
at the nucleus of ~100 kG during a nuclear lifetime of
~10 psec, is only tenths of a degree, preliminary measurements (29) on the 0.891- and 2.211-MeV levels have shown
that this is enough to observe statistically significant
effects.

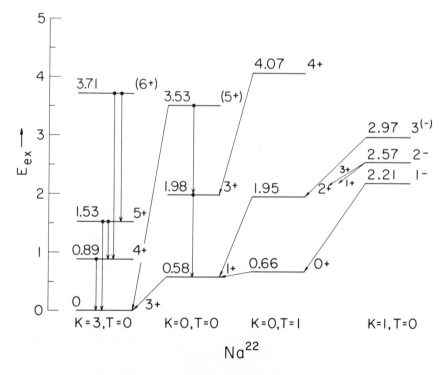

Fig. 15. Level diagram showing the major γ-ray transition
connecting low-lying rotational bands of Na^{22}.

III. MODEL CONSIDERATIONS

A rather surprising feature evident from the experimental description of Na^{22}, as thus far obtained, is that the character of the low-lying even-parity levels (see Fig. 11) is predicted with fair success by all three applicable models, i.e., collective-, shell-model, and SU$_3$.

We consider first the collective model, which predicts for Na^{22} that the 6 particles outside the O^{16} core shall have intrinsic spin projections (protons and neutrons) of $\Omega_p = \Omega_n = 3/2$, thus giving rise to three low-lying rotational bands. The lowest has K = $\Omega_p + \Omega_n$ = 3, T=0, and a 3$^+$, 4$^+$, 5$^+$...spin sequence. For K = $\Omega_p - \Omega_n$ = 0, both symmetric and anti-symmetric combinations of the wave functions may exist: the first combination has T=0 and a 1$^+$,3$^+$,5$^+$ spin sequence, while the second has T=1 and

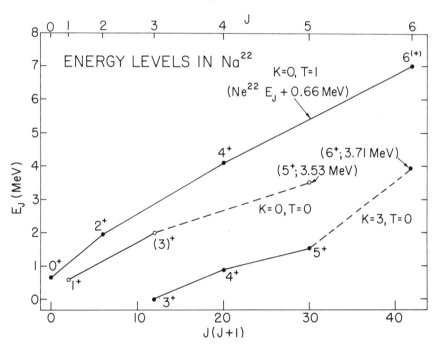

Fig. 16. Plot of E$_J$ vs J(J+1) for the even-parity bands of Na^{22}. Speculative assignments are indicated by parentheses and the dashed connecting lines.

a $0^+,2^+,3^+$...spin sequence. (The T=1 states have already been indicated in Fig. 11.) Our identification of the members of these three even parity bands is given schematically in Fig. 15. Within each band the states are identified according to their excitation energies; spin-parity assignments which have not yet been rigorously determined are given in parentheses. Included in Fig. 15 is our tentative identification of an odd-parity K=1, T=0 band.

Figure 16 shows for the even-parity levels a plot of the excitation energies E_J versus $J(J+1)$, illustrating that the structure obeys approximately the well-known rule for the energy levels of a nearly rigid rotator, namely $E_J = A_1 J(J+1) + A_2 \left[J(J+1) \right]^2$, with $A_2 \ll A_1$. Somewhat more quantitative support for a rotational model description is provided by the diagonal and off-diagonal matrix elements connecting the states of these three bands. Table IV

Table IV. Intrinsic quadrupole moments for the known intra-band E2 transitions of Mass 22 extracted from measured values of B(E2).

Nucleus Transition	J_i, J_f	K,T	10^4B(E2) (e^2-barns^2)	Q_0 (barns)
Na^{22}				
0.891 → 0	4,3	3,0	108 ± 18	+0.56 ± 0.05
1.528 → 0.891	5,4	3,0	76 ± 26	+0.48 ± 0.08
1.528 → 0	5,3	3,0	$25.3^{+7.3}_{-4.4}$	+0.55 ± 0.06
				$Q_0(3,0)$=+0.54±0.04[a]
1.984 → 0.583	3,1	0,0	93^{+25}_{-16}	+0.60 ± 0.06
Ne^{22}				$Q_0(0,0)$=+0.60±0.06[a]
1.275 → 0	2,0	0,1	43 ± 9	+0.46 ± 0.05
3.357 → 1.275	4,2	0,1	54^{+14}_{-9}	+0.44 ± 0.05
				$Q_0(0,1)$=+0.50±0.05[a,b]

[a] Q_0(K,T) is the average Q_0 for a given K,T.

[b] Q_0(0,1) is increased by 10% since the B(E2) are for Ne^{22} and the rotational model predicts that Q_0 is proportional to Z (see Ref. 30).

shows the transition strengths B(E2) obtained from the
measured values of $|M(E2)|^2$ as summarized in Ref. 15,
together with the intrinsic quadrupole moments (Q_0)
extracted from these values using the first-order prediction for the intra-band E2 strengths,

$$B(E2) = \frac{5}{(16\pi)} Q_0^2 (J_1 2K0, J_f K)^2.$$

It is seen from Table IV that the Q_0 for a given band are
consistent with each other, and therefore the relative E2
transition strengths for a given K,T obey the first-order
prediction as given above. (We have taken the positive
sign for Q_0 since local systematics indicate a prolate
deformation for Na^{22}.)

The information available on the intraband M1 matrix
elements also agrees (15) with a rotational model
description of Na^{22}. From the measured values for the
magnetic moments of the ground-state and first-excited
state, the gyromagnetic ratios of the intrinsic and
collective motions are obtained, respectively, as
$g_R = +(0.540 \pm 0.009)$, $g_K = +(0.596 \pm 0.003)$. The value
extracted for g_K is in excellent agreement with that
calculated for the Na^{22} ground state by Bohr and
Mottleson (30), while g_R is consistent with the prediction
$g_R \sim Z/A$. The measured M1 strengths of the $5^+ \rightarrow 4^+$
($1.528 \rightarrow 0.891$) and $4^+ \rightarrow 3^+$ ($0.891 \rightarrow 0$) transitions
are found to be in agreement with an average value
$|g_K - g_R| = 0.034 \pm 0.004$. While this result does not
quite overlap the value $g_K - g_R = 0.056 \pm 0.013$ determined
from the measured magnetic-moments, the agreement is
considered satisfactory in view of the approximations
inherent in the analysis. The predictions of the
rotational model for the signs of the E2/M1 mixing ratios
are

$$\text{sng} \left[x(E2/M1) \right] = - \text{sgn} \left[(g_K - g_R)/Q_0 \right]$$

where the phase convention is that of Rose and Brink (31).
Since the rotational model predicts both Q_0 and $g_K - g_R$
to be positive it thus also predicts that the $1.528 \rightarrow$
0.891 and $0.891 \rightarrow 0$ transitions have negative values of
$x(E2/M1)$, in agreement with experiment.

The identification of the odd-parity band (Fig. 15)
is somewhat more speculative, in that the parity of the
J=3 level is not yet established. However, the strengths
of the observed E1 decays support (16) the assumption that
these are 3 members of the same negative parity band, and
the level spacing is also consistent with a moment of
inertia given by the positive parity bands (see Fig. 16).
In summary then, the collective-model description of Na^{22}
is found to agree quite well with the experimental
evidence thus far established.

We note also that the general features of the even-parity band-structure are predicted almost equally well by both the shell-model, and by SU_3. In the SU_3 model the deformation necessary to generate collective bands must be produced by the six peripheral nucleons in the unfilled $(s_{1/2}-d_{5/2})$ shell. Since A=22 corresponds to the mass region where the quadrupole interaction is a near maximum, it is not surprising that the SU_3 model can produce an equivalent deformation, and thus a description approximately identical to that of the Nilsson form of the collective model. In contrast, the principle dif-ficulty encountered in a shell-model interpretation of these Na^{22} states would seem to originate from the inability of the shell model to provide a sufficient core-deformation. The shell model does succeed in predicting the low-lying even-parity states which belong to the three bands discussed above; but some discrepancy arises in obtaining the energies of these bands relative to each other, and those states corresponding to the (K,T)=(0,0) band are depressed to the extent that the 1^+ state lies below the 3^+ ground state. However, the intraband E2 transitions linking the even-parity states are found to be in satisfactory accord with experiment if an effective charge of ∼0.5e is used in calculating transition rates. (32).

In summary, while the comparisons of the experimental and theoretical descriptions of A=22 indicate quite good overall agreement (15,16,32), it is also clear that more quantitative experimental information is required on the higher-lying excited states. Crucial to this comparison are rigorous determinations of parity for the suggested J=3 member of the odd-parity band and of both spin and parity for the (6^+) and (5^+) members of the even-parity bands (see Fig. 15). Points of interest with respect to operable selection rules for the transitions linking various band members have also been discussed (16).

Experimental work designed to clarify these points of the experimental description for the higher-lying states of Na^{22} have been considerably aided by the now available Ge(Li) detectors of size ∼40 cc, whose increased peak efficiency makes them suitable for studies of p-γ coin-cidence spectra. In this case the Ge(Li) detector can easily resolve the various γ-ray transitions proceeding from the doublet and triplet states, which was not resolved by the particle detector. The simultaneous particle detection also defines the Na^{22} recoil direction, so DSAM studies of line-shapes may be extended to reactions such as $Ne^{20}(He^3,p\gamma)Na^{22}$. This work is presently under way at BNL.

REFERENCES

1. A.E. Litherland, E.B. Paul, G.A. Bartholomew, and H.E. Gove, Phys. Rev. 102, 208 (1956).
2. S.G. Nilsson, Kgl. Danske Videnskab. Selskab. Mat.-Fys. Medd. 27, No. 16 (1955).
3. E.K. Warburton, J.W. Olness, and A.R. Poletti, Phys. Rev. 160, 938 (1967).
4. P.M. Endt and C. Van Der Leun, Nucl. Phys. A105, (1967).
5. A. Gallmann, G. Frick, E.K. Warburton, D.E. Alburger, and S. Hechtl, Phys. Rev. 163, 1190 (1967).
6. J.G. Pronko, C. Rolfs, and H.J. Maier, Phys. Rev. 167, 1066 (1968).
7. A.E. Blaugrund, A. Fisher, and A. Schwarzschild, Nucl. Phys. A107, 411 (1968).
8. R.W. Kavanagh, Bull. Am. Phys. Soc. 12, 913 (1967).
9. A.R. Poletti, E.K. Warburton, J.W. Olness, and S. Hechtl, Phys. Rev. 162, 1040 (1967).
10. E.K. Warburton and H.J. Rose, Phys. Rev. 109, 1199 (1958).
11. A.E. Litherland and A.J. Ferguson, Can. J. Phys. 39, 788 (1961).
12. A.R. Poletti and E.K. Warburton, Phys. Rev. 137, B595 (1965).
13. F.W. Prosser, Jr., in Proceedings of the Second Symposium on the Structure of Low-Medium Mass Nuclei, edited by P. Goldhammer and L.W. Seagondollar, (1966— unpublished).
14. A.R. Poletti, E.K. Warburton, and J.W. Olness, Phys. Rev. 164, 1479 (1967).
15. E.K. Warburton, A.R. Poletti, and J.W. Olness, Phys. Rev. 168, 1232 (1968).
16. P. Paul, J.W. Olness, and E.K. Warburton, Phys. Rev. (to be published).
17. D.H. Wilkinson, in Nuclear Spectroscopy, edited by F. Ajzenberg-Selove (Academic Press Inc., New York, 1960), Part B, p. 863 ff.
18. Electromagnetic Lifetimes, E.K. Warburton, in Nuclear Research with Low Energy Accelerators, Edited by J.B. Marion and D.M. Van Patter (Academic Press, New York, 1967), pp. 43-74.
19. T.K. Alexander and K.W. Allen, Can. J. Phys. 43, 1563 (1965).
20. J.W. Olness and E.K. Warburton, Phys. Rev. 151, 792 (1966).
21. A.E. Blaugrund, Nucl. Phys. 88, 501 (1966).
22. See for example: A.E. Litherland, M.J.L. Yates, B.M. Hinds, and D. Eccleshall, Nucl. Phys. 44, 220 (1963).
23. A.W. Sunyar and P. Thieberger, Phys. Rev. 151, 910 (1966).

24. L. Davis, Jr., D.E. Nagle, and J.R. Zacharias, Phys. Rev. 78, 1068 (1949).

25. H. Schmidt, J. Morgenstern, H.J. Körner, J. Braunsfurth, and S.J. Skorka, Phys. Letters 24B, 457 (1957).

26. A.R. Poletti and D.B. Fossan, Phys. Rev. 160, 883 (1967).

27. L. Grodzins, R. Borchers, and G.B. Hagemann, Phys. Letts. 21, 214 (1966).

28. R. Kalish and W.J. Kossler, Phys. Rev. Letts. 20, 271 (1968).

29. D.B. Fossan, J.W. Olness, and E.K. Warburton, (to be published).

30. A. Bohr and B.R. Mottleson, Kgl. Danske Videnskab Selskab. Mat.-Fys. Medd. 27, No. 16 (1953).

31. H.J. Rose and D.M. Brink, Rev. Mod. Phys. 39, 306 (1967).

32. J.B. McGrory, E.C. Halbert, and B.H. Wildenthal, Bull. Am. Phys. Soc. 13, 609 (1968).

DISCUSSION

ENDT: Your gamma ray energy measurements were done at 90°?

OLNESS: Yes, you're worried about Doppler shifts on the accuracies? They're measured at 90°, and so that's taken care of.

PRONKO: What about 3- and 5- elimination in polarization measurements?

OLNESS: They were equally well ruled out. The same measurements also ruled out those possibilities. They just were not shown on the slide. In fact, the fits were even worse than for the one which I did reject.

PHILLIPS: You commented earlier that the $F^{19}(\alpha,n,\gamma)$ reaction would cause alignment that even without observing the neutrons on axis the residual states would be aligned because you believe the neutrons were s-waves. Have you any evidence that this is so for such a large neutron energy?

OLNESS: No, there is only the qualitative information that is the angular distributions of the de-excitation gamma rays measured in the (α,n) reaction were virtually identical with those obtained in the (p,γ) correlation measurements where one did restrict the substate populations to the same values.

PRONKO: I would like to comment on that remark. I think in general one probably would not have any problems eliminating the spin. But, if there were a mixing ratio involved you might find that the minimum would shift a little bit introducing a little bit of inaccuracy in the mixing ratio if you were, let's say, analyzing the χ^2 sort of fit and looking for the mixing ratio. We have done this sort of thing with the $O^{18}(\alpha,n)$ reaction and we have found for a 700 keV neutron that there was a variation in the angular correlation with the solid angle. It was very small and would never cause any problems in eliminating spins anyway, but I'm sure it would introduce an error in the mixing ratio itself if you were to use the case where the counter is very close. You get a very large solid angle.

OLNESS: Yes, I should say that the conclusions on spins, parities and mixing ratios were not based on the (α,n) distribution results other than just the most obvious restrictions on the minimum spins that could be involved.

PROSSER: I wanted to add a comment on looking at the Doppler attenuation using the shape of the line, a word of caution perhaps more than anything else. A research associate here, Peter Cockburn, has been involved in some investigations of what amounts to just the opposite of your case, say for instance $F(p,\alpha\gamma)$, where one brings in very little momentum but has a great deal of recoil as a result of the heavy outgoing particle. In this case a great deal of angular information is in the line shape as well. Again one can, if he knows the spin sequence, get lifetimes out of this much the same way you have, or turn this around to get some spin information as well. However, in cases where there are heavy outgoing particles which give a great deal of recoil there will be angular information involved, which then needs to be taken into account in any attempt to measure lifetimes this way. This, of course, does not apply to your experiment where most of the momentum is a result of the incident particle.

OLNESS: I agree. It would be interesting to see a line shape analysis of the $(p,\alpha\gamma)$ case you described.

V. A. RECENT DEVELOPMENTS ON THE DYNAMITRON ACCELERATOR

Marshall R. Cleland
Radiation Dynamics, Inc.
Westbury, New York

I. INTRODUCTION

Radiation Dynamics is an established industry, having recently completed 10 years in the business of manufacturing particle accelerators. During this time the company has grown to employ 110 people and now occupies 35,000 square feet of space in three buildings in the Westbury Industrial Park. Twenty-nine high voltage particle accelerators have been delivered to customers and four new machines are under construction. They are classified in Table I according to energy and type of particle. Most of the lower voltage units are being used for studies of radiation effects such as radiation polymerization, molecular cross-linking and radiation damage effects in solid state systems. Most of the 4.0 megavolt machines and the tandem will be used for nuclear structure of research. Because of the rather recent application of Dynamitron accelerators to nuclear studies, this type of machine is not widely known to people in this field. The author welcomes this opportunity to discuss the new developments which are now being undertaken by RDI to adapt these machines to the needs of the nuclear structure physicist.

II. GENERAL DESCRIPTION OF THE DYNAMITRON SYSTEM

The new 4 million volt Dynamitron[1] is shown Figs. 1 and 2, wherein the essential features of the high voltage generator can be seen. These are: the rectifier tubes located along the sides of the high voltage column, the split corona rings connected to each rectifier, the semi-cylindrical electrodes which supply RF power to the rectifier cascade, and the pressure vessel which contains the high pressure gaseous insulation. The large radio frequency transformer which energizes the electrodes is shown in Fig. 3. In the 4.0 MV units and in the tandem, this transformer is located in a side pid directly connected to the low voltage end of the pressure vessel.

A pictorial diagram of the high voltage circuit is shown in Fig. 4. Both high vacuum rectifiers and solid state diodes are indicated in the cascade, but all machines delivered to date have been equipped with hot cathode, high vacuum rectifiers. (A development program is now under way

TABLE I

Summary of Dynamitron Accelerators Built or Under Construction

Maximum Voltage (MV)	Particle Type	Number of Machines
1.0	Electron	3
1.5	Electron	8
2.0	Electron	1
3.0	Electron	3
3.0	Ion	12
4.0	Ion	5
8.0 (tandem)	Ion	1

Fig. 1. 4 MV Dynamitron accelerator stack, viewed from terminal enclosure with pressure vessel removed.

to design silicon rectifier cartridges as direct replacements for the tubes, but these have not yet been evaluated in an accelerator). The capacitors shown between the cylindrical electrodes and the corona rings are composed entirely of the stray capacitance which exists between the corona rings and the electrodes. The dielectric consists of pure SF_6 gas at 100 lbs/in^2. This gaseous capacitor can insulate the maximum

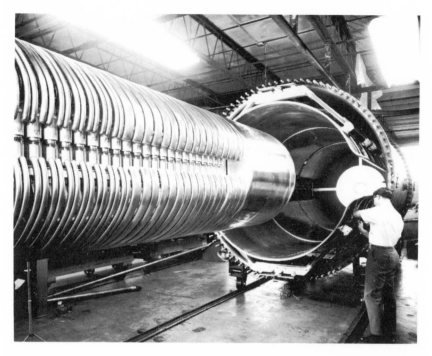

Fig. 2. View of the open accelerator pressure vessel showing
the RF electrodes.

output voltage of the generator and is self-healing in case
of spark breakdown during the conditioning process. The radio
frequency voltage is applied to the large electrodes as a
balanced, push-pull signal so that very little RF voltage (less
than a kilovolt) appears at the high voltage terminal of the
cascade circuit. RF voltages do appear at the corona rings
and so it is necessary to insert RF blocking chokes at both
ends of the cascade circuit in order to extract a pure dc
potential.

The toroidal RF transformer is indicated at the bottom of
this diagram by the center-tapped inductor. This is energized
at its natural resonant frequency by a high-powered triode
oscillator which is connected in a self-tuning circuit. The
RF capacitance indicated in parallel with the transformer
represents the stray capacitance between the cylindrical
electrodes and the pressure vessel. The dc filter capacitance
indicated from the high voltage terminal to ground is the
inherent surface capacitance of this terminal with respect to
the pressure vessel. From this description, one can see that
the necessary capacitive elements of the high voltage generator
are all formed by means of the capacitance of metallic
electrodes in combination with the insulating gas as the dielectric material. This concept is essential to the successful performance of these high voltage machines in that the

Fig. 3.   Toroidal RF Transformer.

total capacitance of the system is small and therefore the
electrical energy stored within the system is minimized. This
enables the machine to survive occasional spark breakdowns
which will occur during the conditioning period of the machine.
In this characteristic the Dynamitron design preserves one of
the most important features of the Van de Graaff electrostatic
accelerator.

III. HIGH CURRENT RATING OF THE
DYNAMITRON GENERATOR

It is well known that the dc current rating of a multi-stage cascaded rectifier circuit is limited by the internal impedance of the circuit. In the case of the conventional Cockroft-Walton machines, the internal impedance increases as the cube of the number of rectifier stages. For this reason, these machines are designed with about 10 stages[2]. In the Dynamitron, (because of the parallel excitation of the rectifiers) the internal impedance varies as the first power of the number of stages, and a much larger number of stages

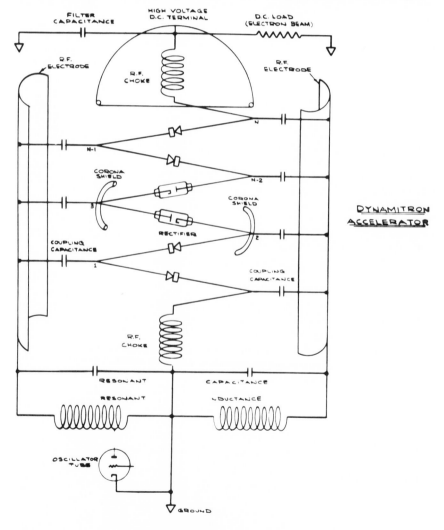

Fig. 4. Pictorial representation of the Dynamitron high
voltage generator.

can be employed. In the 4 million volt version, 94 rectifier tubes are used and the impedance of the cascade circuit is still low enough to supply a 10 mA resistive load.

The essential difference between the Cockcroft-Walton, series-coupled circuit and the Dynamitron parallel-coupled circuit is shown in Figs. 5 and 6. The high impedance of the series-coupled circuit comes about because of a gradual atten-uation of the ac voltage signal as it passes from stage to stage through the coupling capacitors. In the parallel-coupled circuit this attenuation is completely avoided and all rectifier stages are excited to the same amplitude. A useful parameter which describes the current rating of a power supply is the voltage regulation under load, expressed as the percentage drop in output voltage per unit load current. This can be obtained from the ratio of the first two terms in the voltage equations in Figs. 5 and 6. In the Cockcroft-Walton circuit load regulation varies as the square of the number of stages, whereas, in the Dynamitron the load regulation is independent of the number of stages. This explains why it is possible to employ so many stages of rectification. There are, of course, practical advantages to be gained in the selection of components if the ac voltage and the dc voltage per stage can be kept within moderate limits. The nominal single-stage voltage used in all Dynamitrons built to date is just under 50 kV dc which is well within the rating of standard commercial rectifier tubes.

Measurements of the stack impedance using an electron beam as a variable load have confirmed the approximate formula given in Fig. 5. The data are presented in Fig. 7. This impedance of about 25 megohms causes a voltage droop of about 250 kV at 10 mA load which is about 8% of an output voltage of 3.0 MV. In a research machine this droop is auto-matically compensated by the closed-loop voltage regulation system[3] which maintains constant output voltage by increasing the dc voltage applied to the oscillator. The results of a maximum power electron beam test of the 3 million volt Dynami-tron delivered to Brookhaven National Laboratories are shown in Fig. 8. A beam current of 11 mA was delivered on target at 3 million volts and successively higher currents up to 20 mA were delivered at lower voltages.

This data demonstrates the high power characteristic of these machines which has been put to good use in the pro-duction of electron beams for industrial radiation applica-tions. New developments are now being undertaken to take advantage of this unique power capability in the field of ion beam applications.

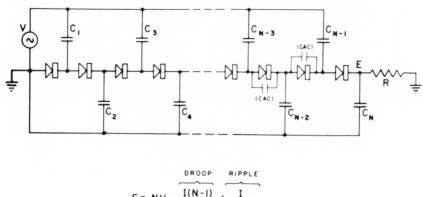

PARALLEL COUPLED VOLTAGE MULTIPLIER CIRCUIT

$$E = NV - \overbrace{\frac{I(N-1)}{fCk}}^{DROOP} \pm \overbrace{\frac{I}{2fCk}}^{RIPPLE}$$

$$k = 1 + \frac{4(CAC)}{C}$$

$$N_{OPTIMUM} = \infty$$

Fig. 5. Schematic diagram of the parallel-coupled cascaded rectifier circuit.

SERIES COUPLED VOLTAGE MULTIPLIER CIRCUIT

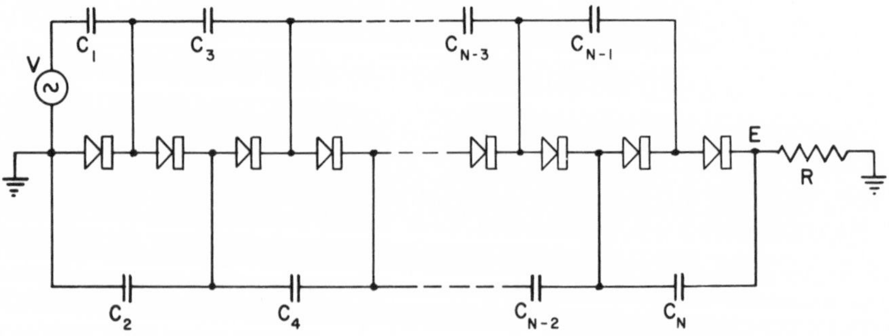

$$E = NV - \overbrace{\frac{I(N^3 + 3N^2/4 + N/2)}{12\,fC}}^{DROOP} \pm \overbrace{\frac{I(N^2 + 2N)}{16\,fC}}^{RIPPLE}$$

$$N_{OPTIMUM} = \sqrt{\frac{4fCV}{I}}$$

Fig. 6. Schematic diagram of the series-coupled cascaded rectifier circuit.

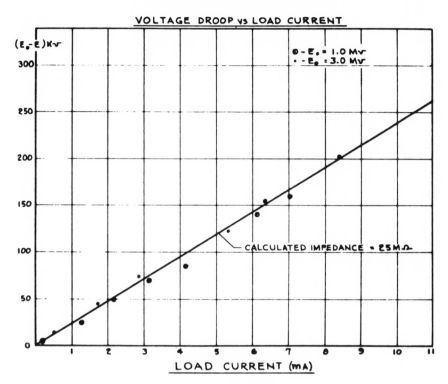

Fig. 7. Determination of stack impedance from load regulation
data.

IV.   HIGH INTENSITY ION BEAM
ACCELERATION

A.   Beam Current Objective

The long range objective of the ion beam development program at RDI is to fully utilize the high current capability
of the Dynamitron power supply for the acceleration of intense
ion beams. This is justified by the belief that useful applications will be found once the practicality of the machines
has been demonstrated. To further this objective the duoplasmatron type of ion source has been chosen in preference to
the more commonly used RF sources which are limited in their
output to a few milliamperes of hydrogen ions. RDI has
developed its own version of the duoplasmatron which is sold
under the trade name of the Dynamag ion source. This is shown
in Fig. 9, and has been described in detail elsewhere[4]. The
output of the Dynamagon is adjustable from 10 microamperes
to more than 10 mA of hydrogen ions. When equipped with this
source, Dynamitrons have produced intense, well-focused ion
beams of several milliamperes (unanalyzed).

Marshall R. Cleland

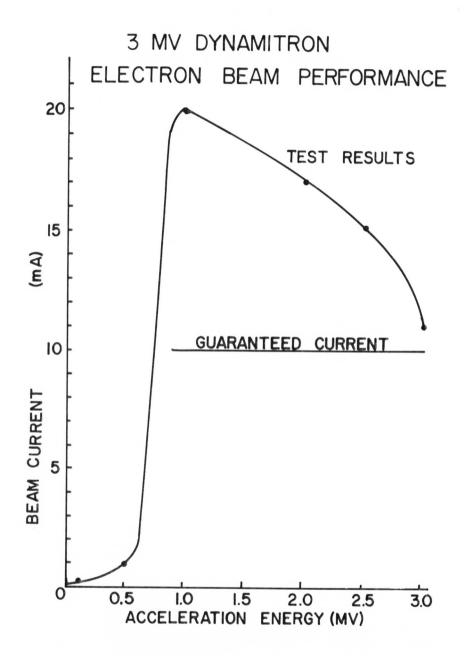

Fig. 8.   Electron beam performance of a 3 MV Dynamitron.

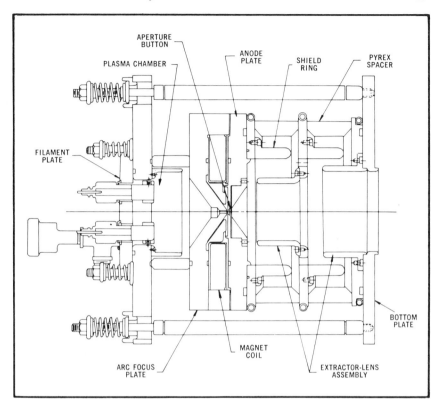

Fig. 9. Dynamag positive ion source.

The maximum hydrogen ion current is stable and of good quality and is machine voltage dependent. The most favorable point usually occurs at about 2.0 MV with a 3.0 MV machine. A typical relationship is shown in Fig. 10. The data were obtained with the Dynamitron produced for the University of Ottawa. Although this current is small compared to the electron beam data, the ion current and the beam power density on target are substantially greater than has been available from the Van de Graaff type machines. The power density may have exceeded 50 kW per square centimeter in some tests. A typical beam profile is shown in Fig. 11. This was ob-tained with the water-cooled vibrating wire device developed at Brookhaven[5].

These high intensity beams cannot be used with thin film targets, but can be tolerated by water-cooled copper backing plates. For the even more powerful ion beams anticipated in the next few years, windowless gas targets or high speed rotating targets will be required. Several designs for rotating targets have appeared recently[6,7], and this technique is quite practical for those studies where a heavy backing plate can be tolerated, such as neutron scattering measure-ments, for example.

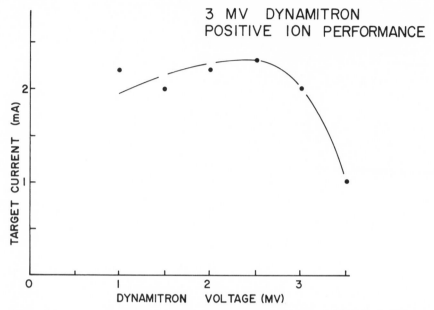

Fig. 10. Positive ion beam performance of a 3 MV Dynamitron.

B. Limiting Mechanisms

    The present achievements in ion current acceleration have
not come easily. Whereas there was no particular difficulty
in accelerating up to 20 mA of electrons through a long
column, with ions there were several limiting mechanisms
which had to be overcome to achieve stable, high-current beams.
One of these limitations was a tendency of the beam to wander
on target. This was traced to an accumulation of electrostatic charges on the glass rings of the acceleration tube.
The cure for this problem was found in the re-entrant dynode
design developed at Brookhaven by C. Turner. This is shown
in Fig. 12, where the completely shielded dynode configuration
is contrasted with a more conventional partially shielded
configuration. The re-entrant design provides complete iso-
lation of the glass from scattered ions and also from backstreaming electrons and has proven to be very satisfactory.
    Another problem associated with high current beams was
the overheating of the tip of the beam extraction electrode.
When a conventional, narrow extractor tip was used to pull
the ions from the plasma, it was observed that severe heating
and, in some cases, actual melting occurred on the side of
the extractor facing away from the ion source. This was due
to an intense, high energy beam of backstreaming electrons
coming from the acceleration tube. This problem was circum-
vented by changing to a large-apertured extractor design which
is shown in Fig. 9. This extraction geometry produces higher

quality beams without reduction of emission from the ion
source. This has been discussed in greater detail in Ref. 4.
Other incidental advantages were also obtained with this open
extractor geometry, particularly, improved vacuum pumping
speed to the source aperture which reduced the pressure and
the beam scattering in this region. Another advantage was a
reduction in the criticality of alignment of the extractor
electrode with respect to the ion source anode.

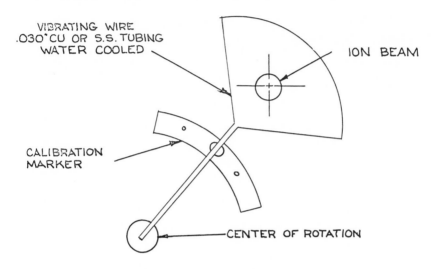

BEAM PROFILE MONITOR

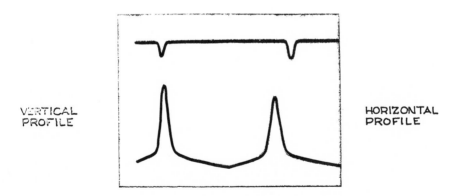

VERTICAL
PROFILE

HORIZONTAL
PROFILE

4.0 MEV 1.35 Ma 2.5 m.m. LENS 24 Kv EXTRACTOR 19 kv
19 Kv HALO 3/19 = 16 %

Fig. 11. Beam profiles measured by the water-cooled vibrating
wire scanner.

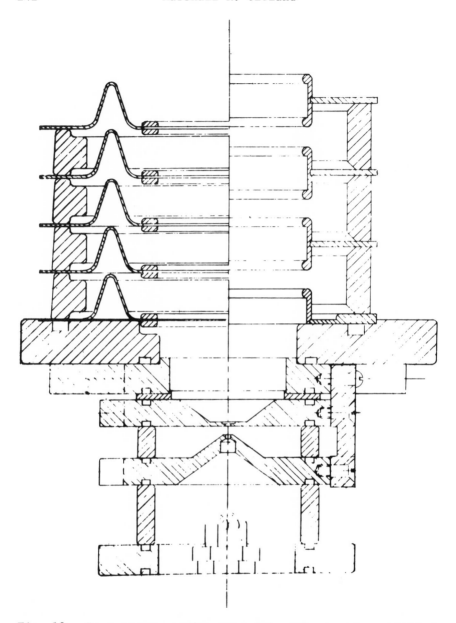

Fig. 12.   Re-entrant acceleration tube illustrating shielded
dynode configuration.

        In spite of the design improvements described above,
which were of considerable practical value, the maximum
stable ion beam current was still limited to a few milliamperes. If an attempt was made to increase the current,
several undesirable effects would occur, including: the
rapid worsening of the vacuum, the rapid increase in internal

X-ray intensity produced by backstreaming electrons, an
increase in the intensity of the halo of particles surround-
ing the primary beam, an increase in the leakage current
through the insulating gas, and ultimately the onset of a
pulsing instability in the beam current arriving at the
target of the accelerator. This pulsing has been observed
to be a blow-up indicating a loss of proper focus control,
presumably due to sparking between electrodes in the acceleration column or in the extractor-lens assembly. All of these
effects can be explained through the mechanism of scattering
of the primary ion beam by residual gas in the acceleration
column. Such scattering can account for the large diameter
halo which is evident in the beam profile shown in Fig. 11.
These scattering events can also be the source of the backstreaming electron current, and this electron current is the
source of the observed X-radiation which, in turn, is
responsible for the ionization leakage through the insulating
gas of the accelerator[8].
    The rapid worsening of the vacuum, in spite of a con-
stant gas feed to the ion source, must be caused by outgassing of the interior surfaces of the acceleration column
due to bombardment by scattered high energy paritlces. The
mechanism is re-generative, because outgassing produces more
scattering which in turn produces more outgassing. In extreme
cases where the system has been recently exposed to air, the
pressure within the vacuum system may rise continually even
with a constant ion beam current, leading eventually to a
violent electrical discharge throughout the column. These
symptoms have been observed on all of the positive ion
Dynamitrons when an attempt was made to force the ion beam
current beyond a certain critical value. Therefore, it is
clear that the problem of achieving a goal of 5 mA of protons
on target is not so simple as just having a proper ion
source. The limiting mechanisms do not appear to be in the
source or in the high voltage power supply, but somehow are
determined by the interaction of the beam with residual gas
in the acceleration column.

C. Advantages of Terminal Pumping

    Most of the side effects described above have been sup-
pressed and a dramatic improvement in ion beam transmission
has been obtained through the use of a small, electrostatic,
titanium gett-ion pump at the high voltage end of the column.
This pump was evaluated on the first 4.0 MV Dynamitron built
for the University of Stuttgart. This machine is quite
large and employs an acceleration column 12 feet in length
(compared to 8 feet for the 3.0 MV machines). This length
reduces the vacuum pumping speed and aggravates the problem
of gas scattering. The maximum stable current was only
about 0.6 mA without terminal pumping. This was increased

by 500% to 3.0 mA through the use of a 4 inch NRC Orb-Ion
pump at the high voltage end of the column.

Comparative data showing the effects of terminal pumping on several important machine parameters are shown in
Figs. 13 through 17. Fig. 13 shows the correlation between
ion current and base vacuum measured at the target end of
the accelerator. The initial pressure with the source gas
turned off and with the terminal getter pump turned off was
1.4×10^{-7} Torr. The hydrogen gas leak rate from the source
increased the base vacuum to 2.3×10^{-7} Torr. When the ion
beam was accelerated, the base vacuum increased linearly with
the beam current to a value of 4.4×10^{-7} Torr at 0.6 mA of
beam on target. The rise of pressure with beam must have
been caused by outgassing of the internal surfaces since
the gas flow to the source was held constant. At 0.6 mA
the beam pulsing began and the current could not be further
increased. The maximum current depended on the gas flow
rate at the source and the previous conditioning history of
the accelerator.

With the terminal pump turned on, the correlation between
beam and vacuum was quite different. The initial pressure
rise due to source gas was reduced and the outgassing caused
by beam acceleration was dramatically suppressed. It was
possible to increase the ion beam to slightly more than 3.0
mA and to hold this condition in a stable manner for more than
an hour. Beam pulsing was again observed at 3.2 mA at a
vacuum corresponding to the onset of the instability at 0.6
mA at a vacuum corresponding to the onset of the instability
at 0.6 mA without terminal pumping. This observation suggests that with a larger terminal pump the maximum current
could be further increased.

Fig. 14 shows the correlation between ion beam current and
the current flowing through the resistor column which provides
the intermediate potentials along the acceleration tube. With
the terminal pump turned off the resistor column current increased from the normal flow of 240 microamperes at 0 beam
up to 335 microamperes with 0.6 mA of beam. This was an increase of 40% in the resistor current presumably caused by
the interception of scattered particles by the dynodes of
the tube. This must have produced severe distortion of the
voltage gradient along the column and could easily have caused
sparking between stages which could have been the cause of
the pulsing instabilities which were observed in the beam.
With the terminal pump on, the column loading was very much
reduced. There was a range between 0.5 and 2.5 mA of target
current where the interaction between the beam and the tube
was negligible. At 3.0 mA the loading effects increased
rapidly, again approaching the 40% increase observed at 0.6
mA without terminal pumping.

Fig. 15 shows the correlation between "corona current"
(ionization leakage through the insulating gas) and beam cur-

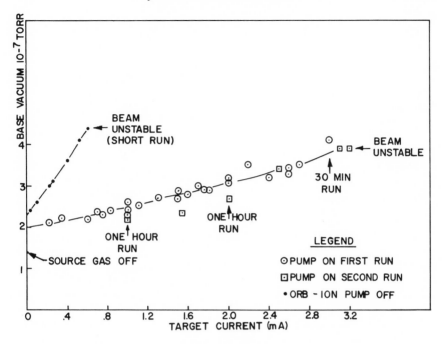

Fig. 13. Correlation between ion beam current and base vacuum.

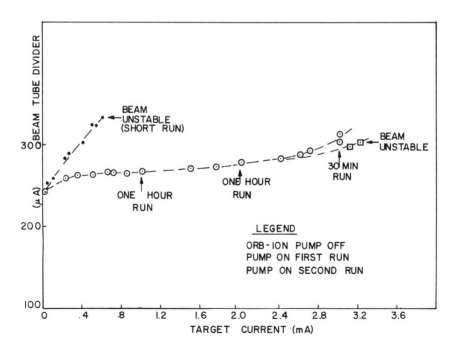

Fig. 14.   Correlation between ion beam current and resistor
column current.

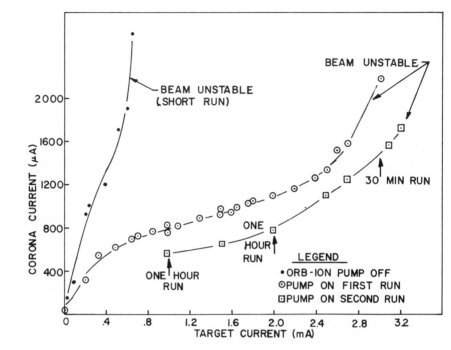

Fig. 15.   Correlation between ion beam current and corona
(leakage) current.

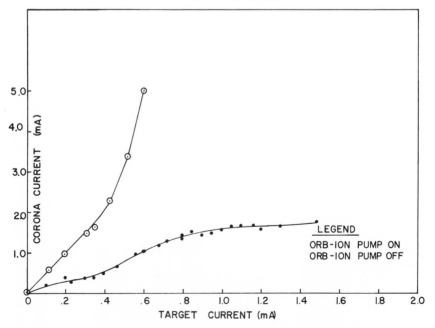

Fig. 16.   Correlation between ion beam current and corona
(leakage) current for 4 MV operation.

rent. This leakage current is collected on the cylindrical
RF electrode system which surrounds the high voltage column
within the pressure vessel of the accelerator. The current
is presumably due to the migration of SF_6 ions between the
high voltage terminal and the electrodes. This current
correlates with the intensity of X-radiation caused by backstreaming electrons. The residual corona current observed
when the ion beam is turned off is negligible. The difference
in leakage current with and without the terminal pump is
dramatic. It is clear from this data that the backstreaming
electron current is strongly dependent on the residual gas
in the column. The data cannot distinguish whether these
electrons are released from the gas itself or from the
accelerating dynodes of the tube under bombardment by high
energy ions. This question is not important in practice
because if the vacuum is sufficiently good the ions will not
be scattered and the electrons will not be liberated in
either case.

In Fig. 16 a similar correlation between leakage and beam
current is shown at 4.0 MV. The leakage current went as high
as 5.0 mA without terminal pumping and was 8 times greater
than the beam current. This insulation leakage imposes an
intolerable load on the high voltage generator and it would
set a low limit on the maximum ion current even if the beam
pulsing instability did not appear. The use of terminal
pumping reduces this leakage by a factor of 5 to a quite
acceptable level about equal to the ion beam current.

The beam halo is also markedly reduced by the use of the
terminal pump. This was measured by intercepting the halo
on a 1 cm aperture plate mounted just in front of the target.
The data is shown in Fig. 17. As in the other measurements,
the intensity of the halo is strongly reduced by terminal
pumping. At 0.6 mA of beam the halo is 70 microamperes
without the pump and 8 microamperes with the pump. As the
beam current is further increased, the halo rises again,
indicating a gradual worsening of the vacuum condition in the
column.

The gas scattering effects described above are associated
with steady state beam conditions and are not present during
pulsed beam operation. The Stuttgart machine was also equipped
with a slow arc-pulsing circuit for the ion source. Beam
pulses up to 8.0 mA at 4.0 MV were recorded on target with
pulse lengths up to 2000 microseconds duration. The pulse
repetition rate was in the range from 10-100 pulses per second
so that the average beam current was low. There was no
apparent effect on any measurable parameter when the terminal
pump was turned on. This may be explained by the fact that
the major portion of the vacuum rise is due to outgassing
caused by scattered beam bombardment. In pulsed mode, the
average beam current is too low to cause significant out-

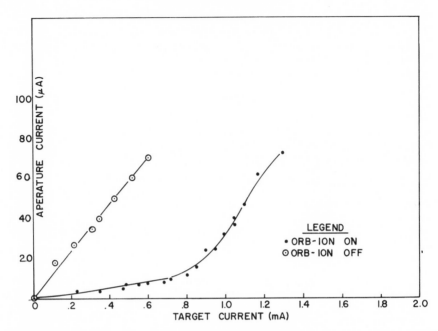

Fig. 17. Beam halo intensity as a function of target current
for 4 MV operation.

gassing and therefore the re-generative build-up in the
residual gas pressure does not occur.

A strong correlation was observed between the peak ion
current and the high voltage terminal potential. This is
shown in Fig. 18. The ion source was not current limited,
but if the emission control was raised, the target current
would diminish. This would seem to indicate that the maximum
pulsed current is limited by the optical design, i.e., the
match between the acceptance of the accelerator tube and the
emittance of the beam from the ion source. The pulsed beam
data shows that the optical design is more than adequate for
the long range goal of fully utilizing the high dc power
capability of the Dynamitron high voltage generator.

The maximum dc beam current has not yet been determined
for 4.0 MV operation because of the perforation of the water-
cooled copper target by the beam. This target withstood a
beam power density which may have been as high as 50 kW/cm^2
for an hour during the 3.0 MV test run and failed midway
through the 4.0 MV run. It thus appears that the limit of
stationary target capability has been reached. In order to
go on it will be necessary to use moving targets or moving
beam techniques in order to prevent target burn-out.

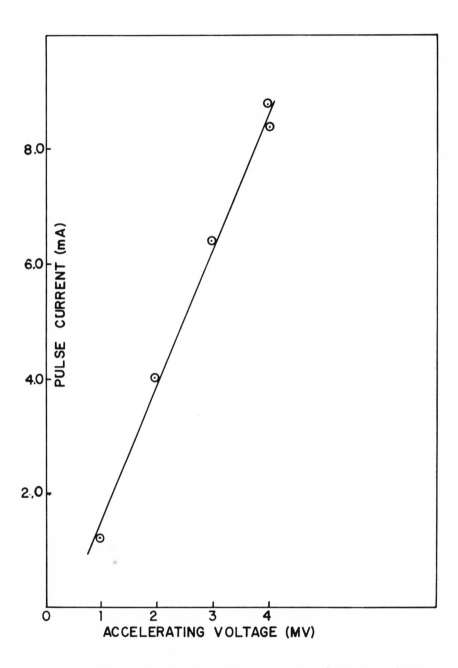

Fig. 18.   Pulsed ion beam performance of a 4 MV Dynamitron.

D. Advantages of Terminal
Mass Analysis

Although the Duoplasmatron type of ion source is capable
of very high emission, the hydrogen beam is not composed
solely of protons. It also contains substantial percentages
of diatomic and triatomic molecular hydrogen ions. Under the
most favorable plasma conditions the proton yield may sometimes be as high as 70% of the total current, but more
frequently the yield may be as low as 30%. With the common
practice of analyzing the beam after acceleration, part of
the machine power is wasted in accelerating the molecular
components. Of even greater significance to the goal of
achieving a maximum proton current, the molecular ions are
more prone to being scattered by residual gas and they cause
substantially greater loading effects than an equivalent
current of protons.

The contribution to column loading from these molecular
hydrogen ions has been separately measured with the second
4.0 MV Dynamitron recently delivered to the University of
Montreal. This machine is equipped with a crossed-field mass
analyzer located within the high voltage terminal. This ion
source, lens and analyzer assembly was supplied by ORTEC,

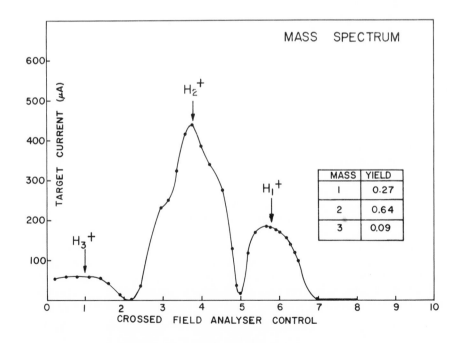

Fig. 19. Mass spectrum of the hydrogen ion beam obtained
with the cross-field analyzer, located in the high voltage
terminal.

Oak Ridge, Tennessee. It is an adaptation of their nano-
second pulsing gun which is based on a design developed at
Oak Ridge National Laboratory [8]. A mass spectrum of the beam
is shown in Fig. 19, where the accelerator target current is
shown as a function of the voltage control of the cross-field
analyzer in the terminal of the machine. It is evident that
the analyzer completely resolves the 3 mass components. The
plasma conditions for this rather low beam current favored
the production of the diatomic molecular ions, the proton
component being only about 27% of the total. The proton
percentage increases with increasing arc current in the source
which would be the case for maximum beam current. In Fig. 20
the X-ray induced leakage current is plotted against the same
analyzer control. Here one can see the loading effect of each
beam component separately. It is evident that whereas the
proton current was about 3 times greater than the triatomic
ion current, the loading effects were 2.5 times greater than
the heavy ions. The ratio of the leakage current to the beam
current is shown in Fig. 21. This curve shows that with protons the leakage current is only 7% of the beam current, while
with diatomic ions it is 22% and with triatomic ions, 62%.
Therefore, most of the loading effects are due to the molecular
ion components. The large spikes on the curve of Fig. 21
occur in the valleys between the mass component and are probably
due to the scattering of ions off the edge of the mass separation aperture within the cross-field analyzer. These spikes
have been ignored in the interpretation of the data as the
curve seems to be quite flat and regular in the central region
of the mass peaks as shown on Fig. 19. The beam halo was
also measured as a function of ion species and it was obvious
that the molecular ions contribute more strongly to the beam
halo than do the protons.

If one considers the evidence presented above, that a
Dynamitron equipped with terminal pumping can accelerate
3.0 mA of a mixed hydrogen ion beam, and that most of the
undesirable side effects are caused by the molecular species
in the beam; then it does not seem unreasonable to expect
that the accelerator column could accept a much higher pure
proton beam, perhaps in excess of 5.0 mA. The ion source and
analyzer package delivered with the Montreal machine are not
capable of such high performance. The maximum available
proton current is probably about 2.0 mA. However, the way
has been shown by these measurements. One of the important
future developments for the Dynamitron is a powerful source,
analyzer and pumping package for the high voltage terminal.

V.   FINE VOLTAGE REGULATION

The terminal voltage of the Dynamitron is regulated by
means of a closed loop feedback system working through the

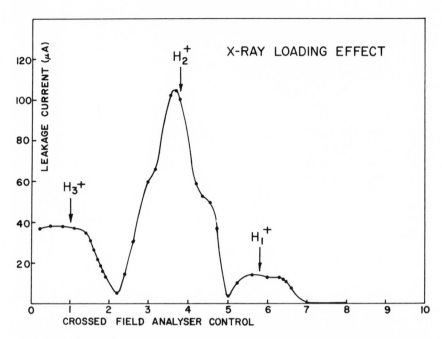

Fig. 20. X-ray induced loading effects for the three atomic ions of hydrogen, obtained with the terminal cross-field analyzer.

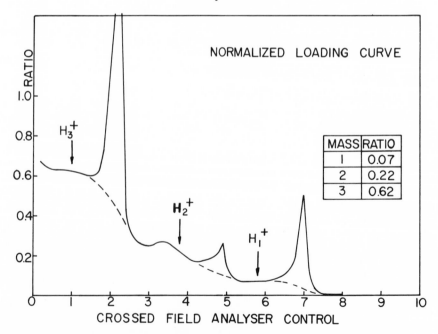

Fig. 21. Ratio of the X-ray induced leakage current to the ion beam current, for the three atomic ions of hydrogen obtained with the terminal crossed-field analyzer.

power oscillator to modulate the RF voltage on the cylindrical
electrodes which energize the rectifier cascade. The sampling
voltage is obtained from the ground end of a high voltage
resistor column which is mounted inside the machine alongside
the accelerator tube. This resistor is not connected to the
dynodes of the tube and is supplied in addition to the beam
tube divider resistor column. This system has been more fully
described elsewhere[3]. The motivation for this method is to
make sure that the machine is always in regulation whether
the ion beam is present on target or not. This is an important consideration for a high power machine where the voltage
cannot be stabilized by the corona load.

The dc voltage stability under varying beam load is
shown in Fig. 22. The data were obtained by monitoring the
error voltage at the summing point of the regulation amplifier. The regulation is ± 0.02% for an electron beam load
variation from 0 to 6 mA. This would also be the case for
reasonable variations of the ac voltage from the power lines.

The ac ripple voltage at the high voltage terminal is
also important as this determines the energy spread of the
ion beam. The ripple can come from various components of
the system; from the RF electrodes; from the ac signals at
power line frequency in the oscillator or voltage regulation
amplifier, and also from the ion source control circuits
within the high voltage terminal. A spectrum analysis of
the main ripple components are shown in Fig. 23. The most
significant component is the 125 kilo-Hertz signal coming
from the oscillator. This data indicates an energy spread
of 1.0 kV, full width (peak to peak) at 2.0 MV. The data
were obtained with a capacitive probe located in the vicinity
of the high voltage terminal, and connected to a pre-
calibrated oscilloscope. The energy spread of the proton
beam from the University of Ottawa machine has been
measured to be about 2 keV using a resonance reaction with
a thin target[9]. Additional data are anticipated from this
institution.

The high frequency signal which is present on the
high voltage terminal is thought to be due to an imbalance
of the RF voltages on the cylindrical electrodes. No
attempt has been made to minimize this effect. It can
probably be reduced to a few hundred volts by including an
adjustable trimming capacitance in the RF circuit or within
the high voltage terminal. The fact that the ac signals are
repetitive offers hope for their eventual elimination by
ordinary means. There does not appear to be any significant
contribution from random noise such as that generated by
the charging belt in a Van de Graaff machine.

For the absolute energy calibration required by nuclear
structure work, it will be necessary to include a feedback
signal from beam slits located at the image point of an
analyzing magnet in the usual manner. This beam slit regu-

lation feature will be provided by Varian, Inc. for the 4.0
MV Dynamitrons. It will be based on the new conditional
mode system recently developed at the Rutgers-Bell tandem
laboratory[11]. The Varian-RDI system will automatically
switch from beam slit control to resistor board control in
case the beam current falls below a critical level. This
will protect the machine from the danger of open-loop operation and also simplify the problem of threading the beam
through the beam transport system.

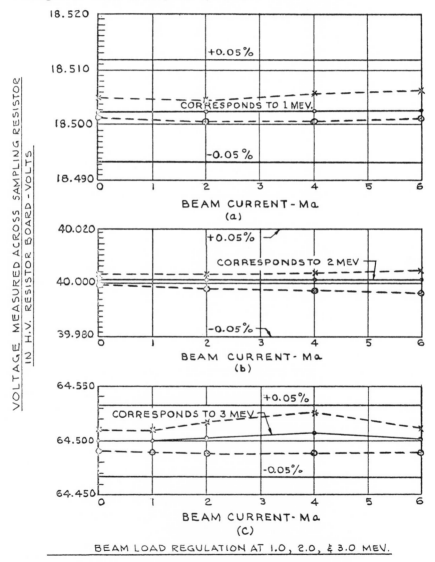

Fig. 22. Beam load regulation of a 3 MV Dynamitron, using
using resistor board feedback control.

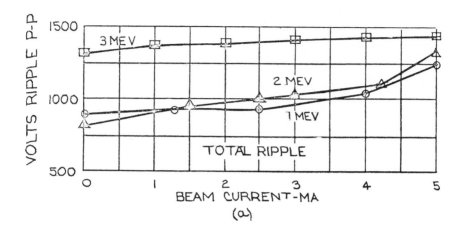

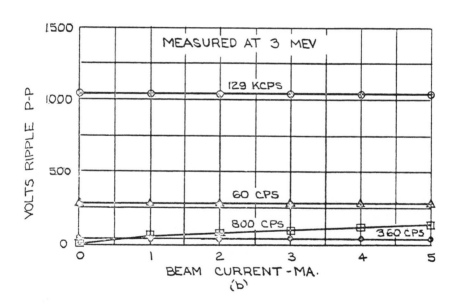

RIPPLE MEASUREMENTS · DC HEATED
OSCILLATOR TUBE FILAMENTS

Fig. 23.   Terminal ripple measurements obtained with a
capacitive probe.

Although the Dynamitron has acquired the reputation of being primarily a high power device, better suited to industrial radiation applications than to nuclear structure work, this is really not a true picture of the machine. The ion beams produced by these machines are good, low emittance, low energy spread beams in spite of their power characteristics, and there are reasons to believe that the energy spread and stability can be reduced below the level now generally available from other dc machines. When this is done, it will be of significant value for nuclear investigations where there seems to be no limit to the fineness of the energy levels exhibited by some nuclear states.

VI. TANDEM DYNAMITRONS

In years past, tandem beam currents were limited by the negative ion injector to about 10 microamperes. Some recent developments in negative ion source technology have changed the picture so that now the tandem current is limited by the high voltage generator.

The direct extraction method using a duoplasmatron ion source with a displaced arc is now capable of producing about 100 microamperes of H⁻ current[11,12]. The hollow cathode arc (diode) source recently announced by High Voltage Engineering Corp. is good for 500 microamperes H⁻[13]. The PIG source with radial beam extraction has recently yielded a current of 2.0 mA of H⁻ with a beam emittance low enough to be accepted by a tandem accelerator[14,15]. These sources may provide the means for obtaining proton beams with tandems that are comparable in intensity to beams now available only from single-ended machines at lower voltages. In addition to giving higher particle energy, the tandem configuration has of course added advantages in the availability of the ion source outside of the machine. This availability enables rapid servicing for complex pulsing of polarization apparatus.

If an attempt is to be made some day to accelerate 2 mA of protons through a tandem, this will require at least 4 mA of current from the power supply (2 mA up and 2 mA down). In addition to the beam current, the X-ray induced leakage current will probably be comparable so that at least 8 mA will be required. Then the resistor boards will need at least 1 milliampere so that a 10 mA high voltage generator would be necessary.

The first Dynamitron tandem is now being built for Argonne National Laboratory. Factory tests are scheduled for October of 1968. The terminal potential is conservatively guaranteed for 4.0 MV (8.0 MeV protons) and will very likely go to 5.0 MV, since the column dimensions are similar to the HVEC Model EN Tandem. The accelerating length is 12 feet and the corona ring diameter is 42 inches. The overall length of the pressure vessel is 34 feet. The dc proton current is guaranteed to be 50 microamperes on target through the 90 degree analyzing magnet.

The 150 kV injector assembly is being built by ORTEC. This will be similar to the one they supplied for HVEC-FN tandem at Los Alamos. The source is a direct extraction duoplasmatron and the beam will be pulsed by the usual technique of chopping and velocity bunching. The pulsed beam objective is 1.0 mA peak at 1.0 nanosecond (full width at half maximum). The injector will be compatible with the ORTEC He$^-$ source which utilizes the principle of charge exchange in an alkali metal vapor canal. It will also be able to accept the polarized beam apparatus now being developed under the direction of B. Donnally of Lake Forest College[16].

One of the unique features of the Dynamitron tandem will be the beam stripping assembly, located within the high voltage terminal. This will employ a large gas stripper canal (1/2" diameter by 5' long) and a diffusion pump recirculation system to collect and re-use the stripper gas. The canal diameter has been specified to insure that the beam acceptance will be large enough for future, high intensity, negative ion sources. If this canal is to be supplied with the proper gas pressure for at least 90% stripping efficiency, 1300 micron-centimeter for 4.0 MeV H$^-$ ions[17], the gas flow rate would be about 54 atm-cc/hr. This is far too much to be conducted down the acceleration columns as the beam scattering effects would be intolerable.

The recirculation system shown in Fig. 24 solves this problem in a simple manner. The stripper canal will be located within a larger manifold to which a diffusion pump will be attached. The pump outlet will be connected through a proper oil trap back to the inlet pipe for the stripper gas. The gas pressure in the center of the canal will be about 17 microns which is a good backing pressure for the diffusion pump. The 3/4" aperture plates placed at each end of the pumping manifold will divert most of the gas away from the acceleration tubes and into the pump. The gas leak rate through each aperture will be about 1.4 atm-cc/hr which is less than the leak rate down the low energy tube of conventional tandems.

A pair of 6" Orb-Ion getter pumps will be mounted just beyond the aperture plates to pump on the acceleration tubes. One of these pumps will be used in the single-ended mode of operation which is another feature of this machine. In this mode, the stripper assembly will be removed and a positive ion source assembly will be installed in its place.

The Argonne machine will embody a number of other new design innovations which will give it a character of its own. It will not in any way be a copy of the well-known HVE tandem machines. It is the fervent wish of RDI that this

new machine will prove to be more than satisfactory for nuclear
studies, and that its high current rating will make possible
some new investigations which cannot be done at this time.

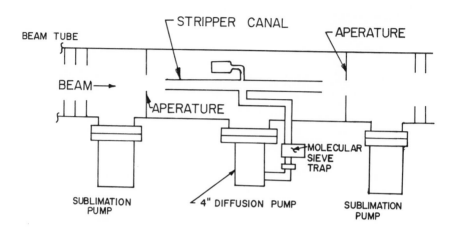

TERMINAL STRIPPER CANAL

Fig. 24. Terminal stripper assembly showing the recirculating
          diffusion pump and the titanium sublimation pumps.

VII.   CONCLUSIONS

There are no plans at the present time to try to extend
the voltage rating of the Dynamitron beyond 5.0 MV. This can,
in principle, be done by scaling up the size of the machine.
It is the opinion of RDI's technical staff that the development
effort should be directed toward improvements in voltage regulation, beam current, beam emittance, nanosecond pulsing, beam
polarization, heavy ion acceleration, etc. These qualities
are all of value if Dynamitrons are to be used in nuclear
structure work.

It is felt that much can be done to achieve these goals.
As each machine is built and tested, better understanding of
the accelerator is obtained and new design approaches are
conceived in greater number than can be utilized. Let no one
think that the field of "low voltage" dc particle accelerator
design is stagnant. On the contrary, it is moving so fast
that it is hard to keep abreast of all the new developments.

BIBLIOGRAPHY

1. Dynamitrons of the Future, M. R. Cleland and P. Farrell,
    IEEE Transactions on Nuclear Science NS-12, 227 (1965).

2. A Generator for Three Million Volts Direct Current, A. Bonwers and A. Kuntke, Zeits. F. Tech. Physik 18, 209 (1937).

3. Multi-Loop Feedback System for Dynamitron Voltage Regulation, C. C. Thompson, IEEE Transactions on Nuclear Science, NS-14, 169 (1967).

4. Dynamag Ion Source with Open Cylindrical Extractor, M. R. Cleland and R. A. Kiesling, IEEE Transactions on Nuclear Science, NS-14, 60 (1967).

5. High Current Beam Scanner, H. E. Wegner and I. L. Feigenbaum, IEEE Transaction on Nuclear Science, NS-14, 1099 (1967).

6. Rotating Neutron Target System, R. Booth, IEEE Transactions on Nuclear Science, NS-14, 938 (1967).

7. A Rotating Target Assembly for 10^{12} neutrons/second, D. Cossuta, Proceedings of the 34th Conference on Accelerator Targets Designed for the Production of Neutrons (held at Liege, Belgium) EUR 3895 d-f-e 191 (1968).

8. Time-of-Flight Techniques, J. H. Neiler and W. M. Good, Fast Neutron Physics, Part I, Chapter IV. A. 509 (1960), Interscience Publishers, Inc., NY.

9. Private Communication, I. Robson, University of Ottawa.

10. An Improved Control System for Van de Graaff Accelerators, E. A. Gere, H. P. Lie and G. L. Miller, IEEE Transactions on Nuclear Science, NS-14, 161 (1967).

11. Production of Protons and Negative Ions with Low Energy Spread, L. E. Collins, R. H. Gobbett and P. T. Shroud, IEEE Transactions on Nuclear Science, NS-12, 247 (1965).

12. Direct Extraction of Negative Ion Beams of Good Intensity from a Duoplasmatron, G. P. Lawrence, R. K. Beauchamp and J. L. McKibben.

13. The Diode Source, A Negative Ion Source, High Voltage Engineering Corp., Technical Note No. 16.

14. Design Considerations for High-Intensity Negative Ion Sources, K. W. Ehlers, IEEE Transactions on Nuclear Science, NS-12, 811 (1965).

15. Model NS-150 Negative Ion Injector System for Continuous or Nanosecond Pulsed Operation, Equipment Specifications No. A-7005, The Cyclotron Corporation, Berkeley, California, Jan. 15, 1968.

16. Negative Polarized Ions from Metastable Hydrogen Atoms,
    B. Donnally, Bull. Am. Phys. Soc., 12, 1170, Abstract
    EA4 (1967).

17. The Production and Acceleration of Ion Beams in the Tandem
    Accelerator, P. H. Rose and A. Galejs, Progress in
    Nuclear Techniques and Instrumentation, Vol. II, (F. J. M.
    Farley, Ed.), North Holland, Amsterdam (1967).

DISCUSSION

DAVIS: What is the material of your electrodes?

CLELAND: The disk electrodes are stainless and they have a
little aluminum ring pressed onto the inside to reduce x-ray
production. The stainless is an odd type, 316 or something,
that is chosen for its drawing properties, in order to be
stamped into those dish shapes.

DAVIS: In the forthcoming tandem, what do you have in mind
for the stripper gas?

CLELAND: We are thinking of oxygen.

DAVIS: Straight off oxygen. You did not consider or at least
had a reason for discarding the possibility of some other
material, something which would be easier to pump, for example?

CLELAND: Well, we really haven't got that sophisticated in
our thinking about it. We'll see how the first one works.
But, if the diffusion pump circulator works actually it will
pump oxygen all right and it will reduce the leak rate I
think to a tolerable level. The various pumping speeds that
you can assume which are reasonable, indicate that the gas
flow rate out of the central region into the orb will be very
low.

DAVIS: How much power do you have available in the terminal?

CLELAND: Well we use basically a georater generator which can
deliver 4 kilowatts at 800 cycles. One could put more than
one of those in the terminal.

DUNNAM: The filling gas obviously affects the coupling between
your driver electrodes and the terminal structure?

CLELAND: Well, it doesn't affect it very much. The dielectric
constants of most gasses is very close to unity.

DUNNAM: So it's not enough then so that variations in filling
or in gas mixture would do very much to the achievable voltage?

CLELAND: Yes, the gas really affects the DC sparking voltage and the DC corona properties, but it doesn't have much effect on the rf coupling scheme.

DUNNAM: Have you tried your machine with ions other than hydrogen since you have installed the terminal pump?

CLELAND: No, one of our customers, the McClellan Air Force Station in Sacramento, has accelerated helium in the single ended machines and finds that the machine won't accept as much helium as it will hydrogen.

DUNNAM: That is with the pump?

CLELAND: No, without a pump. And we haven't any data with the pump. I would expect that since the pump will not be very effective, it is a titantium getter ion pump, it's not going to be very effective for helium. It might not help much. On the other hand, since that data [was obtained] the vacuum rise data shows that most of the trouble really comes from the outgassing material, the pump might handle that all right. So there may be some benefit.

DUNNAM: In an "unloaded" machine, that is one without much beam coming down, will terminal voltage go much higher than the four million volts that you have mentioned?

CLELAND: Four and a half seems quite reasonable and we have touched five momentarily, but frankly on a new model like this we had so many debugging problems that we really haven't had the opportunity to push it to its maximum voltage. There have been a number of the features of the machine which were satisfactory at 3 million volts which have suffered spark damage at 4, it took about a year to debug the first 4 million volt machine and get it reliable, and that's where the time goes, so that's a good reason incidentally why you shouldn't, any of you, think of building your own accelerator.

V. B. HEAVY ION ACCELERATION

Peter H. Rose and William E. Starks
Robert J. Van de Graaff Laboratory
High Voltage Engineering Corporation
Burlington, Massachusetts

INTRODUCTION

This paper concentrates on certain aspects of heavy ion
acceleration in the tandem which are important in the
present state of the art. More general descriptions of the
tandem accelerator can be found in the literature.[1,2]
Before proceeding to detail it is interesting to review the
evolution of the tandem accelerator since it first went
into operation only ten years ago. Fig. 1 shows a layout
of the first tandem installation at the AECL Laboratory in
Chalk River. The figure shows an accelerator with a sophisticated high energy beam handling system and an elementary
injector designed for hydrogen ions. Despite the poor resolution of the injector analyzing system, important new research
was successfully undertaken with beams of helium, carbon,
oxygen and other heavy projectiles. Better mass resolution
at the injector was soon realized to be most desirable. The
second figure shows part of the tandem accelerator at Yale
University. The injector of this machine has been considerably improved and has two ion source positions with an
inflection magnet giving a mass resolution of ~40. The
design suffers from the disadvantage that the second source
position is inaccessible when the machine is being operated,
which prevents maintenance or replacement of a source during
operation. As negative ion sources for most heavy ion
species are unreliable at present there can be considerable
loss of machine operating time.

The research accelerator in the R. J. Van de Graaff
Laboratory is being used to prototype a system which
represents a significant improvement on the two previous
schemes. The accelerator has provision for five completely
separate injectors, as shown in Fig. 3. An inflection magnet directs the beams from the injector into the accelerator.
The resolving power of the inflector is ~20 and is increased
where necessary by providing additional analysis in the
individual injector systems.

The original incentive for building the tandem accelerator was to obtain proton beams of twice the energy, and
although this is still extremely important, it is now
apparent that the advantages of having the ion source, or
ion sources, outside the accelerator and maintaining the
machine in operation for twenty-four hours a day over long
periods ranks of nearly equal importance. The energies

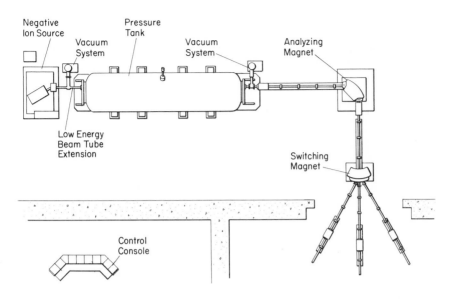

Fig. 1.   A Layout of the EN tandem accelerator at AECL, Chalk
River showing the elementary injection system.

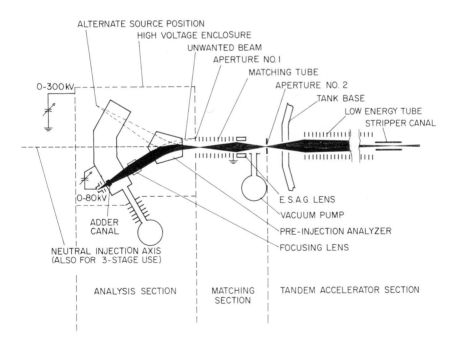

Fig. 2.   The injector end of the Yale MP tandem, showing two
sources and the analyzing system.

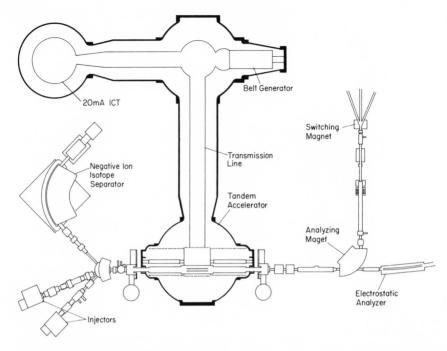

Fig. 3. The tandem accelerator in the R. J. Van de Graaff
Laboratory showing how several separate injectors have been
coupled to the accelerator.

which can be reached by the conventional tandem accelerator
limit the ion species that can be used for research. This
is illustrated in Figure 4 which shows the maximum energies
that can be reached, employing a gas stripper in the
terminal, estimated from the best available charge changing
data. The Coulomb barrier in the laboratory system was
calculated from the expression:

$$E_{CB} = 1.44 \left(\frac{A_1 + A_2}{A_2}\right) \frac{Z_1 \; Z_2}{1.209(A_1^{1/3} + A_2^{1/3}) + 1.9} \; MV \quad (1)$$

The figure shows that the number of elements which can
be studied increases rapidly as the terminal potential
rises. The energies were estimated by taking a component
of the high energy tail of the charge distribution and do
not take into account any shell effects. If, instead of
using gas as a stripper a foil is employed, there will be a
10 or 20 percent increase in energy for the lighter ions
and a significant increase in intensity because of the better vacuum. It is interesting to estimate the terminal
potentials required to accelerate ions above the Coulomb
barrier of a uranium target. Figure 5 shows, that for
iodine ions, a terminal potential of ~ 45 MV is needed if

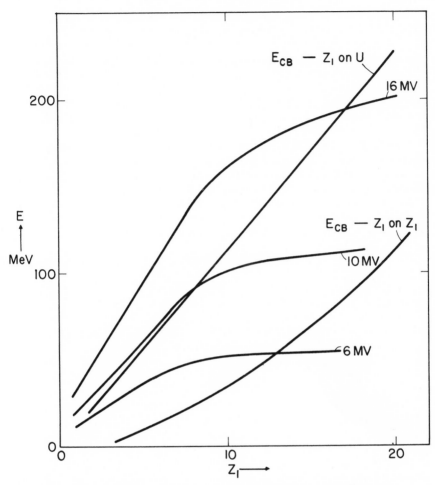

Fig. 4. The energies that can be reached at different
terminal potentials by a tandem accelerator using a gas
    stripper. The Coulomb barriers are shown for reference.

a gas stripper is employed. This figure depends to some
extent on the nature and density of the gas stripper but
the best choice would probably not reduce this voltage by
more than 5-10 percent. A foil stripper reduces the terminal voltage to ˜ 32 MV. Two foils employed, one in the
terminal and one halfway down the high energy column,
reduces the necessary potential to ˜ 24 MV. This method,
although most advantageous, complicates the spectrum of the
beam emerging from the accelerator. This is illustrated by
Figure 6, which shows how the beam breaks up into different
charge and energy components during acceleration. The components of the beam are spaced $V_{T/2}$ apart and retain

excellent energy homogeneity in spite of the stripping
process.

Presently HVE is building a 20 MV tandem accelerator
which will extend the energies and ion species available
to the experimentalist by a large factor. To reach this
voltage, which is twice the rating of the MP accelerator,
the company plans to double the operating gradient rather
than to increase the size of the machine. The operating
gradient in the acceleration tube will then be ~ 70 kV/in.
For the future, more progress in the same direction can be
expected. Columns gradients of over 250 kV/in. have been
obtained in experimental machines. Tube gradients well
above 100 kV/in. have been reached in short sections of
acceleration tube and it can be expected that by developing
materials and geometries, further improvements will result
in a tube matching the performance of the column. Higher
voltage accelerators will therefore not necessarily be
larger, a possibility of great economic significance.

ION SOURCES

The ion sources for tandem accelerators have undergone
considerable development in the last ten years and several
are available which give high currents of many different
ion species. The ions that can be obtained as negative ions
are shown in Table 1. As can be seen, there are very few
light elements that are unavailable. At the present time
the problem is not the availability of negative ion species,
but rather the dependability of the ion source.
Considering the fact that many of the ion species of
interest (e.g. fluorine or sulphur) are chemically active
and attack parts of the ion source, special techniques must
be developed to obtain reasonable source lifetimes and,
almost as important, predictable lifetimes. Some of these
negative ions are easily formed and the chemical destruction
of source parts can be kept low by keeping the concentration
of the corrosive gas or material small, by using a carrier
gas, yet still obtaining the beam intensity desired.
There are a number of other factors which must be evaluated when considering accelerating the heavier ions in
DC tandems. For example, the high mean charge state after
stripping in the terminal increases the current drain on the
accelerator. In order to minimize this loading, it is
extremely useful to preanalyze the injected negative ion
beam to remove all unwanted isotopes. This would require
a resolution of 1:40 for beams through chlorine and much
higher, of course, for uranium. If the projectile is an
isotope of low abundance this is particularly important.
To improve the mass resolution, and incidentally at the same
time the minimum burst length for pulsed beams, it is necessary to minimize the energy inhomogeneity of the injected
beam, which puts a premium on ion sources of low energy

spread - i.e. < 10 eV. To make effective use of this low
energy spread the stability of the power supplies and
analyzing magnet must be 1:10,000 or better, and could in
addition involve a slit-feedback system based on the
inflection analyzing magnet similar to the slit-corona
control techniques used on the tandem accelerator.

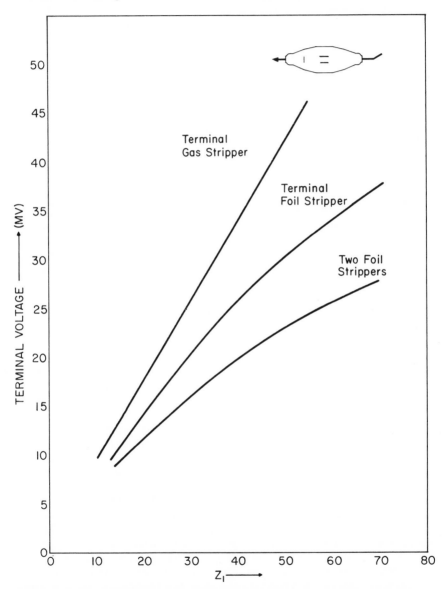

Fig. 5. The terminal potentials required to accelerate an
ion above the Coulomb barrier of a uranium target. Three
stripper configurations are shown (a) A gas stripper, (b) a
foil stripper and (c) two foils, one in the terminal and the
second halfway down the H.E. tube.

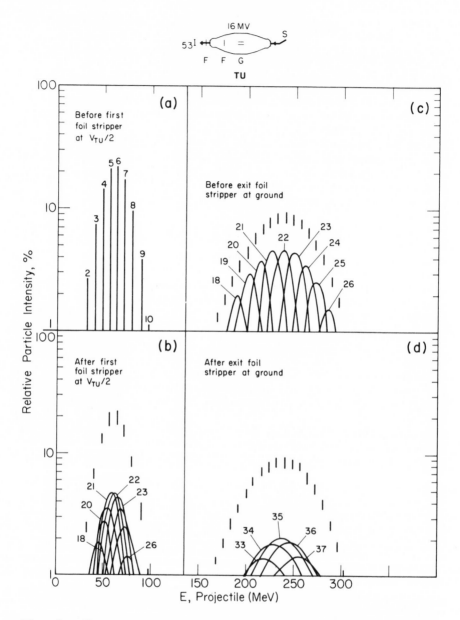

Fig. 6. The energy spectrum of an iodine beam from a tandem
employing a gas stripper in the terminal and foil stripper at
the half potential point of the H.E. tube. (a) Before the
first foil stripper (b) after the foil stripper, showing the
re-distribution of charge states and (c) the same at ground
potential.

CHARGE CHANGING COLLISIONS

If in the process of acceleration the ion changes in an
uncontrolled manner, either during acceleration or in the
beam transport system, two undesirable effects occur.
First, the required beam component is attenuated. Second,
the particles which are lost from the discrete energy spectrum formed in the stripper canal appear as a continuum in
charge and energy. In the case of small beam components,
this continuum may represent an appreciable contamination
and the additional analysis required complicates beam handling. In general, to separate beams completely it is
necessary to apply both electrostatic and magnetic analysis.
The importance of charge changing effects has not been
investigated until recently when there has been an extension
of interest to heavier ions. The main body of work dealing
with charge changing of heavier ions in either gases or
foils is due to the work of Soviet physicists. Nikolaev
(1965) has reviewed the theoretical and experimental data
that is available for heavy ions.[21] The experimental information is mainly limited to projectiles of mass less than
40 and at energies only relevant to the early states of
tandem acceleration.[22-41] There is scope for experimental
work on capture and loss cross sections for the heavy ions
at high energies before accurate predictions can be made.
For example, data on the stripping cross sections of heavy
negative ions is completely lacking. However, the present
experimental knowledge enables theories to be tested and
sensible estimates to be made, particularly in the early
stages of acceleration where most difficulty is likely to
be encountered.

ELECTRON LOSS

The electron loss cross section rises with increasing
energy to a broad maximum at an energy where the generalized
Bohr criterion is satisfied, i.e.

$$v = \gamma v_e \tag{2}$$

Where v is the ion velocity and v_e the orbital velocity of
the electron being removed from the ion. This expression
can be regarded as equivalent to the Massey adiabatic
criterion

$$\frac{a\Delta E}{\hbar v} \sim 1 \tag{3}$$

Where ΔE is the difference in binding energy before and
after the collision, and a is the collision distance. The
quantity $\Delta P_i = \Delta E/v$ can be identified as the change of mom-

entum of the ion in the ionizing collision. As ΔE is approximately the binding energy of the electron being removed and v can be replaced by γv_e, a can be written

$$a = \frac{2\gamma\hbar}{mv_e} \tag{3a}$$

$\frac{1}{2} mv_e^2$ being the amount of energy that must be transferred to the electron to remove it from the ion.

Therefore $\Delta P_{i}/mv_e = \frac{1}{2\gamma} \sim \frac{1}{3}$ (4)

or the electron loss cross section reaches a maximum when the change in momentum of the ion amounts to a definite fraction of the momentum imparted to the ionized electron.

According to Nikolaev v_e is determined by the binding energy I (eV) of the electron being removed and

$$v_e \sim 6 \times 10^7 \, \frac{I^{\frac{1}{2}}}{\gamma} \tag{5}$$

The loss cross section therefore rises to a maximum at an energy given by Eq. (2) and has a value $\sim \pi a^2$. Bohr and Lindhard[42,43] show that when $v > \gamma v_e$ the electron loss cross section falls with increasing energy and is given by

$$\sigma_1 = \pi a_0^2 \, Z_1^{1/3} \, Z_2^{*2} \left(\frac{v_o}{v}\right)^3 \tag{6}$$

Where Z_1 is the atomic number of the projectile,

Z_2 is the atomic number of the target for light targets and is more nearly

$$Z_2^* = Z_2^{1/3} \, v/v_o \tag{6a}$$

for heavy targets for which nuclear screening is important.

ELECTRON CAPTURE

The probability of electron capture is highest when $Z_2 v_o \sim v$, the ion velocity, and are captured into states with an orbital velocity $v_e = \frac{Z_1 v_o}{n} \sim v$. The capture into more highly excited states varies as $(Z_1/n)^3$. In the energy range of interest, the cross section for electron capture by heavy ions decreases monotonically as the energy increases. Bohr and Lindhard have shown that for collisions with light targets the capture cross section is given by

$$\sigma_c = \pi a_o^2 \, Z_1^3 \left[\frac{v_c}{v}\right]^7 \frac{Z_2^{*2}}{n^3} \tag{7}$$

where Z_2^* is the screened nuclear charge. In a heavy target the capture cross section for a highly ionized particle is given by

$$\sigma_c = \pi a_o^2 \, Z_1^2 \, Z_2^{1/3} \left[\frac{v_o}{v}\right]^3 \tag{8}$$

For a number of different ions Betz[40] has obtained the curves shown in Figure 7 which show the variation of the capture and loss cross sections as a function of energy, using the expressions for capture and loss and some experimental points for normalization. Another example of capture and loss cross sections is shown in Figure 8 from the data of Martin [41] for the case of oxygen in argon. From this brief summary it is evident that reasonable cross section estimates can be made for most elements but experimental verification is usually lacking.

EQUILIBRIUM CHARGE DISTRIBUTION

Dimitriev and Nikolaev[44] have completed the most systematic survey of the available data and derived empirical formulas for the mean charge and the charge distribution. The formulas are based on the physical model proposed by Bohr, generalized to include parameters necessary to give a good fit with the experimental data. Brunings et al[45] showed that

$$v_e \sim Z_1^\alpha \, f\,(q/Z_1) \tag{9}$$

where the component α can have a value between 1/3 and 2/3, depending upon the assumptions made. From this expression it can be seen that since (9) can be written in the form

$$\ln v = \alpha \ln Z_1 + \ln f \,(\bar{q}/Z_1) \tag{9a}$$

$\ln Z_1$ is a linear function of $\ln v$ for given values of $\bar{q}/Z_1$. The curves obtained by Dimitriev and Nikolaev based on the available experimental data[22-41] were found to obey this general relation in both gaseous and solid targets. However, they found the slope of the lines decreased monotonically with decreasing $\bar{q}/Z_1$, particularly in solids. This is in all probability connected with the fact that ions passing through a solid remain excited between collisions and therefore tend to be more highly ionized. The experimental data can be fitted by an expression of the form

Rose and Starks

Table 1

A Table of the Known Negative Ions

Period	Group I	Group II	Group III	Group IV
1	$_1$H$^-$,700 µA (a) (3)			
2	$_3$Li$^-$,1 µA (d) (7) $_3$Li$^-$,2 µA (c) (6)	$_4$BeH$^-$,0.2 µA	$_5$B$^-$,0.05 µA (d) (7) $_5$B$^-$,0.7 µA (c) (3)	$_6$C$^-$,<1 µA (d) (7) $_6$C$^-$,0.3 µA (c) (8)
3	$_{11}$Na$^-$, 1 µA (d) (7)	$_{12}$Mg$^-$,0.2 µA (e) (9) $_{12}$MgH$^-$,0.7 µA (e) (9)	$_{13}$Al$^-$, (10)	$_{14}$Si$^-$ (15)
4	$_{19}$K$^-$,<1 µA (d) (7) $_{29}$Cu$^-$,(12)	$_{20}$Ca$^-$,<1 µA (d) (7)		$_{22}$Ti$^-$, (11)
5	$_{37}$Rb$^-$,(15) $_{47}$Ag$^-$,(12)			
	$_{55}$Cs$^-$,(15)			
	$_{79}$Au$^-$,(12)	$_{80}$Hg$^-$,(16)		
6 Lanthanides				
7 Actinides	$_{92}$UF$_n^-$,1 µA (d) (4)			

a = Duoplasmatron with Charge Exchange
b = Duoplasmatron with Direct Extraction
c = Duoplasmatron with Collision Attachment

Table 1 (cont.)

Group V	Group VI	Group VII	Group VIII
			$_2$He⁻,12μA (a) (6)
$_7$N⁻,0.25μA (c) (8) $_7$NO⁻,1μA (d) (7)	$_8$O⁻,20μA (d) (4)	$_9$F⁻,100μA (d) (4)	
$_{15}$P⁻,(18)	$_{16}$S⁻,20μA (d) (7)	$_{17}$Cl⁻,50μA (d) (4)	
	$_{24}$Cr⁻,(12)		$_{26}$Fe⁻, (13) $_{27}$Co⁻,0.02μA (d) (7) $_{28}$Ni⁻, (13)
$_{33}$AsH⁻ (c)(8)	$_{34}$Se⁻,(14)	$_{35}$Br⁻,50μA (d) (4)	
	$_{42}$Mo⁻,(f)(20)		
$_{51}$Sb⁻,(14)	$_{52}$Te⁻,2μA (a)(6)	$_{53}$I⁻,10μA (d)(4)	
$_{73}$TaF⁻,2μA (d) (4)	$_{74}$WO⁻,(f)(19)		
$_{83}$Bi⁻,2μA (d)(7)			

d = Diode Source with Direct Extraction
e = Penning Source
f = Surface Ionization Source

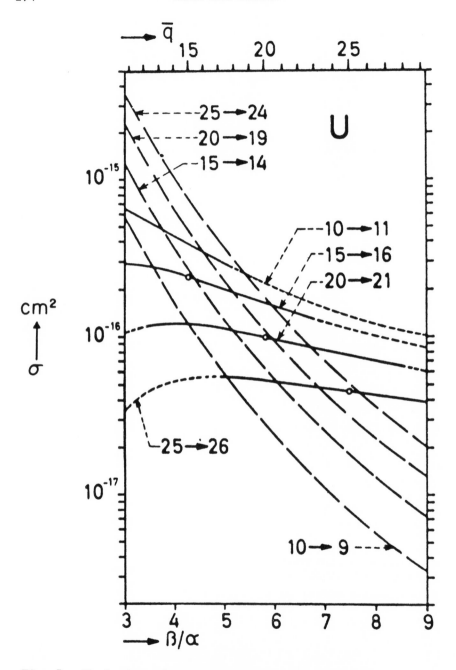

Fig. 7. Variation of capture and loss cross sections of U as
a function of energy in air. Betz.

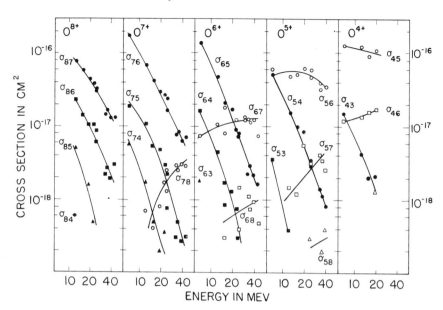

Fig. 8. Capture and loss cross sections for oxygen ions passing through argon as a function of energy. Martin.

$$\bar{q}/Z_1 = \ln\left[v\ \frac{z_1^{\alpha 1}}{m}\right]/\ln\ (n\ Z^{\alpha 2}) \qquad (10)$$

with the extra constants α_1, α_2, m and n which are listed in

Table 2. The ion velocity v is expressed in units of 10^8
cm/sec. α_1 and α_2 are related to α of Eq. (9) by the
relationships

$$\alpha = \alpha_1 + \bar{q}\ Z_1^{-1}\ \ln\ \alpha_2 \qquad \ln\ f = m + \bar{q}\ Z_1^{-1}\ \ln\ n \qquad (11)$$

As applied to real atoms and ions, the expression of
Eq. (10) ignores shell effects, but these are generally
small in the region of validity of the formula because of
the smoothing effect of the number of electrons in the shell,
its population, and the average charge $\bar{q}$.
     The charge distribution can be fitted by the expression

$$F_i = \frac{1}{\sqrt{2\pi}\cdot\sigma}\cdot\ \exp\left[-(q_i - \bar{q})^2 / 2\sigma^2\right] \qquad (12)$$

Dimitriev and Nikolaev were able to calculate a value of σ
from (10) in close agreement with experimentally measured
values, they found

$$\sigma = d_o\ Z_1^K \qquad (13)$$

Table 2

Values of the Coefficients used in Eq. (10) as
Determined by Dimitriev and Nikolaev

Medium	α_1	α_3	m	n	k	d_o
H_2			1.2	4.0	0.43	
He	0.4	0.3	1.3	4.5		
N_2			0.9	7.0	0.45	0.32
A_r			0.9	7.0		
Foil	0.1	0.6	1.2	5.0	0.40	0.38

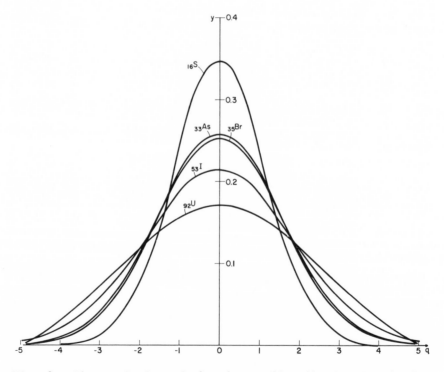

Fig. 9.   The variation of the charge distribution in air for
different Z after Nikolaev.

Values for d and K are given in Table 2. The curves calculated using Eq. (12) are shown in Figure 9.

Betz et al.[46] have more recently measured the charge distribution and mean charge of S, As, I, and U ions between 10 and 70 MeV and found that the mean charge in this energy region could be accurately represented by the expression

$$\bar{q}/Z_1 = 1 - C \exp\ (-\delta\beta/\alpha) \qquad (14)$$

for $\beta \gtrsim \alpha$. For convenience the parameters C and δ are listed in Table 3.

Expressions (10) and (14) are compared in Figure 10 in the case of iodine ions. The experimental data obtained by Grodzins et al.[47] in carbon foils is also known. It is apparent that the expression of Dimitriev and Nikolaev fits the data more accurately at high energies.

Table 3

Experimental Values of C and δ as determined
by Betz et al.

Ion	Gas		Solid	
	C	δ	C	δ
S	1.135±.049	0.159±.007	1.083±.020	0.187±.004
As	1.117±.007	0.111±.001	1.098±.006	0.153±.001
I	1.065	0.078±.001	1.030±.002	0.128±.001
U	(1.01)	(0.042)	1.030±.002	0.100±.001

SCATTERING

Unfortunately the stripping process is accompanied by scattering. Hortig has shown that scattering may be calculated with considerable accuracy using Moliere's theory, provided plural scattering is taken into account. The expected scattering of various ions in 10 and 20 $\mu g/cm^2$ foils as a function of energy is given in Table 4. The calculations for these small angles was based on the expression

$$\langle \theta^2 \rangle = 0.157 \; \frac{Z_2 \; (Z_2 + 1) \; Z_1^2}{A_2} \; \frac{t}{(Pv)^2} \; B \tag{15}$$

where $\langle \theta^2 \rangle^{1/2}$ is in radians, t is in $\mu g/cm^2$, pv is in MeV, A_2 is the mass of the target material, and B is defined by Bethe and Ashkin[48]. It is worth noting that the maximum angle of a single elastic collision θ for $M_1 >> M_2$ is

severely restricted by center of mass considerations to:

$$\theta < \frac{M_2}{M_1} \tag{16}$$

For the case of uranium ions on carbon, θ must be less than 0.02 radians.

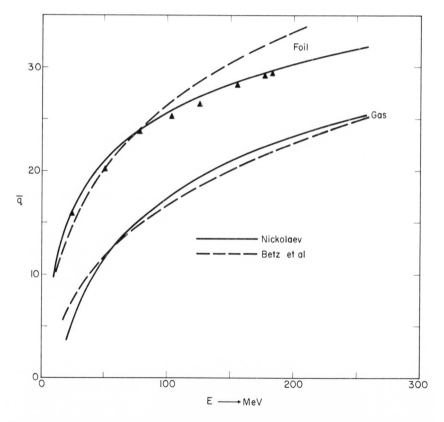

Fig. 10. A comparison of the variation of the mean charge as a function of energy for iodine ions as determined by Nikolaev Eq. (10) and Betz et al. Eq. (14). The data of Grodzins et al. is also shown.

Table 4

The multiple Scattering $\langle \theta^2 \rangle^{\frac{1}{2}}$ in Milliradians
for S, Br, I, and U ions in 10 and 20 $\mu g/cm^2$
foils as a function of energy

Energy					Thickness
MeV	$_{16}S$	$_{35}Br$	$_{53}I$	$_{92}U$	$\mu g/cm^2$
10	2.2	4.8	7.3	13.0	10
	3.4	7.5	11.0	20.0	20
20	1.1	2.4	3.6	6.3	10
	1.7	3.7	5.7	10.0	20
50	0.44	0.96	1.4	2.5	10
	0.67	1.5	2.3	3.9	20
100	0.22	0.48	0.73	·1.26	10
	0.34	0.75	1.10	2.0	20
200	0.11	0.24	0.37	0.63	10
	0.17	0.37	0.55	1.0	20
400	0.055	0.12	0.18	0.32	10
	0.086	0.19	0.28	00.50	20

ENERGY LOSS AND STRAGGLING

The energy loss of the heavy ion beam after traversing
the stripper in the terminal may be calculated using the
stopping cross section per atom given by Lindhard and
Scharff[49]

$$S_e = \zeta_e \, 8\pi \, e^2 \, a_o \, \frac{Z_1 \, Z_2}{Z} \, v/v_o \tag{17}$$

where $\zeta_e \simeq Z_1^{1/6}$, $Z^{2/3} = Z_1^{2/3} + Z_2^{2/3}$, and a_o and v_o are the
radius and the velocity of the electron in the first Bohr
orbit of the hydrogen atom. For the heavier elements this
expression gives values which are too low. The spread in
the energy loss of homogeneous particles traversing uniform
foils is primarily due to nuclear (atom-atom) scattering;
the spread due to interaction with atomic electrons is
negligible.

Table 5

Energy loss, keV/μgcm^{-2} for Br, I, Ta, and U Ions in
Beryllium and Carbon Foils. The figures for Ta
compare the calculated and measured energy losses in
carbon; otherwise the figures in parentheses are
calculated

Energy	$_{35}$Br		$_{53}$I		$_{73}$Ta		$_{92}$U	
	Be	C	Be	C	C	C	Be	C
10	22	22	19	19	(13)	14	(13)	(12)
20	30	30	28	31	(19)	28	(18)	(17)
50	43	48	49	56	(30)	60	(28)	(27)
100	50	53	64	75	(43)	105	(40)	(38)
200	(67)	(70)	80	80	(61)		(57)	(53)
400	(95)	(98)	(87)	(92)	(86)		(80)	(75)

Experimental values for the energy loss for Br, I, Ta
and U are given in Table 5.

Energy straggling due to the nuclear component of the
energy loss can be estimated from the relationship[49] :

$$\delta E = \Delta E \frac{2}{3}. \quad \frac{M_1 \, M_2}{(M_1 + M_2)^2} \tag{18}$$

Lindhard, Scharff, and Schiott[50] give curves for the
straggling, taking into account the considerable reduction
in relative straggling as the electronic component of the
energy loss becomes important and these can be used to
estimate the energy spread of the beam in the stripping
media. For example, the energy straggling of iodine in a
thin carbon foil at 16 MeV is ~ 8% of the energy loss and
decreases at higher energies to 1-2%.

The energy dispersion due to inhomogeneity in stripper
thickness can introduce a much larger energy spread than
straggling. In this respect a gas target has a significant
advantage, as its thickness is uniform over its area. The
dependence of the energy loss on the value of the initial
charge state is difficult to estimate for targets which
are less than equilibrium thickness.

VACUUM REQUIREMENTS

To show the importance of maintaining a good vacuum in the accelerator, it is instructive to calculate the magnitude of the losses in heavy ion beams due to residual gas in the accelerator tubes. For example, if in the negative ion acceleration tube, the pressure of the acceleration tube increases linearly as the terminal is approached, and the loss cross section $\sigma_{-11} + \sigma_{-10}$ varies as $1/E$, it can be seen that

$$\frac{-dn}{n} = 3.3 \times 10^{13} \, (P_1 + bx) \, (\sigma_1 - ax), \qquad (19)$$

where
$$a = \frac{\sigma_1 - \sigma_2}{L} \qquad b = \frac{P_2 - P_1}{L}$$

and n is the beam intensity

P_1 is the base tube pressure (μ),

σ_1 is the cross section for stripping at the entrance to the tube,

σ_2 is the cross section at exit,

P_2 is the pressure at exit,

and L is the length of acceleration tube.

Integrating Eq. (19),

$$\ln N_1/N_2 = 3.3 \times 10^{13} \, \dot{P_1} \sigma_1 L + (b\sigma_1 - aP_1)L^2 - abL^3 \,, \quad (19a)$$

where N_1/N_2 is the ratio of the number of incoming ions of fixed charge state to the number of exiting ions of the same charge. If we take as an example a 0^- beam injected at 40 keV and accelerated to a potential of 6 MV; then assuming the following pressures and cross sections:

$$\sigma_1 = 1.8 \times 10^{-15} \text{ cm}^2 \text{ (at 40 KeV)} \qquad P_1 = 10^{-3} \mu$$

$$\sigma_2 = 4 \times 10^{-16} \text{ cm}^2 \text{ (at 6 MeV)} \qquad P_2 = 10^{-2} \mu$$

$$L = 5 \times 10^{2} \text{ cm}$$

The attenuation

$$\eta = \frac{N_1 - N_2}{N_1} \backsimeq 1 - \frac{1}{\exp(\ln N_1/N_2)} \qquad (20)$$

is 8%. If, however, the pressures increase to

$$P_1 = 5 \times 10^{-3} \mu, \qquad\qquad P_2 = 5 \times 10^{-2} \mu$$

n becomes 34%.

It must be pointed out that the cross sections are estimates and the pressure distribution in the tube is not accurately known - thus the efficiencies shown are not necessarily correct, but they do suggest that the pressure range in which the average tandem accelerator operates is a critical region in that it is approximately at the break-point on the attenuation curve. It also must be noted that the cross sections increase as the ion mass increases and could well be a factor of 2 or more for S^- ions under the same conditions.

The net result of residual gas stripping both in negative and positive ion acceleration tubes is to create a background continuum at the expense of ions in the discrete energy spectrum. The energy homogeneity of the components of a heavy ion beam is such that taking into account short term terminal potential fluctuations and straggling $\Delta E/E$ ~$1:10^4$. Consequently if magnetic analysis shows the existence of a background amounting to $1:10^3$ of a beam component, it can then be deduced that a substantial fraction of the beam is being lost during acceleration.

BUNCHING

Since short duration pulses for time of flight studies or the measurement of very short lifetimes are important in nuclear structure studies, something must be said about the specific problems and limitations of obtaining nano-second bursts from DC tandem accelerators. There are two important factors which affect this problem, the first of which is the energy spread of the beam emerging from the injector.

It is apparent that the most appropriate place to do bunching, by well-known velocity modulation techniques, on a tandem machine, is between the ion source and the accelerator proper. If one considers what effect the energy dispersion of the beam has upon the minimum acceptable burst length, it is easily discovered that because the acceptance of the tandem is energy dependent, there is a maximum amplitude of velocity modulation which can be applied to a particular beam without seriously reducing the amplitude of the accelerated pulse. The transit time t_o of a particle in a drift region is given by

$$t_o = L\sqrt{m/2E_o},\qquad(21)$$

where m   is the mass,

E_o is the energy of the particle,

and L   is the field-free drift length

for a small energy dispersion ΔE_1, Eq. (21) becomes

$$\Delta t_2 = L \sqrt{(m/8E_o^3)}\ \Delta E_1 \tag{21a}$$

This says that for an energy dispersion of ΔE_1, the spread in transit time for fixed E_o and length L is Δt_2. There-fore, if Δt_2 represents the minimum acceptable burst length at the target at a distance L, then ΔE_1 represents

the maximum allowable energy inhomogeneity from the source. It can also be shown that, if Δt_1 is the burst duration to be compressed in a bunching length L, then ΔE_2 is the

energy modulation which must be applied to do so. It is now obvious that

$$\frac{\Delta E_1}{\Delta t_2} = \frac{1}{L}\sqrt{\frac{8E_o^3}{m}} = \frac{\Delta E_2}{\Delta t_1}, \text{ or} \tag{22}$$

$$\Delta E_1\ \Delta t_1 = \Delta E_2\ \Delta t_2, \tag{22a}$$

where ΔE_1, Δt_1 are the energy spread and pulse length before

bunching, and ΔE_2, Δt_2 are the conditions at the end of the drift length L. It is assumed that the length of the buncher is negligible.

It is seen from Eq. (22a), neglecting mechanical con-straints, that very small pulse durations can be obtained only by sacrificing energy homogeneity. The first limita-tion comes about because the tandem machine can only accept a certain maximum $\Delta E/E_o$ and still transmit a reasonable

portion of the beam. Typical numbers for $\Delta E/E_o$ which are

the maximum that avoid transmission loss in a HVE tandem are 4.8% at 1 MV terminal potential and 8.1% at 12 MV. In practice, pulses of the order of 2 nanoseconds (half width) and 500 µamps amplitude have been obtained. The equation (22a) has been generalized by Fowler and Good

$$\Sigma(\Delta P_{x_i}\ \Delta X_i) + \Delta t\Delta E = \text{const}$$

which shows clearly that the emittance of a beam is unavoidably increased by the bunching process. There is a second problem which affects the minimum bunched length available on target and that is the isochronism of the beam analyzing and switching system. A finite emittance implies that the individual trajectories of the beam will have different path lengths and hence transit times when passing through the typical magnet systems used in most accelera-tors. Care must be taken to provide an isochronous path along which the beam travels. This can be done, for

example, by providing beam trajectories as indicated in
Figure 11 which keeps the crossovers in the center of the
analyzing and switching magnets, thus keeping the path
lengths of the extreme rays the same. The major disadvantage of doing this, however, is that it requires opening up
the slits on the analyzing magnet, thus reducing considerably the energy resolution of the analyzing system.

Adjusting the beam handling system in this way is not
easy since complete knowledge of the beam characteristics
at all times is required in order to determine proper settings of the various focusing and steering devices to hold
crossovers in the proper position to achieve isochronism.
Because of the nature of this difficulty, it can be seen
that this is an area in which a process control computer
would be useful.

COMPUTER CONTROL

When accelerating heavy ions, machine operators have a
much harder time selecting the desired beam component from
the many exiting from the accelerator, and to do so must
be accurate in calculating and setting up the operating
conditions for the various lenses, magnetic and electrostatic separation devices in the beam handling system. The
beam setup time tends to become an appreciable fraction of
the available machine time, and in addition during operation
a careful watch must be kept on all machine parameters to
insure that the proper beam is kept on target. Confusion
can easily arise because of the ambiguity of simple beam
analyzing systems and for heavy ion acceleration at least
it becomes obvious that a process control computer has many
advantages.

The most important of these is the computer's ability
to identify and to optimize the desired beam. This can be
done quite easily by specifying the mass, charge and energy
of the beam and beam handling components. The computer can
quickly perform an optimization calculation involving all
the beam handling elements and make the appropriate settings
in a controlled sequence and rate. Small variations of the
settings to peak the beam on the target or on a monitor can
then be made by a relaxation program. Optimization after
calculation of the operating parameters will almost always
be necessary because of small variations in the accelerator
system caused by changes in voltage gradients, temperatures,
pressures, etc. In performing this control function the
computer will be much faster than the human operator, once
the programming has been successfully accomplished.

There are also other benefits which the process control
computer can provide. These include simplified machine

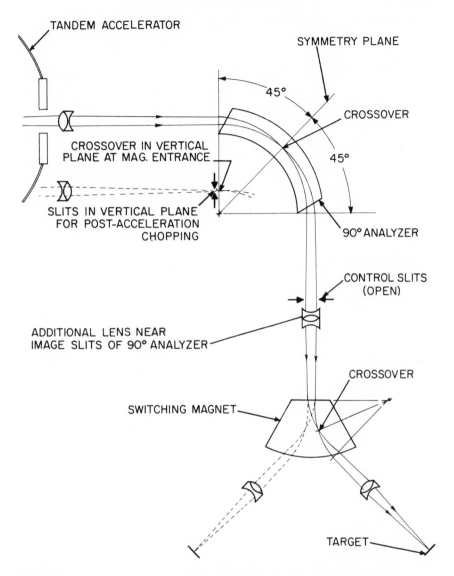

Fig. 11.   Isochronous beam transport system for multiple
                       target locations.

operation, automatic data logging, warning of slow-speed
destructive events, automatic startup of injectors and
accelerators, remote operation, and the ability to program
automatic changes in beam characteristics (e.g. energy) as
might be directed by an on-line data reduction computer.

Because a computer can scan all incoming data channels
in less than a second, it can compensate for changes immediately and control situations which might otherwise lead to
equipment failure before a human operator would have had

time to react to an unusual meter reading. The ease of
operation of a computer-controlled accelerator is self-
evident in these days and needs no elaboration. All an
experimenter would have to do to obtain beam for his experiment is specify mass, charge, energy, intensity, spot size,
and experimental beam location on a typewriter, leaving the
rest to the computer.

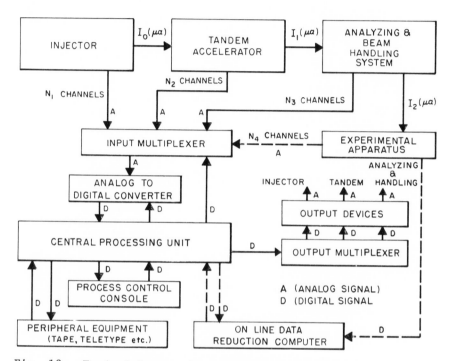

Fig. 12.   Typical layout for correction of a process control
computer to a tandem accelerator.

A schematic of the way we hope to couple a computer to
the Van de Graaff Laboratory's accelerator is shown in
Figure 12. The solid information lines indicate the simple
control system and the dashed lines show how an on-line data
reduction system would fit into the picture. The process
operator console provides all the controls necessary for
minor modifications during operation as well as display
devices to read out data from the accelerator. This console
would also provide manual control of the machine during the
computer's learning period or while debugging new systems.

The addition of a computer to control an accelerator is
not without specific problems. Typically we have to
acquire data across some sort of high voltage interface,
i.e. from the injector ion source controls or even from
the high voltage terminal itself. This situation can be
handled in a number of ways. Techniques of data trans-

mission using frequency modulation, laser beams and light pipes have been developed and one has only to determine which method best suits the lightning-like environment in which it has to work. Figure 13 suggests a method in which data could be conveniently transmitted from the ion source to ground so that the process control computer can handle the information.

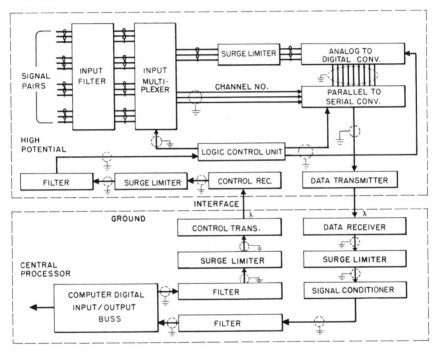

Fig. 13. One method of crossing high voltage interfaces utilizing light pipes for data transmission.

In this case, the choice of techniques for handling the data at each end of the telemeter link is based quite heavily on the fact that surge potentials are quite often many orders of magnitude greater than the normal signal level. Advantage can be taken of the fact that the signals involved (such as source pressure, arc current, and all other source parameters) are, in general, slowly varying and, as such, can be filtered extensively to reduce the amplitude of the surge potentials without sacrificing response time.

As can be seen in the diagram, the analog data signals are individually filtered before entering the multiplexer and also surge-limited at the output of this unit. The multiplexing unit could be as simple as a stepping relay which is free-running, allowing continuous transmission

of the available data. If the quantity of data words turns
out to be large (say, greater than 20), the multiplexer
would probably take the form of a randomly accessible device
so that particular data words can be obtained by the computer on demand. Because of the importance of avoiding
damage from surges, the multiplexing equipment could be
mechanical, since the switching time between input channels
can be slow.

Once the signals are multiplexed they are transferred
to a thoroughly r-f shielded analog to digital converter
to transform the data to a more suitable form for transmission across the high voltage interface. The digital
information would then be transferred into serial form to
be transmitted across the interface by one of the previously
mentioned methods, say, for example, by a single light pipe.

After the information is transmitted to ground it must
be again filtered to remove transient surges and shaped into
a form acceptable to the computer. Special care must be
taken to avoid any surges from entering the computer frame
as the resultant damage could well be disastrous. We can
add at this point that this would be true of any signal or
other connection made between the computer and its surround-
ing environment, i.e. all connections to the computer must
be well isolated from the surge conditions encountered in
an accelerator.

If, as was mentioned previously, the computer might
wish to direct the operations of the multiplexing and
converting hardware on the high potential side of the interface, then a second data link, this time from ground up
across the interface, could easily be added. To be
successful, extensive precautions must be taken to isolate
all sensitive electronic hardware from the surge environment.

REFERENCES

1. P. H. Rose and A. Galejs, Progress in Nuclear Techniques
    and Instrumentation, Ed., J.M. Farley, North Holland
    Publishing Company, Amsterdam.

2. W. D. Allen, Nuclear Structure. Ed. A. Hossain, Harum-
    ar-Rashid, M. Islam. Publishers, North Holland Publish-
    ing Co., Amsterdam.

3. R. Bastide, N. B. Brooks, A. B. Wittkower, P. H. Rose
    and K. H. Purser, IEEE, NS-12, 775 (1965).

4. N. Brooks, HVE, private communication (1966).

5. K. W. Ehlers, IEEE, NS-12, 811 (1965).

6. R. Middleton, Univ. of Pennsylvania, private communication (1967).

7. R. Bastide, HVE, private communication (1967).

8. Jahresbericht, Max-Planck Institut fur Kernphysik, Heidelberg (1965).

9. K. Bethge, E. Heiniscke and H. Baumann, Phys. Letters 23, 532 (1966).

10. R. H. Sloane and C. S. Watt, Proc. Phys. Soc. 61, 217 (1948).

11. V. M. Dukelskii, E. Ya. Zandberg, Doklady Akad. Nauk SSR 86, 263 (1952).

12. V. M. Dukelskii, Doklady Akad. Nauk SSR 105, 955 (1955).

13. V. M. Dukelskii and V. M. Sokolov, JETP 8, 569 (1959).

14. V. M. Dukelskii, N. I. Ionov, Doklady Akad. Nauk SSR 81, 767 (1951).

15. V. M. Dukelskii, E. Ya. Zandberg and N. I. Ionov, Doklady Akad. Nauk SSR 68, 31 (1949).

16. H.S.W. Massey, Negative Ions, (Cambridge Univ. Press, 1950).

17. S. Geltman, J. Chem. Phys. 25, 782 (1956).

18. A.J.C. Nicholson, J. Chem. Phys. 29, 1312 (1958).

19. V.E. Krohn, Jr., J. Appl. Phys. 33, 3523 (1962).

20. M. Perdrix, S. Paletto, R. Goutte, C. Guillaud, Nucl. Instr. and Methods 56, 23 (1967).

21. V. S. Nikolaev, Soviet Physics Uspekii 8, 269, 1965.

22. N. O. Lassen, Dan. Mat. Fys. Medd. 26, 5, 12 (1958).

23. N. O. Lassen, Ibid. 30, 8 (1955).

24. Korsunskii, Pivovar, Markus and Leviant, Dan SSSR 103, 399 (1953).

25. Leviant, Korsunskii, Pivovar and Podgornyi, ibid. 103, 403 (1955).

26. R. L. Gluckstern, Phys. Rev. 98, 1817 (1955).

27. Reynolds, Wyly, and Zucker, Phys. Rev. 98, 1825 (1955).

28. K. G. Stephens and D. Walker, Phil. Mag. 46, 563 (1955).

29. B. Cohen, and Coley, Phys. Rev. 104, 1046 (1956).

30. Nikolaev, Fateeva, Dimitriev and Teplova, JETP 33,
     306 (1957); Soviet Phys. JETP 6, 239 (1957).

31. Afrosimov, Il'in, and Solov'ev, ZhTF 30, 705 (1960);
     Soviet Phys. Tech. Phys. 5, 661 (1961).

32. Allison, Cuevas, and Garcia-Munoz, Phys. Rev. 120,
     1266 (1960).

33. Nikolaev, Dimitriev, Fateeva and Teplova, JETP 40,
     989 (1961); Soviet Phys. JETP 13, 695 (1961).

34. Nikolaev, Fateeva, Dimitriev and Teplova, JETP 41,
     89 (1961); Soviet Phys. JETP 14, 67 (1961).

35. Dimitriev, Nikolaev, Fateeva and Teplova, JETP 42,
     16 (1962); Soviet Phys. JETP 15, 11 (1962).

36. Dimitriev, Nikolaev, Fateeva, and Teplova, JETP 43,
     361 (1962); Soviet Phys. JETP 16, 259 (1963).

37. Pivovar, Tubaev and Novikov, JETP 41, 26 (1961);
     Soviet Phys. JETP 14, 10 (1961).

38. Pivovar, Novikov and Tubaev, JETP 42, (1962);
     Soviet Phys. JETP 15, 1035 (1962).

39. Szostak, Martin and Marmier, Helv. Phys. Acta 34,
     485 (1961).

40. H. D. Betz, and C. Scnmeltzer, Unilac, Bericht-Nr. 1-67
     Heidelberg.

41. F. Martin, to be published.

42. N. Bohr, Dansk, Videnskab Selsk. Mat. Fys. Medd. 18,
     No. 8 (1948).

43. N. Bohr and J. Lindhard, Videnskab Selsk. Mat. Fys.
     Medd. 28, 7, (1954).

44. I.S. Dimitriev and V.S. Nikolaev, Soviet Phys. JETP 20,
     409 (1965).

45. Brunings, Knipp, Teller, Phys. Rev. 60, 657, (1940).

46. H. D. Betz, G. Hortig, E. Seischner, C. L. Schweitzer,
     B. Stadler and J. Weinrauch, Phys. Letters, 22, 643,
     (1966).

47. L. Grodzins, R. Kalish, D. Murnick, R. J. Van de Graaff,
     F. Chmara, P. H. Rose, Phys. Lett. 24B, 282, (1967).

48. H. A. Bethe, Phys. Rev., 89, 1256, (1953).

49. J. Lindhard, M. Scharff, Phys. Rev. 124, 128 (1961).

50. J. Lindhard, M. Scharff and H. E. Schiott, Kgl. Danske
     Videnskab. Selskab. Mat. Fys. Medd. 33, 14, (1963).

     J. Lindhard and M. Scharff, Kgl. Danske Videnskab.
     Selskab. Mat. Phys. Medd. 27, (1953).

51. T. K. Fowler and W. M. Good, Nucl. Instr. and Methods,
     7, 245, (1960).

DISCUSSION

DAVIS: What limitation do you place on the gradient due to
the belt?

ROSE: They have run, the gradients, in excess of 300 kilo-
volts per inch at voltages of about 3 million volts.

DAVIS: Are there any other stripping techniques other than
gas or foil which might be solutions to the sticky problems?

ROSE: Yes of course and we are going to look into some of
them, one that many of you know about is Dr. Van de Graaff's
proposal using dust strippers, a bit of a horrifying thought,
when you think about soot blowing around on the inside of
your accelerator, but on the other hand we have got them
running for periods of several hours before the grime is
transmitted to the outside and we are going to do some
stripping measurements on them but they may not be successful
because the dust particles are small enough, you want them
small enough so that statistically it goes through several;
otherwise, you get an awful lot of energy straggling, that
in between the collisions the ions will de-excite and therefore it may be very little better than the gas type. Other
techniques which are really very interesting are some sort
of electron--high energy--or fairly high temperature plasma
with electrons, but there the problem is cross-sections. You
really have to go through these things repeatedly to get

advantage out. I don't know if any of you have read an
article by Janes, Levy, Bethe and Feld in the Physical Review,
[145 925 (1966)] I think about a year ago, on a thing they
call the "HIPAC" in which they use oscillating electrons to
ionize, or plan to use, they haven't done it except in model
form, [they] plan to use these oscillating electrons of about
10 keV energy to ionize uranium to a very high degree 60+.
The electrons get more energetic than 10 keV to get
accelerated in this device. But, it takes many many
traversals. So it would be - it is perhaps the most important
problem we have, namely to increase the mean charge that we
can get by stripping. So we are looking at everything and
anything but at the moment there are no practical solutions
other than the foil and the gas.

LIST OF PARTICIPANTS

A. Arima	University of Tokyo
	(Rutgers University)
R. G. Arns	Ohio State University
M. Baranger	Carnegie Institute of Technology
R. Bearse	Argonne National Laboratory
J. A. Becker	Lockheed Missles and Space Co.
G. J. Borse	Lehigh University
R. T. Carpenter	State University of Iowa
M. R. Cleland	Radiation Dynamics, Inc.
P. M. Cockburn	University of Kansas
R. S. Cox	University of Kansas
R. Y. Cusson	Chalk River Nuclear Laboratories
J. P. Davidson	University of Kansas
R. Davis	Florida State University
F. E. Dunnam	University of Florida
J. P. Elliott	University of Sussex
P. M. Endt	Rijksunversiteit, Utrecht
N. Freed	Pennsylvania State University
D. A. Gedcke	Ortec, Inc.
P. Goldhammer	University of Kansas
G. M. Griffiths	University of British Columbia
E. Halbert	Oak Ridge National Laboratory
S. S. Hanna	Stanford University
G. I. Harris	Aerospace Research Laboratories
H. Hennecke	Aerospace Research Laboratories
D. S. Koltun	University of Rochester
R. W. Krone	University of Kansas
D. Kurath	Argonne National Laboratory
J. C. Legg	Kansas State University
M. de Llano	University of Mexico
A. E. Litherland	University of Toronto
J. R. MacDonald	Bell Telephone Laboratories
R. Nordhagen	Universitet I Oslo
J. W. Olness	Brookhaven National Laboratory
W. R. Phillips	University of Manchester
	(University of Minnesota)
J. G. Pronko	Yale University
F. W. Prosser, Jr.	University of Kansas
K. H. Purser	University of Rochester
G. Ripka	Centre D'Etudes Nucleaires de Saclay
	(Princeton and Rutgers Universities)
J. Risser	Rice University
P. Rose	High Voltage Engineering Corp.
M. L. Roush	University of Maryland
L. W. Seagondollar	North Carolina State University
W. E. Starks	High Voltage Engineering Corp.
I. Taylor	Columbia University
D. R. Tilley	North Carolina State University

E. W. Titterton	Australian National University
S. Varma	University of Kansas
J. Walinga	Aerospace Research Laboratories
R. W. West	University of Kansas
S. A. Williams	Iowa State University
H. Willmes	Aerospace Research Laboratories